**Automation and Control
Engineering Series**

THE MATHEMATICAL THEORY
OF LINEAR SYSTEMS

Automation and Control Engineering Series

EDITED BY JOHN F. COALES, O.B.E., M.A.,
M.I.E.E., F.Inst.P.

THE
MATHEMATICAL THEORY
OF LINEAR SYSTEMS

★

B. M. BROWN, M.A.

Assistant Professor of Mathematics,
Royal Naval College, Greenwich

NEW YORK

JOHN WILEY & SONS INC.

440 FOURTH AVENUE

1961

PRINTED IN GREAT BRITAIN BY
HAZELL WATSON AND VINEY LTD
AYLESBURY AND SLOUGH

FOREWORD

By John F. Coales, O.B.E., M.A., M.I.E.E., F.Inst.P.

This second book in the series is also the first volume of what is intended to be a textbook on the principles as opposed to the applications of control engineering. This does not mean that it is only suitable for control engineers. All engineering—and indeed all science—involves the study of linear systems to a greater or less extent and to all of these the mathematics set out in this book is equally applicable. It should, therefore, prove a most useful textbook for all engineering students. No branch of engineering is more dependent than control on a clear understanding of the mathematics by means of which the concepts can be formally expressed. The use of mathematics not only plays a vital part in providing a basis for the routine calculations of analysis and synthesis but also enables complicated logical processes to be presented in concise forms. In this way, important general principles are frequently disclosed. Further, by expressing different problems in the same standard or canonical forms, similarities are often high-lighted and it is frequently in this way that inventions arise.

The essence of control engineering is that systems be considered as a whole. There is always some 'plant' that has to be controlled, the design of which is more or less decided by the duty it has to perform. The design of the controls, on the other hand, is usually in the hands of the control engineer and it is for him to decide, by consideration of the system as a whole, what are the best components to use, whether they be chemical, electrical, hydraulic, mechanical, optical or pneumatic. The only thing that can be said about them in advance is that they will all be physical systems and, if they are linear, they must be describable by the mathematics contained in this book. How to use the mathematics in the practical design of systems will be the subject of a later volume. It is further intended that there shall also be a volume on non-linear systems, but for the student it is as well to get a clear understanding of the behaviour of linear systems before starting on the much more difficult problems involved in the design of non-linear systems. The best foundation for any study of control systems is, therefore, a good understanding of the mathematics of linear physical systems and in this book will be found all that is necessary and sufficient to this understanding. Every effort has been made to present it in an easily assimilable form, starting, if the appendices are included, from what every schoolboy should know.

J. F. C.

Cambridge, 1961

AUTHOR'S PREFACE

THE SPECTACULAR DEVELOPMENT in automatic control in the last twenty years has resulted in the appearance of many textbooks on the subject of linear systems. The majority of these have been written by engineers for engineers and, very naturally, the emphasis has been on the applications rather than on the mathematical methods used. These methods have in the main been adaptations of older techniques, already familiar to engineers in their applications in such fields as communication engineering. Such new methods as have appeared have usually been taken over in the forms in which their initiators first presented them. Now it is natural that research workers should feel that their efforts and time are better spent in breaking fresh ground rather than in tidying up existing theory. For these reasons much of the basic theory in existing books tends to be unnecessarily complicated, or to use techniques which are more advanced than the various applications warrant.

My justification for adding to the long list of books already available lies in an attempt to serve the student by presenting the different parts of the basic theory in as general a form as possible, using the most elementary mathematical techniques. From this, it is hoped that he may acquire a clear concept of the underlying principles of the subject. Another aim of the book has been to show the research worker the most efficient methods for carrying out standard analytical processes and calculations.

The earlier chapters of the book are based on a series of lectures on linear systems which I have given for a number of years to officers of the Royal Navy taking advanced courses in ordnance engineering and in gunnery. Since much of the elementary theory of the subject is concerned with systems whose behaviour can be represented by linear differential equations with constant coefficients, I make no apology for discussing the properties and methods of solution of these equations *ab initio* and in considerable detail. In this respect I have departed from a current tendency among engineers to use transform and harmonic response methods for the basic discussion. It is true that the latter frequently allow certain results to be obtained by rule of thumb processes, but I feel that a knowledge of the properties of linear differential equations is necessary for a proper understanding of the general principles of the subject.

An important feature of the book is the use of operational notation and methods. In the first instance these provide a method of obtaining the solutions of a wide class of linear differential and difference equations which is, in general, at least as efficient as any other. Further, operators provide a symbolism that expresses unambiguously the relations between the various elements and signals in a system. Moreover, the form of an operator frequently reveals at a glance important characteristics of the element it represents.

The operator **D** and its properties are introduced in stages in the first two chapters. The treatment here follows, with certain modifications, that to be found in elementary textbooks on differential equations. It is, however, presented in such a way as to stress both the scope and the limitations of the method. In the third chapter the unilateral Laplace transformation is introduced as an alternative method for solving initial value problems, and its efficiency for this purpose is compared with that of operational methods.

Chapters 4 and 5 are devoted to Fourier series and integrals and Fourier and Laplace transforms. Another departure from present practice is the exclusive use, from this stage onwards, of bilateral transforms. There are three reasons why I have chosen to do this. First, there are occasions where the greater generality of application is an advantage; second, the use of bilateral transforms simplifies the statement and application of certain general properties; and third, when integrals with finite limits arise, as for example the convolution integral, this is because the *functions* involved are one-sided rather than the transformation.

In view of the important part played by step and impulse functions, there follows a chapter in which these are defined carefully and their properties discussed fully. This is followed in turn by four chapters in which linear systems are defined and the standard properties of the more elementary types are developed. A feature here is a simplified derivation and statement of the Nyquist stability criterion.

The book divides naturally into two halves at this stage and the chapters that follow are concerned with the more advanced parts of the subject. First there are two chapters on statistical methods and the optimisation theory of Wiener. I have attempted to present these in a way which, while much simpler than that to be found in existing textbooks, is sufficiently general for application to a wide range of engineering problems. The key to this is the use of ensemble rather than time averages for the definition of correlation functions. This not only simplifies the basic analysis, it is also more appropriate, since a treatment which relates a single time average to another is not, strictly speaking, statistical.

The increasing use in recent years of digital computation and of sampling elements in control systems has made a knowledge of the calculus of sequences and of difference equations more necessary than ever to the engineer. The elements of those parts of the subject relevant to linear systems are given in Chapter 13. Extensive use is made of operators and these are approached in the same way as in earlier chapters.

Chapter 14 is devoted to a brief account of the general linear operator. In particular, it is shown how such operators can be represented and classified in different ways. The last two chapters cover the elements of sampling and interpolation systems, using a new approach based on operators.

The thirteen appendices form an important part of the book. They cover miscellaneous topics whose inclusion in the main text would interrupt unduly the logical development of the subject. Such topics are on the one hand elementary algebraic techniques which the student who is out of practice mathematically may wish to revise or to learn how to carry out efficiently. Other appendices give proofs of results quoted in the text which the average engineer may be prepared to accept, but which the more mathematically minded reader may wish to study.

One of the difficulties of planning a book of this type, not based on a particular examination syllabus and with no one class of reader in mind, is that of deciding at what level to write. In this respect I have made no attempt to be consistent throughout the book. For the earlier chapters I have assumed that the reader is familiar with the elements of the differential and integral calculus, including the methods of integration by parts and by substitution, but that he may be out of practice with his technique. For this reason I have given explanations and algebraic reasoning in full, at the risk of being tedious to the more experienced student. On the other hand, I have assumed that the reader whose interest lies mainly in the later chapters is mathematically more mature.

Another problem is that of deciding the standard of rigour to adopt. Since I have assumed that the reader is not a professional mathematician, I have made no attempt to state and prove the various results in their most general forms. I have tried to use reasoning which is as simple as possible but which, if incomplete, is not, I hope, unsound. Thus, it is frequently necessary in this subject to invert the order in which a double limit is evaluated. When this is done, it is assumed that the functions involved are such that the procedure is valid.

To keep the size of the book within reasonable limits, I have chosen my worked examples primarily to illustrate the mathematical processes used. I hope that the various practical applications will be discussed more fully in other volumes of this series. For the same reason, the comparatively small number of exercises included have been designed to give the student an opportunity to practice the techniques described in this book.

In view of the vast amount of literature on the subject, I have not attempted to give a comprehensive bibliography or to acknowledge systematically the sources of my information. Such references as are given in footnotes are therefore, in general, only to books and papers wherein may be found amplification of the relevant topics in the text.

In acknowledging the help of several friends in the various stages of the preparation of this book, I would like to mention first Mr. J. F. Coales, the general editor of this series. It was he who suggested that this book should be written and the fact that his ideas on the scope and form of the text have coincided so closely with my own has made my task very much easier. He has also read the manuscript and made a number of valuable comments. Next, I am greatly indebted to Professor T. A. A. Broadbent, Professor of Mathematics in the Royal Naval College, who has given me much useful advice from time to time. My colleague, Mr. R. B. Harvey, has read both the manuscript and the proofs and has made a large number of detailed and carefully considered suggestions. The proofs have also been read by another colleague, Dr. A. G. Howson, as a result of which a number of important misprints and other errors have been eliminated. To all these I offer my gratitude and thanks. The book will be very much the better for their efforts. I should also like to thank Messrs. Chapman and Hall, and in particular Mr. G. Parr and Mr. E. W. Hamilton, for their co-operation and help at all times in the production of this book.

Royal Naval College, Greenwich.   B. M. BROWN
March, 1961

NUMERATION

SECTIONS are numbered serially in each chapter. Equations are numbered serially in each section. Figures and tables are numbered according to the sections to which they refer. Specimen cross-references are given below.

Section **6.3** refers to the third section in Chapter 6.

Equation **3.2**(5) refers to equation (5) in section **3.2**.

Fig. 7.4(*d*) refers to the fourth figure in Section **7.4**.

Table 13.1(B) refers to the second table in Section **13.1**.

CONTENTS

CHAPTER 1

LINEAR DIFFERENTIAL EQUATIONS WITH CONSTANT COEFFICIENTS

1.1 Differential equations

If x is a function of t, any equation formed from x or t or both and one or more of the derivatives dx/dt, d^2x/dt^2, etc., which is satisfied identically for all values of t within a certain range is called a *differential equation*. Examples are

$$\frac{dx}{dt} = \lambda x, \tag{1}$$

$$\frac{d^2x}{dt^2} = 6t^2, \tag{2}$$

$$x\frac{d^2x}{dt^2} = \left(\frac{dx}{dt}\right)^2, \tag{3}$$

$$\frac{d^2x}{dt^2} + 5\frac{dx}{dt} + 6x = t^3, \tag{4}$$

$$\frac{d^3x}{dt^3} + x\frac{dx}{dt} + x^4 = \sin t. \tag{5}$$

Differential equations arise in many problems in geometry, mechanics and physics; for example, they play a large part in the theories of electric currents and of oscillations in mechanical systems. The differential equation is usually the expression of some physical law, the explicit relation connecting x and t being unknown in the first place. When determined, this relation is called a *solution* of the differential equation.

The highest order of derivative appearing is, by definition, the *order* of the differential equation. Thus in the above examples, (1) is of the first order, (2), (3) and (4) are of the second order, while (5) is of the third order.

Consider the equation (2). This is a trivial example, and the solution can be found directly by two successive integrations as follows:

$$\frac{d^2x}{dt^2} = 6t^2,$$

$$\frac{dx}{dt} = 2t^3 + C_1,$$

$$x = \tfrac{1}{2}t^4 + C_1 t + C_2, \tag{6}$$

where C_1 and C_2 are arbitrary constants.

In general, any differential equation can be solved by a number of integrations. In a number of simple types these integrations can be performed explicitly, as in the above example, by transforming the original equation and the intermediate integrals into suitable integrable forms. In other cases numerical methods of integration must be used. Whichever method is used, the number of integrations will be the same as the order of the differential equation and since each integration introduces one arbitrary constant the solution of an equation of order n will contain n arbitrary constants. Such a solution is called the *general solution* or *complete primitive* of the differential equation. For example, (3) above is of the second order and its general solution contains two arbitrary constants. It is easy to verify that the equation is satisfied by

$$x = C_1 e^{C_2 t}, \tag{7}$$

where C_1 and C_2 are any constants. In this book however we shall not require to discuss general methods of finding such solutions.

Since the arbitrary constants can take any values, it is clear that a differential equation has an infinite number of solutions. In order to obtain a unique solution a number of additional conditions must be specified, this number being equal to the order of the differential equation. Thus if, in addition to the differential equation (2), we are given that $x = 1$ when $t = 0$ and $x = 6$ when $t = 1$, substitution in (6) gives two equations which can be solved for C_1 and C_2. The values obtained are $\tfrac{9}{2}$ and 1, so that the required solution is

$$x = \tfrac{1}{2}t^4 + \tfrac{9}{2}t + 1.$$

Such a solution is called a *particular solution* or *particular integral*. Similarly, the particular integral of (3) with the *initial conditions* $x = 2$ and $dx/dt = 6$ when $t = 0$ is easily found from (7) to be

$$x = 2 e^{3t}.$$

1.2 Linear differential equations

A linear differential equation is one which is linear in the dependent variable x and its derivatives dx/dt, d^2x/dt^2, etc. In other words, the equation must contain no powers or other functions, or products of these quantities. Referring to the examples given in the first section, it is easily seen that **1.1** (1), (2) and (4) are linear and that the other two equations are not. The general linear equation of order n can be expressed in the form

$$a_0(t)\frac{d^n x}{dt^n} + a_1(t)\frac{d^{n-1}x}{dt^{n-1}} + \ldots + a_{n-1}(t)\frac{dx}{dt} + a_n(t)x = f(t), \qquad (1)$$

where the coefficients $a_0(t)$, etc. and $f(t)$ are independent of x and its derivatives. Notice that the condition of linearity imposes no restrictions on the independent variable t. The equation

$$a_0(t)\frac{d^n x}{dt^n} + a_1(t)\frac{d^{n-1}x}{dt^{n-1}} + \ldots + a_n(t)x = 0, \qquad (2)$$

containing only terms in x and its derivatives, is called *homogeneous*. For example, **1.1** (1) is homogeneous while **1.1** (2) and (4) are not. Again

$$\frac{d^2 x}{dt^2} + t\frac{dx}{dt} + t^2 x = 0$$

is homogeneous, but

$$\frac{d^2 x}{dt^2} + t\frac{dx}{dt} + t^2 x = t^3$$

is not.

All the differential equations used in this book are linear. Although it is not generally possible to solve such equations formally, it can be proved that their solutions always have a characteristic form. Consider first the homogeneous equation (2). The general solution of this can always be expressed as

$$x = C_1 v_1(t) + C_2 v_2(t) + \ldots + C_n v_n(t), \qquad (3)$$

where $C_1, C_2 \ldots C_n$ are arbitrary constants and $v_1(t)$, $v_2(t)$, $\ldots v_n(t)$ are *linearly independent* particular solutions. This means that none of these functions can be expressed linearly in terms of the others. More precisely, it is impossible to find constants k_1, k_2, $\ldots k_n$, not all zero, such that

$$k_1 v_1(t) + k_2 v_2(t) + \ldots + k_n v_n(t) \equiv 0.$$

The general solution of the non-homogeneous equation (1) can be shown to take the form

$$x = C_1 v_1(t) + C_2 v_2(t) + \ldots + C_n v_n(t) + g(t). \qquad (4)$$

It is seen that this is obtained by adding to the right-hand side of (3), called the *complementary function*, a suitable function $g(t)$, called a *particular integral*. (The particular solution $x = g(t)$ is of course that for which $C_1 = C_2 = C_3 = \ldots = C_n = 0$.) This form of solution is derived later in this chapter for equations in which the coefficients $a_r(t)$ are constants. A formal derivation covering the general case is given in **7.2**.

1.3   Equations with constant coefficients

A very important special class of linear differential equations is that for which the coefficients $a_0(t), a_1(t), \ldots a_n(t)$, are constant. An equation of this type can be written

$$a_0 \frac{d^n x}{dt^n} + a_1 \frac{d^{n-1} x}{dt^{n-1}} + \ldots + a_n x = f(t). \qquad (1)$$

Although any or all the other constants may be zero we will assume that $a_0 \neq 0$. No restrictions are placed on the function $f(t)$. If it should be zero the equation will be homogeneous.

Unlike the general linear equation, when the coefficients are constant it is possible to obtain an explicit solution. In particular the functions $v_r(t)$ in the complementary function are exponential or related functions. In view of the importance of these equations their properties and methods of solution will be developed in detail in this chapter.

Extensive use will be made throughout the book of operators of various types. For the immediate present however they will serve mainly to provide a convenient abbreviated notation. We accordingly introduce the symbol **D** to denote differentiation with respect to t, so that if u is any function of t, $\mathbf{D}u = du/dt$. Extending this, $d^2u/dt^2 = \mathbf{D}(\mathbf{D}u) = \mathbf{D}^2 u$. In general $d^n u/dt^n = \mathbf{D}^n u$. The following properties are immediately evident:

$$\mathbf{D}^m \mathbf{D}^n u = \mathbf{D}^m(\mathbf{D}^n u) = \mathbf{D}^{m+n} u,$$

so that
$$\mathbf{D}^m \mathbf{D}^n \equiv \mathbf{D}^{m+n}, \qquad (2)$$

$$\mathbf{D}(u+v) = \mathbf{D}u + \mathbf{D}v, \qquad (3)$$

$$\mathbf{D}(cu) = c\mathbf{D}u, \qquad (4)$$

where c is any constant. We can form extended operators by combining the elementary operators so far mentioned. For example, $2\mathbf{D}^3 u + \mathbf{D}^2 u$ can be written as $(2\mathbf{D}^3 + \mathbf{D}^2)u$.

The following example shows what happens if two such operators are applied successively.

$$(\mathbf{D}+3)\{(\mathbf{D}+2)u\} = \mathbf{D}\{(\mathbf{D}+2)u\} + 3\{(\mathbf{D}+2)u\}$$
$$= \mathbf{D}^2 u + 2\mathbf{D}u + 3\mathbf{D}u + 6u$$
$$= (\mathbf{D}^2 + 5\mathbf{D} + 6)u.$$

Thus $$(\mathbf{D}+3)(\mathbf{D}+2) \equiv \mathbf{D}^2 + 5\mathbf{D} + 6.$$

By extending this process it is clear that operators which are polynomials in $\mathbf{D}$ can be multiplied together as though they were algebraic expressions. By a reversal of the order of the same steps they can also be factorised. Notice particularly however that this is true only if the coefficients are constant.

The general linear differential equation with constant coefficients can now be written in the form

$$Q(\mathbf{D})x = f(t), \tag{5}$$

where $$Q(\mathbf{D}) \equiv a_0 \mathbf{D}^n + a_1 \mathbf{D}^{n-1} + \ldots + a_{n-1}\mathbf{D} + a_n.$$

1.4 First order equations

The homogeneous first order equation is

$$a_0 \frac{dx}{dt} + a_1 x = 0. \tag{1}$$

Putting $a_1/a_0 = -\lambda_1$ this becomes

$$\frac{dx}{dt} - \lambda_1 x = 0 \quad \text{or} \quad (\mathbf{D}-\lambda_1)x = 0. \tag{2}$$

The solution of this is well known to be

$$x = C e^{\lambda_1 t}. \tag{3}$$

It can be derived by, among others, the method used below for non-homogeneous equations.

The non-homogeneous equation

$$a_0 \frac{dx}{dt} + a_1 x = f(t) \tag{4}$$

is not changed in form if we divide through by a_0, so that we can without loss of generality take $a_0 = 1$ and write

$$(\mathbf{D}-\lambda_1)x = f(t), \tag{5}$$

or $$\frac{dx}{dt} - \lambda_1 x = f(t).$$

This can be solved by integration if we first multiply by the *integrating factor* $e^{-\lambda_1 t}$. The equation then becomes

$$e^{-\lambda_1 t}\frac{dx}{dt} - \lambda_1 e^{-\lambda_1 t}x = \frac{d}{dt}(x e^{-\lambda_1 t}) = e^{-\lambda_1 t}f(t).$$

Integrating, $$x e^{-\lambda_1 t} = \int e^{-\lambda_1 t}f(t)\,dt,$$

or $$x = e^{\lambda_1 t}\int e^{-\lambda_1 t}f(t)\,dt. \tag{6}$$

Since $f(t)$ is known, the integral can be evaluated, either in closed form or numerically. The solution is therefore determined. This most useful expression will be used frequently both as it stands and to give the solutions of higher order equations. If we denote the integral by $h_1(t)+C$, where C is an arbitrary constant, (6) can be written

$$\begin{aligned} x &= e^{\lambda_1 t}\{h_1(t)+C\} \\ &= g_1(t)+C e^{\lambda_1 t}, \end{aligned} \tag{7}$$

where $g_1(t) = e^{\lambda_1 t}h_1(t)$. The second term $C e^{\lambda_1 t}$, being the solution (3) of the corresponding homogeneous equation (2), is the complementary function (see **1.2** (4)). The function $g_1(t)$ is then the particular integral.

An important special case is when $f(t) = e^{\alpha t}$. Then, if $\alpha \neq \lambda_1$,

$$\int e^{-\lambda_1 t}f(t)\,dt = \int e^{(\alpha-\lambda_1)t}\,dt = \frac{1}{\alpha-\lambda_1}e^{(\alpha-\lambda_1)t}+C,$$

so that $$x = \frac{1}{\alpha-\lambda_1}e^{\alpha t}+C e^{\lambda_1 t}. \tag{8}$$

If $\alpha = \lambda_1$ this expression must be modified as follows:

$$\int e^{-\lambda_1 t}f(t)\,dt = \int dt = t+C,$$

so that $$x = t e^{\lambda_1 t}+C e^{\lambda_1 t}. \tag{9}$$

In other words, if $(\mathbf{D}-\lambda_1)x = e^{\alpha t}$, the particular integral is $e^{\alpha t}/(\alpha-\lambda_1)$ if $\alpha \neq \lambda_1$, and $t e^{\alpha t}$ if $\alpha = \lambda_1$. In both cases the complementary function is $C e^{\lambda_1 t}$.

The results of this section hold whether λ_1 and $f(t)$ are real or complex.

EXERCISE   Solve the differential equation $(\mathbf{D}+2)x = 2t$.

1.5 Second order equations

The homogeneous second order equation is

$$a_0 \frac{d^2x}{dt^2} + a_1 \frac{dx}{dt} + a_2 x = 0$$

or
$$(a_0 \mathbf{D}^2 + a_1 \mathbf{D} + a_2)x = 0. \tag{1}$$

Dividing by a_0 we can, as shown in **1.3**, factorise the operator and write the equation

$$(\mathbf{D} - \lambda_1)\{(\mathbf{D} - \lambda_2)x\} = 0.$$

If we regard $(\mathbf{D} - \lambda_2)x$ as dependent variable instead of x and use **1.4** (2) and (3), we obtain as a first integral

$$(\mathbf{D} - \lambda_2)x = C\,e^{\lambda_1 t}.$$

This equation can be solved for x by using **1.4** (8) or (9). If $\lambda_2 \neq \lambda_1$ we have

$$x = \frac{C}{\lambda_1 - \lambda_2}\,e^{\lambda_1 t} + C_2\,e^{\lambda_2 t},$$

or
$$x = C_1\,e^{\lambda_1 t} + C_2\,e^{\lambda_2 t}, \tag{2}$$

writing $C_1 = C/(\lambda_1 - \lambda_2)$. If $\lambda_2 = \lambda_1$ we have instead (with $C_1 = C$)

$$x = (C_1 t + C_2)\,e^{\lambda_1 t}. \tag{3}$$

Before the second order equation (1) can be solved it is necessary to determine λ_1 and λ_2. These are the roots of the quadratic equation

$$a_0 \lambda^2 + a_1 \lambda + a_2 = 0, \tag{4}$$

called the *auxiliary* or *characteristic equation*.† Provided that a_0, a_1 and a_2 are real these roots will either be real and distinct, real and coincident or conjugate complex numbers. Solutions appropriate to the first two cases are given by (2) and (3). If, however, the roots are complex and a solution in terms of purely real quantities is required, (2) can be modified as follows. Let $\lambda_1, \lambda_2 = \mu \pm jv$.

Then
$$\begin{aligned}
x &= C_1 e^{(\mu + jv)t} + C_2 e^{(\mu - jv)t} \\
&= e^{\mu t}(C_1 e^{jvt} + C_2 e^{-jvt}) \\
&= e^{\mu t}\{C_1(\cos vt + j\sin vt) + C_2(\cos vt - j\sin vt)\},
\end{aligned}$$

using equations (7) and (11) of Appendix 1. Thus

$$x = e^{\mu t}(A\cos vt + B\sin vt), \tag{5}$$

† The term *auxiliary equation* is usual in mathematical textbooks on differential equations, while the name *characteristic equation* is used by engineers, particularly when discussing stability.

replacing the constants $C_1 + C_2$ and $j(C_1 - C_2)$ by A and B respectively. An alternative form is

$$x = C e^{ut} \cos(vt - \alpha), \tag{6}$$

where the arbitrary constants are now C and α, given by $C^2 = A^2 + B^2$ and $\tan \alpha = B/A$.

The non-homogeneous equation of the second order

$$a_0 \frac{d^2 x}{dt^2} + a_1 \frac{dx}{dt} + a_2 x = f(t) \tag{7}$$

can be solved by repeated application of the results of the last section. Put $a_0 = 1$ and write (2) as

$$(\mathbf{D} - \lambda_1)\{(\mathbf{D} - \lambda_2)x\} = f(t), \tag{8}$$

so that $(\mathbf{D} - \lambda_2)x = g_1(t) + C e^{\lambda_1 t}, \quad$ from **1.4** (7).

Hence $x = e^{\lambda_2 t} \int e^{-\lambda_2 t} g_1(t)\, dt + C_1 e^{\lambda_1 t},$

using **1.4** (6) and (8) with $C_1 = C/(\lambda_1 - \lambda_2)$. Writing

$$\int e^{-\lambda_2 t} g_1(t)\, dt = h_2(t) + C_2 \quad \text{and} \quad e^{\lambda_2 t} h_2(t) = g_2(t)$$

we deduce $x = g_2(t) + C_1 e^{\lambda_1 t} + C_2 e^{\lambda_2 t}, \tag{9}$

where λ_1 and λ_2 are the roots of the auxiliary equation (4). This shows once more that the general solution of a linear equation is formed by adding the complementary function (see (2)) to the particular integral $g_2(t)$. The form (9) is appropriate only if λ_1 and λ_2 are real and distinct. If they are coincident or complex the forms given in (3) or (5) above must be used for the complementary function.

EXERCISE   Solve the equation $(\mathbf{D}^2 + 3\mathbf{D} + 2)x = e^{-3t}$.

1.6   Equations of order n

The method used in the last section can be extended formally without difficulty to the general equation with constant coefficients of order n,

$$a_0 \frac{d^n x}{dt^n} + a_1 \frac{d^{n-1} x}{dt^{n-1}} + \ldots + a_n x = f(t).$$

Writing this $Q(\mathbf{D})x = f(t) \tag{1}$

where $Q(\mathbf{D}) \equiv a_0 \mathbf{D}^n + a_1 \mathbf{D}^{n-1} + \ldots + a_n,$

we first write down the auxiliary equation. As in the last section this is formed by replacing $\mathbf{D}$ by λ in $Q(\mathbf{D})$ and equating to zero. This gives

$$Q(\lambda) = a_0 \lambda^n + a_1 \lambda^{n-1} + \ldots + a_n = 0, \tag{2}$$

It is known that such an equation always has n roots, distinct or coincident, real or complex. Denoting these roots by $\lambda_1, \lambda_2, \ldots \lambda_n$ and putting $a_0 = 1$, the operator $Q(\mathbf{D})$ can be factorised (see Appendix 2), so that (1) can be written

$$(\mathbf{D}-\lambda_1)(\mathbf{D}-\lambda_2) \ldots (\mathbf{D}-\lambda_n)x = f(t). \tag{3}$$

Integrating step by step as in **1.5**, the general solution of (3) is found to be

$$x = g_n(t) + C_1 e^{\lambda_1 t} + C_2 e^{\lambda_2 t} + \ldots + C_n e^{\lambda_n t}. \tag{4}$$

The particular integral $g_n(t)$ is the last of the sequence of intermediate particular integrals given by the recurrence relation (omitting arbitrary constants)

$$g_r(t) = e^{\lambda_r t} \int e^{-\lambda_r t} g_{r-1}(t) \, dt. \tag{5}$$

At each intermediate integration one more term is introduced into the complementary function, while in general the complementary function terms already obtained remain unchanged in form (see **1.5** (9)).

The case of repeated roots requires special consideration. Although these do not affect the determination of the particular integral, the complementary function must be modified as in **1.5** (3). More generally, if λ_1 is a multiple root of order k $(\lambda_1 = \lambda_2 = \ldots = \lambda_k)$ the corresponding complementary function terms are

$$(C_1 t^{k-1} + C_2 t^{k-2} + \ldots + C_k) e^{\lambda_1 t}. \tag{6}$$

With conjugate complex roots the corresponding terms in the complementary function may be written as in **1.5** (5) or (6).

It appears therefore that in order to solve the equation (1) it is first necessary to write down and solve the auxiliary equation (2). This can always be done if numerical values of the coefficients are given. Sometimes the roots can be found by factorising the polynomial $Q(\lambda)$ by inspection. For example, if $Q(\lambda) \equiv \lambda^3 + 6\lambda^2 + 9\lambda + 2$ it happens that $Q(\lambda) \equiv (\lambda + 2)(\lambda^2 + 4\lambda + 1)$. The roots are then -2, $-2 \pm \sqrt{3}$. In general, however, this is not possible. In such cases numerical methods must be used. A brief account of these is given in Appendix 9. When the roots are known the complementary function can be written down. If the original differential equation is homogeneous this will be the general solution. Taking the above example, the general solution of the differential equation

$$(\mathbf{D}^3 + 6\mathbf{D}^2 + 9\mathbf{D} + 2)x = 0$$

is $x = A e^{-2t} + B e^{(-2+\sqrt{3})t} + C e^{(-2-\sqrt{3})t}.$

When the complementary function of a non-homogeneous equation has been found the particular integral must be determined. It is always possible to do this formally or by numerical methods using the recurrence relation (5), but much more direct and revealing methods are usually available. These methods apply to equations of the first and second orders as well as to equations of higher order. They will be discussed in the next chapter.

EXERCISES   Obtain the general solutions of the following homogeneous differential equations:

1. $(\mathbf{D}^3 + 6\mathbf{D}^2 + 11\mathbf{D} + 6)x = 0.$

2. $(\mathbf{D}^2 + 5\mathbf{D} - 7)x = 0.$

3. $(\mathbf{D}^2 + 5\mathbf{D} + 7)x = 0.$

4. $(\mathbf{D}^3 + 3\mathbf{D}^2 - \mathbf{D} - 3)x = 0.$

5. $(\mathbf{D}^4 - 10\mathbf{D}^2 + 9)x = 0.$

6. $(\mathbf{D}^4 + 10\mathbf{D}^2 + 9)x = 0.$

7. $(\mathbf{D}^3 + 8)x = 0.$

CHAPTER 2

SOLUTION BY OPERATIONAL METHODS

2.1 Introduction

If the function $f(t)$ is a polynomial in t, an exponential, circular or hyperbolic function of t, or a product of such functions, the particular integral will be a function of the same type. It is possible by substituting such a function with undetermined coefficients in the differential equation to obtain a set of simultaneous equations in these coefficients. Solving these equations gives the required solution. This method is given in most textbooks on differential equations and is widely used.† An alternative process is to use operational methods. These are always equally if not more effective and they can be applied to a wider range of functions. Moreover, the operational notation is particularly suitable for describing the working of linear systems. For these reasons they will be discussed in detail in this chapter.

2.2 Direct and inverse operators

We call any polynomial in $\mathbf{D}$ a *direct operator*. Using our previous notation, such an operator can be denoted by

$$Q(\mathbf{D}) \equiv a_0 \mathbf{D}^n + a_1 \mathbf{D}^{n-1} + \ldots + a_n. \tag{1}$$

It has the following properties. If α is a constant and u and v any functions of t that can be differentiated n times,

(Ia) $$Q(\mathbf{D}) e^{\alpha t} = Q(\alpha) e^{\alpha t},$$

(IIa) $$Q(\mathbf{D})(e^{\alpha t} u) = e^{\alpha t} Q(\mathbf{D} + \alpha)u,$$

(IIIa) $$Q(\mathbf{D})(u + v) = Q(\mathbf{D})u + Q(\mathbf{D})v.$$

Notice that in (Ia) while $Q(\mathbf{D})$ is an operator, $Q(\alpha)$ is an ordinary numerical multiplier. In order to prove this result it is only necessary to observe that $\mathbf{D}^r e^{\alpha t} = \alpha^r e^{\alpha t}$. Property (IIa) shows that a factor $e^{\alpha t}$ can be shifted

---

† See for example Piaggio, H. T. H., *Differential Equations*. Bell & Sons (London).

outside the operator if $\mathbf{D}$ is replaced in the latter by $\mathbf{D}+\alpha$ wherever it occurs. It is proved as follows:

$$\mathbf{D}(e^{\alpha t}u) = \alpha\, e^{\alpha t}u + e^{\alpha t}\mathbf{D}u = e^{\alpha t}(\mathbf{D}+\alpha)u. \tag{2}$$
$$\mathbf{D}^2(e^{\alpha t}u) = \mathbf{D}\{e^{\alpha t}(\mathbf{D}+\alpha)u\} = e^{\alpha t}(\mathbf{D}+\alpha)^2 u,$$

using (2). This process can be extended to give $\mathbf{D}^r(e^{\alpha t}u)$ and thence $Q(\mathbf{D})(e^{\alpha t}u)$ as stated above. Property (IIIa) is proved by repeated application of **1.3** (3).

The simplest direct operation (other than the trivial one of multiplication by a constant) is differentiation, denoted by $\mathbf{D}$. We shall denote the inverse operation of this, which is of course integration, by $1/\mathbf{D}$ or $\mathbf{D}^{-1}$. Thus

$$\mathbf{D}^{-1}u = \int u\, dt. \tag{3}$$

Alternatively stated,

$$x = \mathbf{D}^{-1}u \quad \text{if} \quad \mathbf{D}x = u. \tag{4}$$

Notice that we have defined this inverse operation as giving an *indefinite* integral. In other words $\mathbf{D}^{-1}u$ represents an infinite aggregate of functions, different members of which are given by different values of the arbitrary constant. It is of some interest and importance to see what happens when the operators $\mathbf{D}$ and $\mathbf{D}^{-1}$ are applied in different orders to a function, for example $3t^2$. Thus

$$\mathbf{D}^{-1}(3t^2) = t^3 + C, \qquad \mathbf{D}\mathbf{D}^{-1}(3t^2) = 3t^2, \tag{5}$$

so that the operational "product" $\mathbf{D}\mathbf{D}^{-1}$ gives the unit or identical operation. This provides a justification for the use of the reciprocal notation for the inverse operation. On the other hand,

$$\mathbf{D}(3t^2) = 6t, \qquad \mathbf{D}^{-1}\mathbf{D}(3t^2) = 3t^2 + C. \tag{6}$$

This shows that the product $\mathbf{D}^{-1}\mathbf{D}$ is not an identical operation. One aspect of this result is that the operators $\mathbf{D}$ and $\mathbf{D}^{-1}$ are not commutative.

The general inverse operator $1/Q(\mathbf{D})$ is defined in the same way, as follows.

If

$$Q(\mathbf{D})x = u \tag{7}$$

then

$$x = \frac{1}{Q(\mathbf{D})}u. \tag{8}$$

In other words the function x given by the inverse operation in (8) is by definition the *general* solution of the differential equation (7). This will therefore include complementary function terms. The indeterminacy which this convention introduces is the cause of a small amount of inconvenience which it is desirable to accept for the following reasons.

If the differential equation (7) is specified without any further conditions all the possible solutions must be regarded as having equal status. It is impossible to pick out one of these to represent a unique inverse operation without sacrificing generality. Further, it is necessary for the logical justification of some of the formulae derived later that the inverse operator shall indicate the whole class or aggregate of functions given by the solution of the differential equation, rather than one particular solution. This means that when we equate two such expressions we imply the equivalence of the corresponding aggregates rather than the equality of a pair of particular functions in the respective aggregates.

As an example, in order to interpret the expression

$$\frac{1}{\mathbf{D}^2+3\mathbf{D}+2}t^2$$

we must solve the differential equation $(\mathbf{D}^2+3\mathbf{D}+2)x = t^2$. It can be verified that the solution of this equation is

$$x = \tfrac{1}{2}t^2 - \tfrac{3}{2}t + \tfrac{7}{4} + C_1 e^{-t} + C_2 e^{-2t}$$

so that $\dfrac{1}{\mathbf{D}^2+3\mathbf{D}+2}t^2 = \tfrac{1}{2}t^2 - \tfrac{3}{2}t + \tfrac{7}{4} + C_1 e^{-t} + C_2 e^{-2t}$,

where the constants C_1 and C_2 can take all possible values.

In order to obtain particular integrals by operational methods we require six properties of inverse operators. The first three of these are extensions of (Ia), (IIa) and (IIIa) above as follows:

(Ib)   a particular integral of $\dfrac{1}{Q(\mathbf{D})} e^{\alpha t}$ is $\dfrac{e^{\alpha t}}{Q(\alpha)}$, provided $Q(\alpha) \neq 0$,

(IIb) $\dfrac{1}{Q(\mathbf{D})}(e^{\alpha t} u) = e^{\alpha t}\dfrac{1}{Q(\mathbf{D}+\alpha)}u$,

(IIIb) $\dfrac{1}{Q(\mathbf{D})}(u+v) = \dfrac{1}{Q(\mathbf{D})}u + \dfrac{1}{Q(\mathbf{D})}v$.

The first and third of these results can be verified immediately by substitution, using (Ia) and (IIIa). The second is proved in Appendix 6 (Theorem 9), which also contains a formal derivation of (Ib).

The other three properties represent algebraic processes which it is permissible to perform on inverse operators. These are quoted without proof here.

(IVb) $$\frac{1}{Q_1(\mathbf{D})Q_2(\mathbf{D})}u = \frac{1}{Q_1(\mathbf{D})}\frac{1}{Q_2(\mathbf{D})}u = \frac{1}{Q_1(\mathbf{D})}\left\{\frac{1}{Q_2(\mathbf{D})}u\right\}.$$

(Vb) Provided the function u operated on has derivatives of all orders, a particular integral may be obtained by expanding the inverse operator $1/Q(\mathbf{D})$ in *ascending* powers of $\mathbf{D}$.

(VIb) The inverse operator $1/Q(\mathbf{D})$ may be expressed in partial fractions.

Proofs of these properties are given in Appendix 6. It will be seen from examples 8 to 11 in the next section that the series given by (Vb) will terminate after a finite number of terms if, and only if, u is a polynomial in t. In other cases an infinite series will be obtained. The expansion of the operator is effected by means of the binomial theorem or by division (see Appendices 3 and 4). In view of the important part which this process will play in this book a fuller account, with examples, is given in Appendix 7.

2.3   Evaluation of particular integrals

Consider the differential equation

$$Q(\mathbf{D})x = f(t). \tag{1}$$

With the notation of the last section the solution can be written

$$x = \frac{1}{Q(\mathbf{D})}f(t). \tag{2}$$

If $f(t)$ is a polynomial in t, an exponential or circular function of t or a product of functions of these types the particular integral, and hence the general solution, can always be evaluated completely. With other types of function it can be expressed as an integral. We show below, with examples, how these solutions are obtained systematically using operational methods.

Firstly, if $f(t) = e^{\alpha t}$, we use property (Ib) (**2.2**).

Example 1 $$\frac{d^2x}{dt^2}+5\frac{dx}{dt}+6x = e^{3t},$$

or $$x = \frac{1}{\mathbf{D}^2+5\mathbf{D}+6}e^{3t}.$$

A particular integral is therefore

$$\frac{1}{3^2+5.3+6}e^{3t} = \frac{1}{30}e^{3t}.$$

The auxiliary equation is

$$\lambda^2+5\lambda+6 = 0,$$

with roots $\lambda = -2$ and -3. The complementary function is therefore $Ae^{-2t}+Be^{-3t}$, so that the general solution is

$$x = \tfrac{1}{30}e^{3t}+Ae^{-2t}+Be^{-3t}.$$

Example 2 $(D^2+4D+13)x = 5e^{-t}.$

The auxiliary equation is

$$\lambda^2+4\lambda+13 \equiv (\lambda+2)^2+3^2 = 0,$$

with roots $-2\pm3j$. The particular integral is $\tfrac{1}{2}e^{-t}$, so that the general solution is

$$x = \tfrac{1}{2}e^{-t}+e^{-2t}(A\cos 3t+B\sin 3t).$$

This method can always be used provided $Q(\alpha) \neq 0$. It can also be used if $f(t) = \cos \beta t$ or $\sin \beta t$ by regarding these functions as the real or imaginary parts of $e^{j\beta t}$ (see Appendix 1).

Example 3 $(D^2+6D+9)x = \cos 2t.$

or $$x = \frac{1}{D^2+6D+9}\mathcal{R}\,e^{2jt},$$

where $\mathcal{R}$ denotes the real part.

The auxiliary equation has two equal roots, -3, and the particular integral is

$$\mathcal{R}\left\{\frac{1}{-4+12j+9}e^{2jt}\right\} = \mathcal{R}\left\{\frac{5-12j}{5^2+12^2}(\cos 2t+j\sin 2t)\right\}$$

$$= \tfrac{1}{169}(5\cos 2t+12\sin 2t).$$

The general solution is thus

$$x = \tfrac{1}{169}(5\cos 2t+12\sin 2t)+(At+B)e^{-3t}.$$

If $f(t) = \sin \beta t$, it can be expressed either as the imaginary part of $e^{j\beta t}$ or as the real part of $-je^{j\beta t}$. More generally, if $f(t)$ contains both $\sin \beta t$ and $\cos \beta t$, it is usually simpler to work with real parts throughout.

Example 4 $(\mathbf{D}^2+4\mathbf{D}+1)x = \cos t+2\sin t.$

The auxiliary equation is

$$\lambda^2+4\lambda+1 \equiv (\lambda+2)^2-(\sqrt{3})^2 = 0,$$

with roots $-2\pm\sqrt{3}$. The particular integral is

$$\mathscr{R}\left\{\frac{1}{-1+4j+1}(1-2j)\,e^{jt}\right\} = \mathscr{R}\{-\tfrac{1}{4}(2+j)(\cos t+j\sin t)\},$$

so that the general solution is

$$x = \tfrac{1}{4}(-2\cos t+\sin t)+A\,e^{(-2+\sqrt{3})t}+B\,e^{(-2-\sqrt{3})t}.$$

The case where $f(t)$ is the product of an exponential and a circular function can be solved as follows:

Example 5 $(\mathbf{D}+2)x = e^{-3t}\cos 2t.$

$$x = \mathscr{R}\left\{\frac{1}{\mathbf{D}+2}\,e^{(-3+2j)t}\right\}$$

$$= \mathscr{R}\left\{\frac{1}{-3+2j+2}\,e^{(-3+2j)t}\right\}+\frac{1}{\mathbf{D}+2}\,0$$

$$= \mathscr{R}\{\tfrac{1}{5}(-1-2j)\,e^{-3t}(\cos 2t+j\sin 2t)\}+A\,e^{-2t}$$

$$= \tfrac{1}{5}e^{-3t}(-\cos 2t+2\sin 2t)+A\,e^{-2t}.$$

In this example we have introduced a useful notation for the complementary function. Since the latter is the general solution of $Q(\mathbf{D})x = 0$, it is convenient to denote it by $\{1/Q(\mathbf{D})\}0$.

We now turn to the case $f(t) = e^{\alpha t}$ where $Q(\alpha) = 0$. When this happens, $Q(\mathbf{D})$ can be written $(\mathbf{D}-\alpha)^k Q_1(\mathbf{D})$ where $Q_1(\alpha) \neq 0$ and k is the multiplicity of the root α. Then

$$x = \frac{1}{Q(\mathbf{D})}\,e^{\alpha t} = \frac{1}{(\mathbf{D}-\alpha)^k}\left\{\frac{1}{Q_1(\mathbf{D})}\,e^{\alpha t}\right\} = \frac{1}{(\mathbf{D}-\alpha)^k}\left\{\frac{e^{\alpha t}}{Q_1(\alpha)}\right\}$$

$$= \frac{1}{Q_1(\alpha)}\,\frac{1}{(\mathbf{D}-\alpha)^k}(e^{\alpha t}1) = \frac{e^{\alpha t}}{Q_1(\alpha)}\,\frac{1}{\mathbf{D}^k}1 = \frac{t^k\,e^{\alpha t}}{k!\,Q_1(\alpha)},$$

using properties (IVb) and (IIb) (2.2) respectively. With the latter the function u is the constant 1, which on integration k times gives $t^k/k!$. Here, as in the following examples, we omit complementary function terms from the various steps of the argument. In practice it makes the working less cumbersome to determine these separately, directly from the auxiliary equation $Q(\lambda) = 0$, and add them to the particular integral at the final stage.

Example 6 $(D^2 + 5D + 6)x = e^{-3t}.$

A particular solution is found as follows.

$$x = \frac{1}{D+3}\left(\frac{1}{D+2}e^{-3t}\right) = \frac{1}{D+3}(-e^{-3t})$$

$$= -\frac{1}{D+3}(e^{-3t}1) = -e^{-3t}\frac{1}{D}1 = -te^{-3t}.$$

Introducing the complementary function, the general solution becomes

$$x = (A-t)e^{-3t} + Be^{-2t}.$$

Example 7 $(D^3 + D^2 - D - 1)x = e^{-t}.$

$$x = \frac{1}{(D+1)^2(D-1)}e^{-t} = -\tfrac{1}{2}\frac{1}{(D+1)^2}(e^{-t}1)$$

$$= -\tfrac{1}{2}e^{-t}\frac{1}{D^2}1 = -\tfrac{1}{4}t^2e^{-t},$$

or, with the complementary function,

$$x = (A + Bt - \tfrac{1}{4}t^2)e^{-t} + Ce^{t}.$$

The case $f(t) = t^m$, where m is a positive integer, can be dealt with using property (Vb), that is by expanding the inverse operator in ascending powers of **D**.

Example 8 $(D+3)x = t^3.$

$$x = \frac{1}{3+D}t^3 = \tfrac{1}{3}(1 + \tfrac{1}{3}D)^{-1}t^3$$

$$= \tfrac{1}{3}(1 - \tfrac{1}{3}D + \tfrac{1}{9}D^2 - \tfrac{1}{27}D^3 + \ldots)t^3 + \frac{1}{D+3}0$$

$$= \tfrac{1}{3}t^3 - \tfrac{1}{3}t^2 + \tfrac{2}{9}t - \tfrac{2}{27} + Ae^{-3t}.$$

Notice that, since the fourth and higher derivatives of t^3 all vanish, terms after the one in $\mathbf{D}^3$ need not be written down. In general, the series obtained by expanding an operator will terminate if, and only if, the function operated on is a polynomial in t.

T.L.S.—2

Example 9 $(\mathbf{D}^2+3\mathbf{D}+5)x = 2+3t^2.$

$$x = \frac{1}{5+3\mathbf{D}+\mathbf{D}^2}(2+3t^2)$$

$$= \tfrac{1}{5}\{1-(\tfrac{3}{5}\mathbf{D}+\tfrac{1}{5}\mathbf{D}^2)+(\tfrac{3}{5}\mathbf{D}+\tfrac{1}{5}\mathbf{D}^2)^2\}(2+3t^2),$$

or, introducing the complementary function,

$$x = (\tfrac{1}{5}-\tfrac{3}{25}\mathbf{D}+\tfrac{4}{125}\mathbf{D}^2)(2+3t^2)+\frac{1}{(\mathbf{D}+\tfrac{3}{2})^2+(\tfrac{1}{2}\sqrt{11})^2}0$$

$$= \tfrac{3}{5}t^2-\tfrac{18}{25}t+\tfrac{74}{125}+e^{-3t/2}\{A\cos(\tfrac{1}{2}\sqrt{11})t+B\sin(\tfrac{1}{2}\sqrt{11})t\}.$$

In both of the above examples the expansions have been obtained from the binomial theorem. An alternative method is to use division. This would certainly be preferable with more complicated operators, particularly if the synthetic method is used (see Appendix 3).

Finally, a combination of the above methods can be used when $f(t) = t^m e^{\alpha t}\cos\beta t$.

Example 10 $(\mathbf{D}+1)x = t\,e^t\cos t$

$$x = \mathscr{R}\frac{1}{\mathbf{D}+1}\{t\,e^{(1+j)t}\} = \mathscr{R}\,e^{(1+j)t}\frac{1}{\mathbf{D}+2+j}t,$$

using property (IIb). If we then expand the operator we have

$$x = \mathscr{R}\,e^{(1+j)t}\left(\frac{1}{2+j}-\frac{\mathbf{D}}{(2+j)^2}\right)t$$

$$= \mathscr{R}\,e^{(1+j)t}\left(\frac{2-j}{5}t-\frac{3-4j}{25}\right),$$

or $x = (\tfrac{2}{5}t-\tfrac{3}{25})\,e^t\cos t+(\tfrac{1}{5}t-\tfrac{4}{25})\,e^t\sin t+A\,e^{-t}.$

Example 11 $(\mathbf{D}^2+3\mathbf{D}+2)x = 2t\,e^{-t}.$

$$x = \frac{1}{(\mathbf{D}+1)(\mathbf{D}+2)}2t\,e^{-t} = e^{-t}\frac{1}{\mathbf{D}(\mathbf{D}+1)}2t$$

$$= e^{-t}\frac{1}{\mathbf{D}}(1-\mathbf{D})2t = e^{-t}\frac{1}{\mathbf{D}}(2t-2)$$

$$= e^{-t}(t^2-2t).$$

With the complementary function,

$$x = e^{-t}(t^2-2t+A)+B\,e^{-2t}.$$

EXERCISES   Solve the following differential equations by operational methods:

1. $(D^2+3D+2)x = e^{-3t}$ (cf. exercise in **1.5**).
2. $(D^2+4D+13)x = 18e^t$.
3. $(D^2-4)x = e^{-2t}$.
4. $(D^2+9)x = \sin 2t$.
5. $(D^2+8D+25)x = 3 \cos 3t+2 \sin 3t$.
6. $(D+2)x = 2t$ (cf. exercise in **1.4**).
7. $(D+2)x = t^4+t$.
8. $(D^2+D+1)x = t^2$.
9. $(D^2+4D+4)x = te^{-t}$.
10. $(D^2+6D+25)x = te^{-3t} \cos 4t$.
11. $(D^3+2D^2+2D+1)x = \cos t$.

2.4   Particular integrals by expansion of the operator

It is apparent from the last section that if $f(t)$ takes the form $t^m e^{\alpha t} \cos \beta t$, where m is a constant positive integer and α and β are constant, then a particular integral can always be found, and this particular integral is a linear combination of a finite number of functions of the same type. With other types of function however, or if $f(t)$ is unspecified, the particular integral will in general take a more complicated form. In the present and the following sections we show two methods of dealing with these more complicated cases.

The method of expanding the operator has already been applied to functions which are polynomials in t, in which case the series obtained have been found to terminate. These are the only cases where this happens, since polynomials are the only functions whose derivatives of all sufficiently high orders can vanish identically. In any other case the series obtained must contain an infinite number of non-vanishing terms.

Consider the general first order equation. It is convenient to write this in the form

$$(TD+1)x = f(t). \tag{1}$$

Here the constant T has the physical dimensions of time, and in systems governed by this equation it is usually called the *time constant*. Then the complementary function is $A e^{-t/T}$. Expansion of the inverse operator in ascending powers of **D** gives as a particular integral

$$(1 - TD + T^2D^2 - T^3D^3 + \ldots)f(t),$$

so that the general solution is

$$x = f(t) - Tf'(t) + T^2f''(t) - T^3f'''(t) + \ldots + A e^{-t/T}. \tag{2}$$

If the infinite series converges it can be verified by direct substitution in (1) that (2) is a solution.

For a solution of this type to be useful it is necessary that the successive terms of the series should diminish in magnitude fairly rapidly. When this is the case we can say that a first approximation to the particular integral is given by $x = f(t)$. The second approximation is

$$x = f(t) - Tf'(T) = f(t-T) \tag{3}$$

approximately, using Taylor's theorem. Physically this means that the solution is represented by the function $f(t)$ delayed by a time T. Better approximations can be obtained by taking further terms of the series, but these have no simple physical interpretation.

Useful approximations can often be obtained from the expansion (2) even when it is not convergent. The explanation of this somewhat surprising fact is that such a series frequently has the property of being *asymptotic* or *semi-convergent*. A formal definition of this property will not be given here; it is sufficient to state that when it occurs the individual terms of the series and the remainders at each stage decrease in absolute value at first, before they start to increase indefinitely (the remainder after the first n terms is defined as the difference between the sum of these terms and the required function). There is therefore a minimum remainder. If this is small enough an adequate approximation can be obtained by terminating the series at this stage.

With many asymptotic series the minimum remainder occurs when the corresponding term is also a minimum. In practice, a satisfactory approximation to the particular integral is often given by the first one or two terms of the expansion, whether the series is convergent or asymptotic.

Appendix 7 contains a number of alternative methods of deriving the expansion (2) together with the remainder at any stage. It also shows by an example how an asymptotic series can arise and be interpreted.

The method of expanding the operator can be extended without difficulty to differential equations of higher order. For example

$$(3\mathbf{D}^2 + 2\mathbf{D} + 1)x = f(t).$$

Then $x = \dfrac{1}{1 + 2\mathbf{D} + 3\mathbf{D}^2} f(t) = (1 - 2\mathbf{D} + \mathbf{D}^2 + 4\mathbf{D}^3 + \ldots)f(t)$

$$= f(t) - 2f'(t) + f''(t) + 4f'''(t) + \ldots.$$

The usefulness or otherwise of this series, like (2), depends on the relative magnitude of successive terms, which of course depends on the nature of the function $f(t)$.

2.5 Solutions expressed as integrals

Consider the general first order equation

$$(\mathbf{D}-\lambda_1)x = f(t). \tag{1}$$

Using property (IIb) (**2.2**) we can solve formally as follows.

$$x = \frac{1}{\mathbf{D}-\lambda_1}f(t) = \frac{1}{\mathbf{D}-\lambda_1}\{e^{\lambda_1 t}e^{-\lambda_1 t}f(t)\} = e^{\lambda_1 t}\frac{1}{\mathbf{D}}\{e^{-\lambda_1 t}f(t)\},$$

or

$$x = e^{\lambda_1 t}\int e^{-\lambda_1 t}f(t)\,dt. \tag{2}$$

This of course is the solution (6) obtained in **1.4**. As was seen in **1.4** the indefinite integral in this expression gives the general solution of (1). If the indefinite integral is replaced by a definite integral in which the lower limit is a constant t_0 and the upper limit the variable t, a particular solution is obtained. Since t is now a limit we must use another symbol, t_1, as the variable of integration. Thus

$$x(t) = e^{\lambda_1 t}\int_{t_0}^{t} e^{-\lambda_1 t_1}f(t_1)\,dt_1. \tag{3}$$

Since the term $e^{\lambda_1 t}$ does not involve the variable of integration, it can be placed under the integral sign, giving the required solution,

$$x(t) = \int_{t_0}^{t} e^{\lambda_1(t-t_1)}f(t_1)\,dt_1. \tag{4}$$

This is the solution which vanishes when $t = t_0$. It can be evaluated, if necessary by numerical integration of (3) or (4), for any value of t and for any value of t_0.

Equations of the second and higher orders can be treated in the same way by expressing the operator in partial fractions. Thus if

$$(\mathbf{D}-\lambda_1)(\mathbf{D}-\lambda_2)x = f(t), \tag{5}$$

$$x = \frac{1}{\lambda_1-\lambda_2}\left(\frac{1}{\mathbf{D}-\lambda_1} - \frac{1}{\mathbf{D}-\lambda_2}\right)f(t)$$

$$= \frac{1}{\lambda_1-\lambda_2}\left\{e^{\lambda_1 t}\int e^{-\lambda_1 t}f(t)\,dt - e^{\lambda_2 t}\int e^{-\lambda_2 t}f(t)\,dt\right\}.$$

This is the general solution. If the indefinite integrals are replaced by definite integrals from t_0 to t, these can be combined into a single integral, which is the particular integral

$$x(t) = \int_{t_0}^{t} \frac{1}{\lambda_1-\lambda_2}\left\{e^{\lambda_1(t-t_1)} - e^{\lambda_2(t-t_1)}\right\}f(t_1)\,dt_1. \tag{6}$$

This solution clearly vanishes when $t = t_0$. It can be verified that its derivative also vanishes then.

Notice that both (4) and (6) are of the form

$$x(t) = \int_{t_0}^{t} W(t-t_1)f(t_1)\, dt_1. \tag{7}$$

It is easily seen that this will be true for the general equation $Q(\mathbf{D})x = f(t)$ and that if we replace $t - t_1$ by τ, the function $W(\tau)$ depends only on the operator $Q(\mathbf{D})$. In the cases we have considered already, if $Q(\mathbf{D}) = \mathbf{D} - \lambda_1$,

$$W(\tau) = e^{\lambda_1 \tau}, \tag{8}$$

while if $Q(\mathbf{D}) = (\mathbf{D} - \lambda_1)(\mathbf{D} - \lambda_2)$

$$W(\tau) = \frac{e^{\lambda_1 \tau} - e^{\lambda_2 \tau}}{\lambda_1 - \lambda_2}. \tag{9}$$

As special cases of (9), if λ_1 and λ_2 are conjugate complex numbers $\mu \pm jv$,

$$W(\tau) = \frac{1}{v} e^{\mu \tau} \sin v\tau, \tag{10}$$

while if $\lambda_2 = \lambda_1$,

$$W(\tau) = \tau\, e^{\lambda_1 \tau}. \tag{11}$$

The last result is obtained by letting $\lambda_2 \to \lambda_1$ in (9), which is equivalent to differentiating (8) with respect to λ_1. Finally, if

$$Q(\mathbf{D}) = (\mathbf{D} - \lambda_1)(\mathbf{D} - \lambda_2) \ldots (\mathbf{D} - \lambda_n),$$

the partial fractions of $1/Q(\mathbf{D})$ are $\sum_{r=1}^{n} 1/\{Q'(\lambda_r)(\mathbf{D} - \lambda_r)\}$ (see Theorem 2 of Appendix 5), so that

$$W(\tau) = \sum \frac{e^{\lambda_r \tau}}{Q'(\lambda_r)}. \tag{12}$$

This expression requires modification when some of the numbers $\lambda_1, \lambda_2, \ldots \lambda_n$ are repeated or are complex.

For the present, the significance of this process lies in the fact that, whatever the form of the function $f(t)$, a particular integral can be calculated with, at worst, a single numerical integration. This particular integral (7) is in fact the one which vanishes together with its first $(n-1)$ derivatives when $t = t_0$. We shall see later in **8.4**, when discussing linear systems, that (7) represents the process of *convolution* and that the function $W(\tau)$ corresponds to a *weighting function*.

2.6 The general rational fraction operator

At this stage we introduce formally the general rational fraction operator $F(\mathbf{D}) = P(\mathbf{D})/Q(\mathbf{D})$ where $P(\mathbf{D})$ and $Q(\mathbf{D})$ are polynomials in $\mathbf{D}$. (Although we have not made use of operators of this type in this chapter they play an important part later in the book in the development of the theory of linear systems.) Then, by definition,

$$F(\mathbf{D}) = \frac{P(\mathbf{D})}{Q(\mathbf{D})} = \frac{1}{Q(\mathbf{D})}P(\mathbf{D}). \tag{1}$$

That is, the general rational fraction operator is the combination of a direct and an inverse operator in which the inverse operator is applied *after* the direct operator. In other words, if $x = F(\mathbf{D})u$, x is the general solution of the differential equation

$$Q(\mathbf{D})x = P(\mathbf{D})u. \tag{2}$$

It is evident that $F(\mathbf{D})u$ will contain complementary function terms represented by $\{1/Q(\mathbf{D})\}0$. We refer to a particular integral of the differential equation (2) as a *particular form* of the expression $F(\mathbf{D})u$.

The rational fraction operators have properties analogous to those of the simple direct and inverse operators enumerated in **2.2**. These are as follows:

(Ic)   a particular form of $F(\mathbf{D})\,e^{\alpha t}$ is $F(\alpha)\,e^{\alpha t}$, provided $Q(\alpha) \neq 0$,

(IIc) $F(\mathbf{D})(e^{\alpha t}u) = e^{\alpha t}F(\mathbf{D}+\alpha)u,$

(IIIc) $F(\mathbf{D})(u+v) = F(\mathbf{D})u+F(\mathbf{D})v.$

In addition, operators of this type can be combined or broken down by algebraic manipulation, with the qualification that the cancellation or introduction of common factors has the effect of the elimination or introduction of complementary function terms. The latter in particular should be avoided. As particular cases operators of this type may be expressed in partial fractions or expanded in series of *ascending* powers of $\mathbf{D}$.

These properties are proved, and a general discussion of operators of this type is given in Appendix 6.

CHAPTER 3

SOLUTIONS WITH GIVEN INITIAL CONDITIONS

3.1 Direct method

The general solution of a differential equation of order n contains n arbitrary constants or constants of integration. It was seen in **1.1** that in order to determine a particular solution to our problem we require n extra conditions. These can take various forms. For example, the values of the dependent variable x can be given for n different values of the independent variable t. Alternatively some or all of these conditions may involve the derivatives of x. In our discussion of the linear equation $Q(\mathbf{D})x = f(t)$ we shall consider only the case in which the values of x and of its first $n-1$ derivatives are given when $t = 0$. These are called the *initial conditions*.

Example 1　To solve $(\mathbf{D}^2 + 5\mathbf{D} + 6)x = 12\,e^t$ if $x = 2$ and $\mathbf{D}x = 1$ when $t = 0$.

Using the method of Chapter 2 the general solution is found to be

$$x = e^t + A\,e^{-2t} + B\,e^{-3t},$$

whence
$$\mathbf{D}x = e^t - 2A\,e^{-2t} - 3B\,e^{-3t}.$$

Substituting the given values,

$$2 = 1 + A + B, \qquad 1 = 1 - 2A - 3B.$$

If these equations are solved we find that $A = 3$, $B = -2$. The required solution is therefore

$$x = e^t + 3\,e^{-2t} - 2\,e^{-3t}.$$

Example 2　To solve $(\mathbf{D}^2 + 4\mathbf{D} + 13)x = 5e^{-t}$ if $x = \mathbf{D}x = 0$ when $t = 0$.

The general solution of this has been found to be (**2.3**, example 2)

$$x = \tfrac{1}{2}e^{-t} + e^{-2t}(A\cos 3t + B\sin 3t).$$

Putting $t = 0$, we have $\tfrac{1}{2} + A = 0$. Differentiating and putting $t = 0$, we have $-\tfrac{1}{2} - 2A + 3B = 0$. Hence $A = -\tfrac{1}{2}$, $B = -\tfrac{1}{6}$, so that

$$x = \tfrac{1}{2}e^{-t} - e^{-2t}(\tfrac{1}{2}\cos 3t + \tfrac{1}{6}\sin 3t).$$

3.2 Laplace transform

An alternative method giving directly the solution of a linear differential equation satisfying given initial conditions makes use of the *Laplace transformation*. In this section we define this and prove some of its more elementary properties.

If $f(t)$ is a function of t defined for values of $t \geqq 0$, its Laplace transform is defined to be $\int_0^\infty e^{-pt} f(t) \, dt$. This integral is a function of p, and is denoted by $\mathfrak{L}f(t)$ or $f^*(p)$. Thus

$$\mathfrak{L}f(t) = f^*(p) = \int_0^\infty e^{-pt} f(t) \, dt. \tag{1}$$

We call $f(t)$ the *inverse Laplace transform* of $f^*(p)$ and denote it by $\mathfrak{L}^{-1} f^*(p)$. The physical significance of the variable p will be considered later, in Chapter 5. For the present purpose it can be any real or complex number for which the integral in (1) converges.

The Laplace transform has the following properties:

$$\mathfrak{L}\{f_1(t) + f_2(t)\} = \mathfrak{L}f_1(t) + \mathfrak{L}f_2(t), \tag{2}$$

$$\mathfrak{L}\{cf(t)\} = c\mathfrak{L}f(t), \tag{3}$$

c being a constant.

$$\mathfrak{L}f'(t) = pf^*(p) - f(0), \tag{4}$$

$$\mathfrak{L}f''(t) = p^2 f^*(p) - pf(0) - f'(0), \tag{5}$$

$$\mathfrak{L}f^{(n)}(t) = p^n f^*(p) - p^{n-1} f(0) - p^{n-2} f'(0) - \ldots - f^{(n-1)}(0), \tag{6}$$

$$\mathfrak{L}\int_0^t f(t_1) \, dt_1 = \frac{f^*(p)}{p}. \tag{7}$$

The first two properties are easily proved, while (4) is derived as follows.

$$\mathfrak{L}f'(t) = \int_0^\infty e^{-pt} f'(t) \, dt = \left[e^{-pt} f(t) \right]_0^\infty + p \int_0^\infty e^{-pt} f(t) \, dt,$$

integrating by parts. If the limits are substituted in the integrated part, (4) follows immediately. Repeated application of (4) gives (5) and (6). Thus

$$\mathfrak{L}f''(t) = p\mathfrak{L}f'(t) - f'(0) = p\{pf^*(p) - f(0)\} - f'(0),$$

and so on. To prove (7) put $\int_0^t f(t_1) \, dt_1 = F(t)$. Then $F'(t) = f(t)$ and $F(0) = 0$. Since

$$f^*(p) = \mathfrak{L}f(t) = \mathfrak{L}F'(t) = pF^*(p) - F(0) = pF^*(p),$$

it follows that $F^*(p) = f^*(p)/p$, which is the required result.

We now obtain the transforms of certain elementary functions, starting with $e^{\alpha t}$, where α is a real constant.

$$\mathfrak{L}\,e^{\alpha t} = \int_0^\infty e^{-pt}\,e^{\alpha t}\,dt = \int_0^\infty e^{-(p-\alpha)t}\,dt = \left[\frac{-e^{-(p-\alpha)t}}{p-\alpha}\right]_0^\infty.$$

Thus
$$\mathfrak{L}\,e^{\alpha t} = \frac{1}{p-\alpha}, \tag{8}$$

provided the real part of p is greater than α. Differentiating (8) m times with respect to α†,

$$\mathfrak{L}t^m\,e^{\alpha t} = \frac{m!}{(p-\alpha)^{m+1}}. \tag{9}$$

Putting $\alpha = 0$,

$$\mathfrak{L}t^m = \frac{m!}{p^{m+1}}. \tag{10}$$

If α is replaced by the complex number $\alpha + j\beta$, (8) becomes

$$\mathfrak{L}\,e^{(\alpha+j\beta)t} = \mathfrak{L}\,e^{\alpha t}(\cos\beta t + j\sin\beta t)$$

$$= \frac{1}{p-\alpha-j\beta} = \frac{p-\alpha+j\beta}{(p-\alpha)^2+\beta^2}.$$

Equating real and imaginary parts we have the two results:

$$\mathfrak{L}\,e^{\alpha t}\cos\beta t = \frac{p-\alpha}{(p-\alpha)^2+\beta^2}, \tag{11}$$

$$\mathfrak{L}\,e^{\alpha t}\sin\beta t = \frac{\beta}{(p-\alpha)^2+\beta^2}. \tag{12}$$

A similar process can be applied to (9).

† The process of differentiating a relation such as this can be justified as follows. Let
$$\mathfrak{L}\,f(t,\,a) = f^*(p,\,a).$$
Then
$$\mathfrak{L}\,\frac{\partial}{\partial a}f(t,\,a) = \mathfrak{L}\lim\frac{1}{\delta a}\{f(t,\,a+\delta a)-f(t,\,a)\}$$

$$= \lim\frac{1}{\delta a}\{f^*(p,\,a+\delta a)-f^*(p,\,a)\}$$

$$= \frac{\partial}{\partial a}f^*(p,\,a),$$

provided $f(t,\,a)$ and $f^*(p,\,a)$ satisfy certain general continuity conditions.

These results and some important particular cases of them are listed in Table 3.2.

$f(t)$	$f^*(p)$	$f(t)$	$f^*(p)$
1	$\dfrac{1}{p}$	$\cos \beta t$	$\dfrac{p}{p^2+\beta^2}$
t	$\dfrac{1}{p^2}$	$\sin \beta t$	$\dfrac{\beta}{p^2+\beta^2}$
t^2	$\dfrac{2}{p^3}$	$e^{\alpha t}\cos \beta t$	$\dfrac{p-\alpha}{(p-\alpha)^2+\beta^2}$
t^m	$\dfrac{m!}{p^{m+1}}$	$e^{\alpha t}\sin \beta t$	$\dfrac{\beta}{(p-\alpha)^2+\beta^2}$
$e^{\alpha t}$	$\dfrac{1}{p-\alpha}$	$t\cos \beta t$	$\dfrac{p^2-\beta^2}{(p^2+\beta^2)^2}$
$t^m e^{\alpha t}$	$\dfrac{m!}{(p-\alpha)^{m+1}}$	$t\sin \beta t$	$\dfrac{2\beta p}{(p^2+\beta^2)^2}$

TABLE 3.2 (A)   Laplace transforms.

Notice that (8), (9), (11) and (12) are special cases of the useful general formula

$$\mathfrak{L}\, e^{\alpha t} f(t) = f^*(p-\alpha). \tag{13}$$

This is easily proved using the definition of $f^*(p)$ given in (1) (see property I of **5.4**).

3.3   Application to differential equations

We are now in a position to solve linear differential equations with constant coefficients by means of the Laplace transformation. Consider first the two examples worked in **3.1**.

Example 1   To solve $\mathbf{D}^2 x + 5\mathbf{D}x + 6x = 12\, e^t$ if $x = 2$ and $\mathbf{D}x = 1$ when $t = 0$.

The first step is to multiply both sides of the equation by e^{-pt} and integrate from 0 to ∞. This is equivalent to taking the transforms of the four terms of the equation. If we denote the transform of x by x^* and use **3.2** (5), (4) and (8) with $f(t) = x$, we obtain

$$(p^2x^* - 2p - 1) + 5(px^* - 2) + 6x^* = \frac{12}{p-1}.$$

Solving for x^*,

$$(p^2 + 5p + 6)x^* = \frac{12}{p-1} + 2p + 1 + 10 = \frac{2p^2 + 9p + 1}{p-1},$$

whence

$$x^* = \frac{2p^2 + 9p + 1}{(p-1)(p+2)(p+3)}.$$

In order to find the function of which x^* is the transform we use partial fractions. Using for preference the inspection method described in Appendix 5, it is easily seen that

$$x^* = \frac{1}{p-1} + \frac{3}{p+2} - \frac{2}{p+3}.$$

Referring again to **3.2** (8),

$$x = e^t + 3e^{-2t} - 2e^{-3t},$$

which agrees with the result obtained in **3.1**.

It is seen that by working with Laplace transforms the solution of a differential equation of this type can be effected by purely algebraic methods. This process is particularly simple when the initial conditions are that x and its first $n-1$ derivatives vanish when $t = 0$. In this case **3.2** (4), (5) and (6) reduce to

$$\mathfrak{L}\,\mathbf{D}x = px^*, \qquad \mathfrak{L}\,\mathbf{D}^2x = p^2x^*, \qquad \mathfrak{L}\,\mathbf{D}^nx = p^nx^*. \tag{1}$$

If $Q(\mathbf{D})$ is a polynomial in $\mathbf{D}$ of degree n it follows that

$$\mathfrak{L}Q(\mathbf{D})x = Q(p)x^*. \tag{2}$$

Example 2   To solve $(\mathbf{D}^2 + 4\mathbf{D} + 13)x = 5e^{-t}$ if $x = \mathbf{D}x = 0$ when $t = 0$.

Taking transforms,

$$(p^2 + 4p + 13)x^* = \frac{5}{p+1},$$

$$x^* = \frac{5}{(p+1)(p^2 + 4p + 13)} = \frac{1}{2(p+1)} - \frac{p+3}{2(p^2 + 4p + 13)},$$

again obtaining the partial fractions by one of the methods described in Appendix 5. In order to find the inverse transform of the second term we write it in the form

$$\frac{\frac{1}{2}(p+2)+\frac{1}{2}}{(p+2)^2+3^2}.$$

so that **3.2** (11) and (12) can be used. It follows that

$$x = \tfrac{1}{2}e^{-t} - e^{-2t}(\tfrac{1}{2}\cos 3t + \tfrac{1}{6}\sin 3t).$$

Example 3   To   solve $(\mathbf{D}^3 + 6\mathbf{D}^2 + 11\mathbf{D} + 6)x = 4e^{-3t}$,   given   that $x = \mathbf{D}x = \mathbf{D}^2x = 0$ when $t = 0$.

Then $$(p^3 + 6p^2 + 11p + 6)x^* = \frac{4}{p+3},$$

or $$x^* = \frac{4}{(p+1)(p+2)(p+3)^2} = \frac{1}{p+1} - \frac{4}{p+2} + \frac{3p+11}{p^2+6p+9}$$

$$= \frac{1}{p+1} - \frac{4}{p+2} + \frac{3(p+3)+2}{(p+3)^2}$$

$$= \frac{1}{p+1} - \frac{4}{p+2} + \frac{3}{p+3} + \frac{2}{(p+3)^2}.$$

We deduce
$$x = e^{-t} - 4e^{-2t} + (3+2t)e^{-3t}.$$

EXERCISES   Solve the following differential equations with the initial conditions given. Check the solutions by operational methods.

1. $(\mathbf{D}^2 + 7\mathbf{D} + 12)x = 0$; $x = 5$, $\mathbf{D}x = 8$ when $t = 0$.
2. $(\mathbf{D}^2 + 10\mathbf{D} + 41)x = 0$; $x = 1$, $\mathbf{D}x = 2$ when $t = 0$.
3. $(\mathbf{D}^2 + 4\mathbf{D} + 3)x = 1$; $x = 3$, $\mathbf{D}x = -2$ when $t = 0$.
4. $(\mathbf{D}^2 + 3\mathbf{D} + 2)x = 2e^{-3t}$; $x = \mathbf{D}x = 0$ when $t = 0$.
5. $(\mathbf{D}^2 + 2\mathbf{D} + 5)x = e^t$; $x = \mathbf{D}x = 0$ when $t = 0$.
6. $(\mathbf{D}^2 + 4\mathbf{D} + 4)x = \cos t$; $x = \mathbf{D}x = 0$ when $t = 0$.

3.4   Comparison of methods

Consider the differential equation of order n, $Q(\mathbf{D})x = f(t)$. If $x = \mathbf{D}x = \ldots = \mathbf{D}^{n-1}x = 0$ when $t = 0$, the Laplace transform of the solution is given by

$$x^*(p) = \frac{f^*(p)}{Q(p)}. \tag{1}$$

With more general initial conditions we have instead of (1),

$$x^*(p) = \frac{f^*(p) + q(p)}{Q(p)}, \tag{2}$$

where $q(p)$ is a polynomial of degree $n-1$ whose coefficients depend on those of $Q(\mathbf{D})$ and on the initial values. For example, if

$$Q(\mathbf{D}) = a_0\mathbf{D}^2 + a_1\mathbf{D} + a_2$$

it is found that

$$x^*(p) = \frac{f^*(p) + a_0(px_0 + x_1) + a_1x_0}{Q(p)},$$

where $x = x_0$, $\mathbf{D}x = x_1$ when $t = 0$.

Now if $f(t)$ is the sum of terms of the types t^m, $e^{\alpha t}$, $\cos \beta t$ or $\sin \beta t$ (where α and β are constants and m is a constant positive integer) or products of these functions, then $f^*(p)$, and hence $x^*(p)$, are proper rational fractions. By expressing $x^*(p)$ in partial fractions the solution for x can be found in terms of functions of the same types. Thus the Laplace transform provides a complete alternative to the operational methods described in the last chapter for solving equations of this type. Since many writers on linear systems use the Laplace transform approach exclusively, it is desirable at this stage to make a comparison of the two methods.

Consider first the problem of determining a solution with specified initial conditions. If operational methods are used both the complementary function and the particular integral can be obtained with a minimum of algebraic manipulation. In order to determine the values of the arbitrary constants it is necessary to substitute the initial conditions and solve the resulting simultaneous equations. With first and second order equations this is usually easy. As the order of the differential equation increases however, the labour of solving the simultaneous equations increases rapidly, so much so that with equations of the fourth and fifth orders it can become very tedious. With the transform method most of the work lies in the extraction of the partial fractions. If this is done by equating coefficients, the solution of the simultaneous equations obtained is just as, if not more, lengthy than that of the similar equations arising in the operational method, so that the transform method offers no advantage. It is only when the more refined inspection methods are used that the transform method is superior, and then only when the order of the original differential equation exceeds three or four. It may be mentioned here that the real advantages of the transform method appear when it is applied to sets of simultaneous differential equations (see **14.6**) or to partial differential equations.

For many purposes the characteristic features of a linear system can be inferred from the general solution of the corresponding differential equation. When this is the case the classical operational method is always more efficient and also more appropriate. This is one of the reasons that operational methods are chosen in this book as the basis for presenting the general theory of linear systems. Nevertheless, Laplace transforms are particularly suitable for certain problems. We shall therefore treat the two methods as complementary rather than as alternatives.

CHAPTER 4

FOURIER SERIES AND INTEGRALS

4.1 Periodic functions

A function $f(t)$ is said to be *periodic* with *period* T if $f(t+T) = f(t)$ for all values of t. Then if such a function is given for $0 \leq t < T$ it is defined by this relation for all other values of t. The graph of a typical periodic function is shown in fig. 4.1(a). It is clear that a function having a period T also has periods $2T$, $3T$, ...

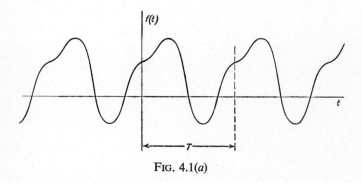

FIG. 4.1(a)

The simplest periodic functions are the pure harmonics $\cos \Omega t$ and $\sin \Omega t$, for the values of these are obviously unchanged when the phase angle Ωt is increased by 2π. The period T is therefore given by $\Omega T = 2\pi$ or $T = 2\pi/\Omega$. The correct name for the constant Ω is the *pulsatance* or *angular frequency*. We shall, however, avoid these cumbersome terms and call it the *frequency*. It should, however, be pointed out that frequency is strictly the number of cycles per unit time, that is,

$$1/T = \Omega/2\pi.$$

Consider now the pairs of functions $\cos 2\Omega t$, $\sin 2\Omega t$; $\cos 3\Omega t$, $\sin 3\Omega t$; .... These pairs have periods $T/2$, $T/3$, ... respectively. It follows that each function also has period T. In this way we can define an infinite number of functions each with period T. This suggests the possibility of expressing a general periodic function as an infinite series of the type

$$\tfrac{1}{2}a_0 + a_1 \cos \Omega t + b_1 \sin \Omega t + a_2 \cos 2\Omega t + b_2 \sin 2\Omega t + \ldots,$$

where $a_0, a_1, b_1, \ldots$ are suitably chosen constants. Such a series is called a *Fourier series*. For reasons which appear later, it is convenient to denote the constant term (which is of course also periodic) by $\tfrac{1}{2}a_0$ rather than a_0.

It can be shown that such an expansion is possible provided $f(t)$ satisfies certain general conditions.† It is possible, assuming the expansion to exist, to calculate numerical values of the coefficients corresponding to a given function $f(t)$. This is demonstrated in the next section.

4.2 Fourier series

Let
$$f(t) = \tfrac{1}{2}a_0 + \sum_{n=1}^{\infty} (a_n \cos n\Omega t + b_n \sin n\Omega t). \tag{1}$$

Then $f(t)$ must have period $T = 2\pi/\Omega$. We shall prove that the coefficients a_n and b_n are given by

$$a_n = \frac{2}{T} \int_{-\frac{1}{2}T}^{\frac{1}{2}T} f(t) \cos n\Omega t \, dt, \tag{2}$$

$$b_n = \frac{2}{T} \int_{-\frac{1}{2}T}^{\frac{1}{2}T} f(t) \sin n\Omega t \, dt. \tag{3}$$

Proof. We require the values of the following integrals, which are easily verified. If m and n are positive integers,

$$\int_{-\frac{1}{2}T}^{\frac{1}{2}T} \cos n\Omega t \, dt = 0, \qquad \int_{-\frac{1}{2}T}^{\frac{1}{2}T} \sin n\Omega t \, dt = 0, \tag{4}$$

$$\int_{-\frac{1}{2}T}^{\frac{1}{2}T} \cos m\Omega t \cos n\Omega t \, dt = 0, \qquad \int_{-\frac{1}{2}T}^{\frac{1}{2}T} \sin m\Omega t \sin n\Omega t \, dt = 0, \tag{5}$$

provided $m \neq n$. If $m = n$ we have

$$\int_{-\frac{1}{2}T}^{\frac{1}{2}T} \cos^2 n\Omega t \, dt = \int_{-\frac{1}{2}T}^{\frac{1}{2}T} \sin^2 n\Omega t \, dt = \tfrac{1}{2}T. \tag{6}$$

Finally
$$\int_{-\frac{1}{2}T}^{\frac{1}{2}T} \cos m\Omega t \sin n\Omega t \, dt = 0, \tag{7}$$

for all integral values of m and n.

† See for example Churchill, R. V., *Fourier Series and Boundary Value Problems*, McGraw-Hill (New York, 1941).

Integrating (1) from $-\frac{1}{2}T$ to $\frac{1}{2}T$ and using (4), we have

$$\int_{-\frac{1}{2}T}^{\frac{1}{2}T} f(t)\,dt = \frac{1}{2}a_0 \int_{-\frac{1}{2}T}^{\frac{1}{2}T} dt = \frac{1}{2}Ta_0,$$

whence $\qquad\qquad a_0 = \dfrac{2}{T}\displaystyle\int_{-\frac{1}{2}T}^{\frac{1}{2}T} f(t)\,dt,$ $\qquad\qquad$ (8)

which is a special case of (2). Again, if we multiply (1) by $\cos m\Omega t$ before integrating we get

$$\int_{-\frac{1}{2}T}^{\frac{1}{2}T} f(t)\cos m\Omega t\,dt = a_m \int_{-\frac{1}{2}T}^{\frac{1}{2}T} \cos^2 m\Omega t\,dt = \frac{1}{2}Ta_m,$$

using (4), (5), (6) and (7). Substitution of n for m gives (2) for non-zero values of n. Notice that, because we have denoted the constant by $\frac{1}{2}a_0$ rather than a_0, (2) covers the case $n = 0$ also. Finally, to prove (3), multiply (1) by $\sin m\Omega t$ and integrate as above.

Equations (2) and (3) are called *Euler's formulae*. Notice that the existence of these constants for a given function $f(t)$ does not in itself imply that the series so generated has sum $f(t)$ or even that it converges. A full discussion of this extensive subject is beyond the scope of this book. It is sufficient to state here that periodic functions which arise in practical problems usually do have convergent Fourier series and that their coefficients are given by Euler's formulae.

Example 1 Consider the periodic function whose graph consists of the alternate rectilinear and parabolic segments shown in fig. 4.2(a). In

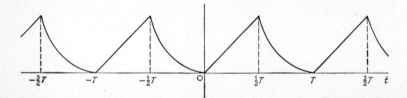

FIG. 4.2(a)

this case $f(t) = kt^2$ for $-\frac{1}{2}T \leqq t \leqq 0$ and $\frac{1}{2}kTt$ for $0 \leqq t \leqq \frac{1}{2}T$. Substitution in (2) gives

$$a_n = \frac{2}{T}\int_{-\frac{1}{2}T}^{0} kt^2 \cos n\Omega t\,dt + \frac{2}{T}\int_{0}^{\frac{1}{2}T} \frac{1}{2}kTt \cos n\Omega t\,dt$$

$$= \frac{2}{T}\int_{0}^{\frac{1}{2}T} k(\tfrac{1}{2}Tt + t^2)\cos n\Omega t\,dt,$$

making the substitution $-t$ for t in the first integral and then combining the two integrals. This integral is now evaluated by parts in the usual way. It is found to give

$$a_n = \frac{k}{n^2\Omega^2}(3\cos n\pi - 1) = \frac{2k}{n^2\Omega^2} \quad \text{or} \quad -\frac{4k}{n^2\Omega^2},$$

according as n is even or odd. The integral for $n = 0$ must be evaluated separately; it is easily verified that $a_0 = 5kT^2/24$. The same method gives

$$b_n = \frac{2}{T}\int_0^{\frac{1}{2}T} k(\tfrac{1}{2}Tt - t^2)\sin n\Omega t\, dt = \frac{4k}{Tn^3\Omega^3}(1 - \cos n\pi).$$

Since $\Omega T = 2\pi$ we have finally

$$f(t) = \frac{5kT^2}{48} + \frac{kT^2}{2\pi^2}\left(-2\cos\Omega t + \tfrac{1}{4}\cos 2\Omega t - \tfrac{2}{9}\cos 3\Omega t + \dots\right)$$

$$+ \frac{kT^2}{\pi^3}\left(\sin\Omega t + \tfrac{1}{27}\sin 3\Omega t + \tfrac{1}{125}\sin 5\Omega t + \dots\right).$$

Example 2 A simpler example is shown in fig. 4.2(b). Here $f(t) = kt$ for $-\tfrac{1}{2}T < t < \tfrac{1}{2}T$. It is easy to verify that

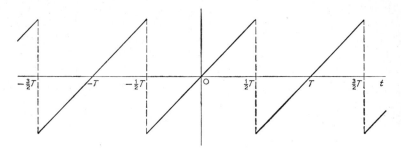

FIG. 4.2(b)

$$a_n = \frac{2}{T}\int_{-\frac{1}{2}T}^{\frac{1}{2}T} kt\cos n\Omega t\, dt = 0,$$

$$b_n = \frac{2}{T}\int_{-\frac{1}{2}T}^{\frac{1}{2}T} kt\sin n\Omega t\, dt = -\frac{2k}{n\Omega}\cos n\pi,$$

so that

$$f(t) = \frac{kT}{\pi}\left(\sin\Omega t - \tfrac{1}{2}\sin 2\Omega t + \tfrac{1}{3}\sin 3\Omega t - \dots\right).$$

Two interesting features are revealed in this example. First there is the absence of cosine terms. This is due to the fact that in this case $f(t)$ is an *odd function*, that is to say a function for which $f(-t) = -f(t)$ for all values of t. It can be proved easily that for such a function a_n is zero for all values of n, including zero, so that the Fourier series contains only sine terms. Each of these sines incidentally is itself an odd function. Likewise an *even function*, for which $f(-t) = f(t)$, will, if it be periodic, have a Fourier series containing only cosine terms. Another feature of odd and even functions is that their power series (if they exist) contain respectively only odd or even powers of t. A general function, such as that in the first example, is neither odd nor even, and its Fourier series will contain both cosine and sine terms. Such a function can always be expressed as the sum of an even function and an odd function by writing it in the form

$$f(t) = \tfrac{1}{2}\{f(t)+f(-t)\}+\tfrac{1}{2}\{f(t)-f(-t)\}. \tag{9}$$

For example,

$$e^{\alpha t} = \tfrac{1}{2}(e^{\alpha t}+e^{-\alpha t})+\tfrac{1}{2}(e^{\alpha t}-e^{-\alpha t}) = \cosh \alpha t + \sinh \alpha t.$$

Secondly, the function $f(t)$ in example 2 has discontinuities for $t = \pm\tfrac{1}{2}T, \pm\tfrac{3}{2}T, \ldots$. If we substitute any of these values in the corresponding Fourier series we get zero. This is a special case of a general result that if $f(t)$ has a simple discontinuity at t_0 the sum of its Fourier series for this value is $\tfrac{1}{2}\{f(t_0+0)+f(t_0-0)\}$, where $f(t_0+0)$ denotes the limit of $f(t)$ as $t \to t_0$ through *positive* values of $t-t_0$, with a similar meaning for $f(t_0-0)$. In example 2,

$$f(\tfrac{1}{2}T+0) = \tfrac{1}{2}kt \quad \text{and} \quad f(\tfrac{1}{2}T_0-0) = -\tfrac{1}{2}kt,$$

so that the sum of the Fourier series must be zero. Incidentally, this property is an example of the unexpected phenomenon of an infinite series of continuous functions whose sum is discontinuous.

The process of expanding a function $f(t)$ in a Fourier series is equivalent to analysing it into sinusoidal components. The constant term $\tfrac{1}{2}a_0$ is simply the mean value of $f(t)$, as is shown by (8). The terms $a_1 \cos \Omega t + b_1 \sin \Omega t$ give the fundamental or first harmonic, whose frequency is the same as that of $f(t)$. In general, the terms $a_n \cos n\Omega t + b_n \sin n\Omega t$ give the nth harmonic, whose frequency is n times that of the fundamental. This harmonic has amplitude $\sqrt{(a_n^2+b_n^2)}$.

In many cases, particularly when $f(t)$ is given only in graphical or tabular form, the integrals in Euler's formulae cannot be evaluated explicitly. When this happens numerical methods must be used.

Obtain Fourier series for the functions $f(t)$ with period T defined as follows:

1. $f(t) = k(\frac{1}{4}T^2 - t^2)$ when $-\frac{1}{2}T \leq t \leq \frac{1}{2}T$,
2. $f(t) = 0$ if $-\frac{1}{2}T < t \leq 0$
   $= kt$ if $0 \leq t < \frac{1}{2}T$.

4.3 Complex Fourier series

Fourier series and the formulae for their coefficients can be expressed much more compactly if complex exponential functions are used instead of sines or cosines. These forms are particularly appropriate for general theoretical discussions. Using Appendix 1 (12) we can write **4.2** (1) in the form

$$f(t) = \frac{1}{2}a_0 + \sum_{n=1}^{\infty} \{\frac{1}{2}a_n(e^{jn\Omega t} + e^{-jn\Omega t}) - \frac{1}{2}jb_n(e^{jn\Omega t} - e^{-jn\Omega t})\}$$

$$= \frac{1}{2}a_0 + \sum_{n=1}^{\infty} \{\frac{1}{2}(a_n - jb_n)e^{jn\Omega t} + \frac{1}{2}(a_n + jb_n)e^{-jn\Omega t}\}$$

$$= \frac{1}{2}a_0 + \sum_{n=1}^{\infty} (c_n e^{jn\Omega t} + \bar{c}_n e^{-jn\Omega t}),$$

where, from **4.2** (2) and (3) and Appendix 1 (7) and (11),

$$c_n = \frac{1}{2}(a_n - jb_n) = \frac{1}{T}\int_{-\frac{1}{2}T}^{\frac{1}{2}T} f(t) e^{-jn\Omega t}\, dt$$

and

$$\bar{c}_n = \frac{1}{2}(a_n + jb_n) = \frac{1}{T}\int_{-\frac{1}{2}T}^{\frac{1}{2}T} f(t) e^{jn\Omega t}\, dt.$$

If we now write c_{-n} for $\bar{c}_n$ the Fourier series becomes

$$f(t) = \sum_{n=-\infty}^{\infty} c_n e^{jn\Omega t}, \tag{1}$$

the coefficients being given by the single formula

$$c_n = \frac{1}{T}\int_{-\frac{1}{2}T}^{\frac{1}{2}T} f(t) e^{-jn\Omega t}\, dt, \tag{2}$$

valid for negative as well as for positive values of n.

The coefficients c_n are complex numbers whose real and imaginary parts are $\frac{1}{2}a_n$ and $-\frac{1}{2}b_n$. Since $\bar{c}_n = c_{-n}$ we have

$$a_n = c_n + c_{-n}, \qquad b_n = j(c_n - c_{-n}). \tag{3}$$

Also $|c_n|$ is half the amplitude of the nth harmonic while ang c_n (see Appendix 1) determines the initial phase of this component of $f(t)$.

4.4 Fourier integrals

The process of analysis of periodic functions into harmonic components developed in this chapter can be extended to certain non-periodic functions $f(t)$. Consider the *periodic* function $f_T(t)$ with period T defined by the equation $f_T(t) = f(t)$ for $-\frac{1}{2}T < t < \frac{1}{2}T$. Then the periodicity condition determines the value of $f_T(t)$ for values of t

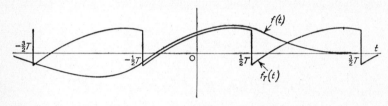

FIG. 4.4(a)

outside this range. If we expand $f_T(t)$ in a Fourier series and then let $T \to \infty$ we will obtain an analogous representation of $f(t)$.

Using the complex form introduced in **4.3**, we have

$$f_T(t) = \sum_{n=-\infty}^{\infty} c_n e^{jn\Omega t}, \tag{1}$$

where
$$c_n = \frac{1}{T} \int_{-\frac{1}{2}T}^{\frac{1}{2}T} f_T(t)\, e^{-jn\Omega t}\, dt. \tag{2}$$

Now if T is large Ω will be small, and as $T \to \infty$, $c_n \to 0$, provided the integral in (2) remains finite. Taking these factors into account it is convenient to make a change of notation. First we denote the frequency $n\Omega$ of a typical harmonic component by ω and the increment Ω between successive frequencies by $\delta\omega$. Then

$$c_n = \frac{\delta\omega}{2\pi} \int_{-\frac{1}{2}T}^{\frac{1}{2}T} f_T(t)\, e^{-j\omega t}\, dt.$$

If we now replace c_n by $c_T(\omega)\delta\omega$, (1) and (2) can be written

$$f_T(t) = \sum_{\omega=-\infty}^{\infty} c_T(\omega)\, \delta\omega\, e^{j\omega t},$$

where $$c_T(\omega)\,\delta\omega = \frac{\delta\omega}{2\pi}\int_{-\frac{1}{2}T}^{\frac{1}{2}T} f_T(t)\,e^{-j\omega t}\,dt.$$

If we now let $T \to \infty$ so that $\delta\omega \to 0$, we obtain

$$f(t) = \int_{-\infty}^{\infty} c(\omega)\,e^{j\omega t}\,d\omega, \tag{3}$$

where $$c(\omega) = \frac{1}{2\pi}\int_{-\infty}^{\infty} f(t)\,e^{-j\omega t}\,dt. \tag{4}$$

Using real functions the forms corresponding to (3) and (4) are

$$f(t) = \int_{0}^{\infty} \{a(\omega)\cos\omega t + b(\omega)\sin\omega t\}\,d\omega. \tag{5}$$

where $$a(\omega) = \frac{1}{\pi}\int_{-\infty}^{\infty} f(t)\cos\omega t\,dt, \qquad b(\omega) = \frac{1}{\pi}\int_{-\infty}^{\infty} f(t)\sin\omega t\,dt. \tag{6}$$

As in the last section $c(\omega) = \frac{1}{2}\{a(\omega)-jb(\omega)\}$.

It should be emphasised that this formal explanation is incomplete mathematically. In order to make it rigorous it is necessary to impose certain conditions on $f(t)$ and to take account of these in the proof. In addition to ensuring the convergence of the two infinite integrals which emerge, these should be such as to render valid the inversion of the two limiting operations of integration and of letting $T \to \infty$. For a rigorous derivation of the relations (3) and (4) the reader is referred to a standard text on the subject.†

The process of expressing a function $f(t)$ as a *Fourier integral* as in (3) or (5) is equivalent to analysing it into harmonic components with a *continuously* varying frequency ω. This contrasts with a Fourier series, in which the frequencies take discrete values. Like c_n in a Fourier series the *coefficient function* $c(\omega)$ is a complex number whose modulus determines the relative amplitudes of the different components. In determining the behaviour of many linear systems the harmonic content of a particular signal is of equal or greater importance than its representation as a function of time. When this is the case it is convenient to refer to $f(t)$ and $c(\omega)$ as the time and frequency functions of the signal respectively. Alternatively, we say that $f(t)$ represents the signal in the *time domain* and that $c(\omega)$ represents it in the *frequency domain*.

† See for example, Churchill, p. 33 *op. cit.*

Example 1   Consider the simple rectangular pulse of duration $2T_1$ in which $f(t)$ has a constant value k for $-T_1 < t < T_1$ and the value zero outside this range. Then

$$c(\omega) = \frac{1}{2\pi}\int_{-\infty}^{\infty} f(t)\,e^{-j\omega t}\,dt = \frac{1}{2\pi}\int_{-T_1}^{T_1} k\,e^{-j\omega t}\,dt$$

$$= \left[\frac{k\,e^{-j\omega t}}{-2\pi j\omega}\right]_{-T_1}^{T_1} = \frac{k}{\pi\omega}\left[\frac{e^{j\omega T_1} - e^{-j\omega T_1}}{2j}\right] = \frac{k}{\pi\omega}\sin\omega T_1,$$

using Appendix 1 (12). Graphs of $f(t)$ and of $|c(\omega)|$ are shown in fig.

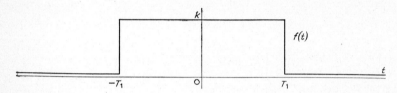

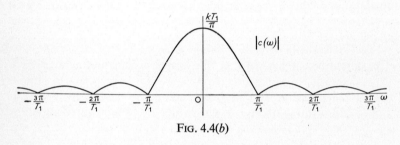

Fig. 4.4(*b*)

4.4(*b*). The Fourier integral for $f(t)$ therefore takes the form

$$f(t) = \frac{k}{\pi}\int_{-\infty}^{\infty} \frac{\sin\omega T_1}{\omega}\,e^{j\omega t}\,d\omega$$

$$= \frac{k}{\pi}\int_{-\infty}^{0} \frac{\sin\omega T_1}{\omega}\,e^{j\omega t}\,d\omega + \frac{k}{\pi}\int_{0}^{\infty} \frac{\sin\omega T_1}{\omega}\,e^{j\omega t}\,d\omega.$$

If ω is replaced by $-\omega$ in the first integral and the two integrals are then combined, we have finally

$$f(t) = \frac{2k}{\pi}\int_{0}^{\infty} \frac{\sin\omega T_1 \cos\omega t}{\omega}\,d\omega.$$

Example 2   If α is a positive constant and $f(t)$ is defined to be $e^{\alpha t}$ for $t < 0$ and $e^{-\alpha t}$ for $t > 0$, as shown in fig. 4.4(*c*),

$$c(\omega) = \frac{1}{2\pi}\int_{-\infty}^{0} e^{(\alpha - j\omega)t}\,dt + \frac{1}{2\pi}\int_{0}^{\infty} e^{(-\alpha - j\omega)t}\,dt$$

$$= \frac{1}{2\pi}\left(\frac{1}{\alpha-j\omega} - \frac{1}{-\alpha-j\omega}\right) = \frac{\alpha}{\pi(\alpha^2+\omega^2)},$$

so that
$$f(t) = \frac{\alpha}{\pi}\int_{-\infty}^{\infty} \frac{e^{j\omega t}\,d\omega}{\alpha^2+\omega^2} = \frac{2\alpha}{\pi}\int_{0}^{\infty} \frac{\cos\omega t}{\alpha^2+\omega^2}\,d\omega.$$

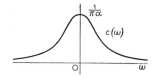
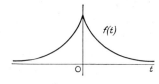

FIG. 4.4(c)

An interesting feature of the Fourier integral is the similarity of form of the integrals in (3) and (4) giving $f(t)$ in terms of $c(\omega)$ and vice versa. Because of this it is possible, given any corresponding pair of functions to obtain an analogous pair in which the roles of t and ω are interchanged. Thus corresponding to the two examples above we have the following.

Example 3   If $c(\omega) = 1$ for $-\omega_1 < \omega < \omega_1$ and zero otherwise,

$$f(t) = \int_{-\omega_1}^{\omega_1} e^{j\omega t}\,d\omega = \frac{2}{t}\sin\omega_1 t.$$

This function, which is of considerable importance in the theory of noise, represents a signal whose frequency components are uniformly distributed over the band from 0 to ω_1, with a sharp cut-off at the upper

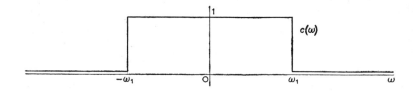

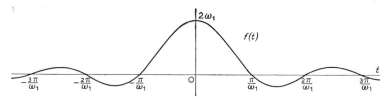

FIG. 4.4(d)

frequency. In particular, if a random noise signal is passed through a perfect low-pass filter the output can be regarded as made up of components which are functions of this type. Graphs of $c(\omega)$ and $f(t)$ appear in fig. 4.4(d).

Example 4 If $f(t) = \dfrac{1}{t_1^2 + t^2}$, then $c(\omega) = \dfrac{1}{2t_1} e^{\pm \omega t_1}$, according as $\omega \lessgtr 0$.

EXERCISE Obtain the coefficient function $c(\omega)$ for the even function $f(t)$ whose value is $T_1 - t$ if $0 \leq t \leq T_1$ and zero if $t \geq T_1$.

CHAPTER 5

FOURIER AND LAPLACE TRANSFORMS

5.1 Fourier transform

In Chapter 3 we introduced the idea of the Laplace transform of a given function $f(t)$ defined as

$$\mathfrak{L}f(t) = f^*(p) = \int_0^\infty f(t)\,e^{-pt}\,dt, \qquad (1)$$

while in the last chapter we saw that if $f(t)$ could be expressed as a Fourier integral it had a coefficient function given by

$$c(\omega) = \frac{1}{2\pi}\int_{-\infty}^\infty f(t)\,e^{-j\omega t}\,dt. \qquad (2)$$

A comparison of these expressions shows that if $j\omega$ is replaced by p and if (2) is multiplied by 2π they become identical, except for the lower limits of the integrals. Accordingly we call $2\pi c(\omega)$ the *Fourier transform* of $f(t)$ and denote it by $\mathfrak{F}f(t)$. Alternatively, ignoring for the time being the difference in the lower limits, we can use the notation of (1) and write the Fourier transform as $f^*(j\omega)$. Thus

$$\mathfrak{F}f(t) = f^*(j\omega) = \int_{-\infty}^\infty f(t)\,e^{-j\omega t}\,dt. \qquad (3)$$

If $f^*(j\omega)$ is given, the corresponding function $f(t)$ is called its *inverse Fourier transform*, and is denoted by $\mathfrak{F}^{-1}f^*(j\omega)$. Using the Fourier integral **4.4** (3) we have

$$\mathfrak{F}^{-1}f^*(j\omega) = f(t) = \frac{1}{2\pi}\int_{-\infty}^\infty f^*(j\omega)\,e^{j\omega t}\,d\omega. \qquad (4)$$

We noted in **4.4** the similarity of form of the integrals appearing in (3) and (4) above. This can be extended one stage further by defining the transform as $\sqrt{(2\pi)}c(\omega)$ instead of $2\pi c(\omega)$; if this is done the same factor $1/\sqrt{(2\pi)}$ appears outside both integrals. This is the usual convention in mathematical texts, but for engineering applications the definition given above is usually more convenient. The difference in the two definitions should however be borne in mind when consulting standard tables of transforms.

The scope of this seemingly powerful technique is severely limited by the necessity that the two integrals involved should converge. Since the factors $e^{\pm j\omega t}$ have unit modulus they neither assist nor retard this convergence in general, so that for practical purposes it is sufficient for the integrals $\int_{-\infty}^{\infty} |f(t)|\,dt$ and $\int_{-\infty}^{\infty} |f^*(j\omega)|\,d\omega$ to converge. This condition usually excludes cases in which either $f(t)$ or $f^*(j\omega)$ does not tend to zero as t or ω tends to infinity.

5.2   Bilateral Laplace transform

We have just seen that the field of application of the Fourier transform is severely limited by convergence requirements. The scope of the method can, however, be extended considerably by the following device. Assume that the integral in **5.1** (3) does not converge as $t \to \infty$ but converges very rapidly as $t \to -\infty$. Bearing in mind that if γ is a positive constant $e^{-\gamma t}$ tends to zero as $t \to \infty$ and to infinity as $t \to -\infty$, it may happen if $f(t)$ is multiplied by $e^{-\gamma t}$, that the integral becomes convergent at the upper limit and yet still remains convergent at the lower limit. For this to happen γ must in general not be too large. Likewise a function $f(t)$ whose Fourier transform integral does not converge at the lower limit may be modified by a factor $e^{-\gamma t}$ with negative γ. What we are doing in effect is to make use of "surplus" convergence at one limit to achieve convergence at the other limit. Taking then the Fourier transform of $f(t)e^{-\gamma t}$,

$$\mathfrak{F}\{f(t)\,e^{-\gamma t}\} = \int_{-\infty}^{\infty} f(t)\,e^{-(\gamma+j\omega)t}\,dt = f^*(\gamma+j\omega),$$

or, putting $\gamma+j\omega = p$,

$$f^*(p) = \int_{-\infty}^{\infty} f(t)\,e^{-pt}\,dt. \tag{1}$$

Comparing (1) with **5.1** (1), it is seen that the two expressions are identical except for the lower limits of the integrals. We call these integrals the *bilateral* and *unilateral Laplace transforms* respectively.

It is clear that the unilateral transform takes no account in any way of the values of $f(t)$ for negative values of t and that, strictly speaking, the solutions of differential equations obtained by this method are valid only for positive values of t. For this reason the bilateral transform provides greater generality. On the other hand, if $f(t) = 0$ when $t < 0$ the two transforms become identical. Using this fact we shall henceforth in this book work exclusively with the bilateral transform. When use is made of results obtained earlier for the unilateral transform it will be assumed that the functions transformed vanish when $t < 0$. Functions of this type will be called *one-sided functions*.

The relation between the two transforms can be expressed conveniently by using the unit step function $H(t)$, which will be discussed fully in the next chapter. This is defined to have the values zero or unity according as $t \lessgtr 0$. Since

$$\int_0^\infty e^{-pt} f(t)\, dt = \int_{-\infty}^\infty e^{-pt} H(t) f(t)\, dt,$$

it follows that the unilateral transform of $f(t)$ is the same as the bilateral transform of the one-sided function $H(t) f(t)$. If the symbol $\mathfrak{L}$ now denotes the bilateral transform we can, for example, rewrite **3.2** (8) and (11) as

$$\mathfrak{L} H(t)\, e^{\alpha t} = \frac{1}{p-\alpha}, \tag{2}$$

$$\mathfrak{L} H(t)\, e^{\alpha t} \cos \beta t = \frac{p-\alpha}{(p-\alpha)^2 + \beta^2}. \tag{3}$$

Apart from its greater generality the bilateral transform has certain other advantages. First, it will be shown that some of the properties to be obtained in **5.4** can be expressed more compactly in terms of bilateral transforms. Again, in linear system theory one of the main applications of the Laplace transform lies in transient analysis. For this it is assumed that at time $t = 0$ the input is switched on or otherwise initiated in a system previously quiescent. Both input and output functions are therefore one-sided. Use of the bilateral transform ensures that this condition is taken into consideration; in particular, the occurrence of steps or impulses when $t = 0$ will be revealed automatically, and no independent determination of the initial conditions for the output for $t > 0$ will be necessary. This point is illustrated in **6.3**.

If $\mathfrak{L} f(t) = f^*(p)$ we say that $f(t)$ is the *inverse Laplace transform* of $f^*(p)$. It is denoted by $\mathfrak{L}^{-1} f^*(p)$. Then since

$$\mathfrak{L} f(t) = f^*(p) = f^*(\gamma + j\omega) = \mathfrak{F}\, e^{-\gamma t} f(t),$$

it follows that

$$e^{-\gamma t} f(t) = \mathfrak{F}^{-1} f^*(\gamma + j\omega) = \frac{1}{2\pi} \int_{-\infty}^\infty f^*(\gamma + j\omega)\, e^{j\omega t}\, d\omega,$$

so that

$$f(t) = \frac{1}{2\pi} \int_{-\infty}^\infty f^*(\gamma + j\omega)\, e^{(\gamma + j\omega)t}\, d\omega = \frac{1}{2\pi j} \int_{\gamma - j\infty}^{\gamma + j\infty} f^*(p)\, e^{pt}\, dp.$$

The relations between the transform pair $f(t)$ and $f^*(p)$ can be summarised thus,

$$f^*(p) = \mathfrak{L}f(t) = \int_{-\infty}^{\infty} f(t)\, e^{-pt}\, dt, \tag{4}$$

$$f(t) = \mathfrak{L}^{-1} f^*(p) = \frac{1}{2\pi j} \int_{\gamma - j\infty}^{\gamma + j\infty} f^*(p)\, e^{pt}\, dp. \tag{5}$$

We are now in a position to give a physical interpretation of the Laplace transform, for (5) shows $f(t)$ analysed into exponential components e^{pt} in the same way as it is analysed into harmonic components in **4.4** (1), (3) and (5). The coefficient p is a continuously varying complex parameter $\gamma + j\omega$ whose real part γ remains constant. If fig. 5.2(a) is an Argand diagram, called the p-plane, representing the complex variable p, the values of p used correspond to points on an infinite line parallel to and at a distance γ from the imaginary or ω axis. For each value of p the function $f^*(p)$ then determines the coefficient of e^{pt} in this representation. In this respect it is a generalisation of the coefficient function $c(\omega)$ in a Fourier integral, and further, of the coefficients a_n and b_n in a Fourier series. If we write $p = j(\omega - j\gamma)$, it appears as j multiplied by a *complex frequency* $\omega - j\gamma$. This concept is of considerable help when discussing applications of the Laplace transform.

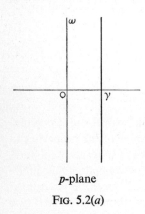

p-plane

FIG. 5.2(a)

The Fourier transform is now seen as a particular case of the Laplace transform in which p is the imaginary number $j\omega$. It is represented in fig. 5.2(a) by points on the imaginary axis. The Fourier transform is particularly appropriate when the oscillatory character of $f(t)$ is of special interest, such as, for example, in a discussion of the nature of noise.

Two examples of the evaluation of bilateral Laplace transforms are given below.

Example 1   If $f(t)$ is the rectangular pulse shown in fig. 4.4(b), whose value is the constant k if $-T_1 < t < T_1$ and zero otherwise,

$$\mathfrak{L}f(t) = \int_{-T_1}^{T_1} k\, e^{-pt}\, dt = \frac{k}{p}(e^{pT_1} - e^{-pT_1}) = \frac{2k}{p} \sinh pT_1.$$

Example 2   If $f(t)$ is the Gaussian probability function $e^{-\frac{1}{2}t^2}/\sqrt{(2\pi)}$,

$$\mathfrak{L}f(t) = \frac{1}{\sqrt{(2\pi)}}\int_{-\infty}^{\infty} e^{-\frac{1}{2}t^2 - pt}\,dt = \frac{1}{\sqrt{(2\pi)}}\int_{-\infty}^{\infty} e^{-\frac{1}{2}(t+p)^2} e^{\frac{1}{2}p^2}\,dt.$$

Making the substitution $t+p = x\sqrt{2}$ and using the well known integral,

$$\int_{-\infty}^{\infty} e^{-x^2}\,dx = \sqrt{\pi},$$

we have $$\mathfrak{L}f(t) = \frac{1}{\sqrt{(2\pi)}} e^{\frac{1}{2}p^2}\int_{-\infty}^{\infty} e^{-x^2}\sqrt{2}\,dx = e^{\frac{1}{2}p^2}.$$

Thus $$\mathfrak{L}\left\{\frac{1}{\sqrt{(2\pi)}} e^{-\frac{1}{2}t^2}\right\} = e^{\frac{1}{2}p^2}.$$

EXERCISE   Obtain $\mathfrak{L} f(t)$ if $f(t) = |t|$ when $|t| < T_1$ and is zero otherwise.

The Laplace and Fourier transforms are specially useful when handling functions $f(t)$ which have discontinuities and impulses or which have different expressions in different intervals, for in such cases the transforms frequently are single functions of an elementary type, as in example 1 above (further examples appear in **6.3**). This is particularly convenient when such functions appear in linear differential equations. For if problems of this type are solved by the methods developed in earlier chapters, the equations usually have to be solved separately for each interval with the initial conditions for each interval matched to the terminal conditions of the previous interval, taking account of any intervening step or impulse. These processes are not only tedious; frequently they require very careful handling. But if transforms are used such situations are taken care of automatically, and the algebraic manipulation necessary is simplified considerably.

5.3   Convergence of transform integrals†

Let $f(t)$ be a function having a Laplace transform $f^*(p)$. Then

$$f^*(p) = \int_{-\infty}^{\infty} f(t)\,e^{-pt}\,dt, \tag{1}$$

$$f(t) = \frac{1}{2\pi j}\int_{\gamma-j\infty}^{\gamma+j\infty} f^*(p)\,e^{pt}\,dp. \tag{2}$$

Writing $p = \gamma + j\omega$ as before, the integrand in (1) becomes $f(t)e^{-\gamma t}e^{-j\omega t}$. But, as we have already stated, the factor $e^{-j\omega t}$ does not influence the

† This section can be omitted from a first reading.

convergence of the integral (1) at either limit, so that we need only consider the function $f(t)e^{-\gamma t}$. Then if γ is a positive constant it is clear that the greater the value of γ the greater is the prospect of convergence at the *upper* limit. Likewise if γ is reduced the possibility of convergence is reduced. In general there is a lower bound γ_1 (which is not necessarily

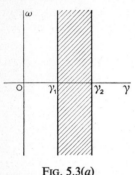

positive) of values of γ for which the integral converges at the upper limit. In the same way there is an upper bound γ_2 for convergence at the lower limit, so that the transform can exist only if $\gamma_1 < \gamma < \gamma_2$. In other words, p must lie in an infinite strip in the p-plane parallel to the imaginary axis as shown in fig. 5.3(a). As special cases of this general result γ_2 can be ∞ or γ_1 can be $-\infty$ or both, so that the domain of convergence in the p-plane can be the

FIG. 5.3(a)

half-plane to the right or left of a given line or the whole plane. (An illustration of the last type is provided by example 2 of the last section.) A given function has a Fourier transform if the strip of convergence includes the imaginary axis. When this is not the case the Laplace transform must be used.

The need for convergence of the integral in (1) results in many common elementary functions not having transforms. For example, if $f(t) = e^{\alpha t}$, where α is real,

$$f^*(p) = \int_{-\infty}^{\infty} e^{(\alpha-p)t}\, dt = \left[\frac{e^{(\alpha-p)t}}{\alpha-p}\right]_{-\infty}^{\infty}.$$

This expression converges at the upper limit only if $\gamma > \alpha$ and at the lower limit if $\gamma < \alpha$. When $\gamma = \alpha$ it does not converge at either limit. There is thus no value of p for which the integral has a proper value. The same is easily seen to be true for the functions $\cos \beta t$, $\sin \beta t$, t^m and products of these functions. None of these functions therefore has a bilateral transform. On the other hand, if $f(t) = H(t)e^{\alpha t}$,

$$f^*(p) = \int_{0}^{\infty} e^{(\alpha-p)t}\, dt = \left[\frac{e^{(\alpha-p)t}}{\alpha-p}\right]_{0}^{\infty} = \frac{1}{p-\alpha},$$

provided $\gamma > \alpha$. This therefore, like many other unilateral transforms, exists for all values of p in the half-plane to the *right* of a certain line.

The integral in (2) giving the inverse transform must be evaluated along a line parallel to the imaginary axis in the strip of convergence of (1).

In fact, any such line in this strip can be used. This expression for $f(t)$ makes available the full resources of the theory of functions of a complex variable and in particular of contour integration for the solution of problems arising in linear systems. This is specially true for systems containing distributed parameters, such as transmission lines, which are represented by partial differential equations. The more elementary problems that we shall discuss, however, can be handled perfectly satisfactorily by less erudite techniques.

The strip in which the integral (2) is to be evaluated should always be specified or implied, for it can be shown that integrals of the same function $f^*(p)$ taken in different strips can lead to different functions $f(t)$ if the lines separating such strips pass through singularities of $f^*(p)$. For example, if $f^*(p) = 2\alpha/(\alpha^2 - p^2)$ where $\alpha > 0$, $f^*(p)$ has poles (see **10.5**) at the points $p = \pm\alpha$. The lines $\gamma = \alpha$ and $\gamma = -\alpha$ divide the

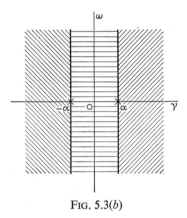

FIG. 5.3(b)

plane into three regions, as shown in fig. 5.3(b). If (2) is evaluated in these in turn it is found that

$$f(t) = (e^{-\alpha t} - e^{\alpha t})H(t) = -2 \sinh \alpha t \, H(t) \quad \text{if } \gamma > \alpha,$$
$$= e^{-\alpha t} H(t) + e^{\alpha t} H(-t) \quad \text{if } -\alpha < \gamma < \alpha,$$
$$= 2 \sinh \alpha t \, H(-t) \quad \text{if } \gamma < -\alpha.$$

It can be verified by substituting in (1) that these three functions all have the same transform $2\alpha/(\alpha^2 - p^2)$, but with the appropriate different strips of convergence.

A full account of this aspect of the subject has been given by van der Pol and Bremmer.†

† van der Pol, B, and Bremmer, H., *Operational Calculus based on the two-sided Laplace Integral*. Cambridge University Press (1950).

5.4   Properties of the Laplace transform

Let $\mathfrak{L}f(t) = f^*(p)$, so that

$$f^*(p) = \int_{-\infty}^{\infty} f(t)\, e^{-pt}\, dt, \tag{1}$$

$$f(t) = \frac{1}{2\pi j}\int_{\gamma-j\infty}^{\gamma+j\infty} f^*(p)\, e^{pt}\, dp. \tag{2}$$

We shall state and prove some of the more important properties of this transformation.

(I) $\qquad\qquad\qquad \mathfrak{L}\{e^{\alpha t}f(t)\} = f^*(p-\alpha).$

Proof $\qquad \mathfrak{L}\{e^{\alpha t}f(t)\} = \int_{-\infty}^{\infty} f(t)\, e^{-(p-\alpha)t}\, dt = f^*(p-\alpha).$

(II) $\qquad\qquad\qquad \mathfrak{L}f(t+\tau) = e^{\tau p}f^*(p).$

Proof $\qquad \mathfrak{L}f(t+\tau) = \int_{-\infty}^{\infty} f(t+\tau)\, e^{-pt}\, dt$

$$= \int_{-\infty}^{\infty} f(t)\, e^{-p(t-\tau)}\, dt, \quad \text{writing } t-\tau \text{ for } t,$$

$$= e^{p\tau}\int_{-\infty}^{\infty} f(t)\, e^{-pt}\, dt = e^{p\tau}f^*(p).$$

This result, sometimes called the *shift theorem*, can also be obtained from (2) by a process similar to that used to prove property (I). These two theorems show that multiplication by an exponential function in the time domain is equivalent to shifting in the frequency domain and vice versa.

(III)   If k is a real constant,

$$\mathfrak{L}f(kt) = \frac{1}{|k|}f^*\!\left(\frac{p}{k}\right).$$

Proof $\qquad \mathfrak{L}f(kt) = \int_{-\infty}^{\infty} f(kt)\, e^{-pt}\, dt$

$$= \int_{-\infty}^{\infty} f(t)\, e^{-pt/k}\, d(t/k), \quad \text{writing } t/k \text{ for } t,$$

$$= \frac{1}{k}f^*\!\left(\frac{p}{k}\right),$$

provided k is positive. If k is negative the limits $\pm\infty$ become interchanged. This accounts for the change in sign. As a special case, if $k = -1$,

(IIIa) $\mathfrak{L}f(-t) = f^*(-p).$

(IV)   If $\mathfrak{L}g(t) = g^*(p)$ then $\mathfrak{L}\displaystyle\int_{-\infty}^{\infty} f(\tau)g(t-\tau)\,d\tau = f^*(p)g^*(p).$

Proof $\mathfrak{L}f(\tau)g(t-\tau) = f(\tau)\,e^{-p\tau}g^*(p),$ using (II),

so that

$$\mathfrak{L}\int_{-\infty}^{\infty} f(\tau)g(t-\tau)\,d\tau = \int_{-\infty}^{\infty} f(\tau)\,e^{-p\tau}g^*(p)\,d\tau$$

$$= g^*(p)\int_{-\infty}^{\infty} f(\tau)\,e^{-p\tau}\,d\tau = g^*(p)f^*(p).$$

This particular method of combining two functions $f(t)$ and $g(t)$ by integrating the product $f(t_1)g(t_2)$ over all values of t_1 and t_2 whose sum is t is called *convolution*. The theorem we have proved, which is called the *convolution theorem*, thus states that convolution in the time domain corresponds to multiplication in the frequency domain. This result has important consequences in the general theory of linear systems, particularly in connection with weighting functions. Notice that the convolution integral can equally well be written $\displaystyle\int_{-\infty}^{\infty} f(t-\tau)g(\tau)\,d\tau.$

(V) $\mathfrak{L}f'(t) = pf^*(p)$

Proof $\mathfrak{L}f'(t) = \displaystyle\int_{-\infty}^{\infty} f'(t)\,e^{-pt}\,dt = \left[f(t)\,e^{-pt} \right]_{-\infty}^{\infty} + p\int_{-\infty}^{\infty} f(t)\,e^{-pt}\,dt,$

integrating by parts. Since $f(t)$ is differentiable and has a transform, the integrated part vanishes at both limits, otherwise the transform integral for $f(t)$ would not converge. This proves the result. An immediate alternative proof is available from (2), by differentiating the integrand with respect to t. Obvious extensions of this property are

(Va) $\mathfrak{L}f^{(n)}(t) = p^n f^*(p)$ and

(Vb) $\mathfrak{L}\{Q(\mathbf{D})f(t)\} = Q(p)f^*(p),$

where $Q(\mathbf{D})$ is a polynomial in $\mathbf{D}$. Finally, if $F(\mathbf{D})$ is a rational fraction $P(\mathbf{D})/Q(\mathbf{D})$,

(VI) $\mathfrak{L}\{F(\mathbf{D})f(t)\} = F(p)f^*(p).$

Proof Let $F(\mathbf{D})f(t) = x(t)$. Then $Q(\mathbf{D})x(t) = P(\mathbf{D})f(t)$. Using the last result, $Q(p)x^*(p) = F(p)f^*(p)$, whence the result follows. Notice that this property presupposes that $x(t)$ *has* a transform. There cannot be more that one such function among the solutions of the above differential equation, for if there were two their difference would be made up of complementary function terms and we saw in the last section that such functions have no transforms. As an important particular case of this property, if $f(t)$ is a one-sided function the solution $x(t)$ given by this method is the one which also is one-sided.

Property (VI) is widely used for solving differential equations and for analysing linear systems when the functions $f(t)$ and $x(t)$ have discontinuities and impulses.

We have already commented on the similarity of form of the direct and inverse Fourier transforms. It is clear from (1) and (2) that the same is true for the more general Laplace transform. Taking account of the difference of signs of the exponents in the integrals in (1) and (2) and the factor $1/(2\pi j)$ in the latter we can deduce a set of properties corresponding to (I) to (VI) above by interchanging the roles of the variables t and p. If this is done it is easily seen that (II) is the image of (I) and vice versa, while (III) is its own image.

The image of (IV) can be shown to be

$$\text{(VII)} \qquad \mathfrak{L}f(t)g(t) = \frac{1}{2\pi j}\int_{\gamma-j\infty}^{\gamma+j\infty} f^*(p_1)g^*(p-p_1)\,dp_1,$$

which states that multiplication in the time domain is equivalent to convolution in the frequency domain. When evaluating this integral the real parts of p and p_1 must be chosen so that p_1 and $p-p_1$ lie in the strips of convergence (see **5.3**) of the transforms of $f(t)$ and $g(t)$ respectively.

The image of (V) is

$$\text{(VIII)} \qquad\qquad \mathfrak{L}tf(t) = -\frac{d}{dp}f^*(p)$$

or, more generally, $\qquad \mathfrak{L}t^nf(t) = \left(-\frac{d}{dp}\right)^n f^*(p).$

These properties can of course be applied to the Fourier transform by replacing p by $j\omega$. The only one of these that calls for special mention is (VI) which gives

$$\mathfrak{F}\{F(\mathbf{D})f(t)\} = F(j\omega)f^*(j\omega). \qquad\qquad (3)$$

We summarise below the qualifications or modifications to the above properties which are necessary when unilateral transforms are used. First, it can be verified that properties (I), (VII) and (VIII) remain unchanged, while (III) is valid provided $k > 0$. Property (II) holds only if $f(t) = 0$ when t lies between 0 and τ. In property (IV) the limits $-\infty$ and

∞ in the convolution integral must be replaced by 0 and t respectively. Properties (V), (Va) and (Vb) are valid provided the appropriate number of derivatives of $f(t)$ vanish when $t = 0$. Otherwise the forms given by **3.2** (4) and (6) must be used. These restrictions must be taken into account when the more general property (VI) is used.

All these conditions point to the desirability of using in general the bilateral rather than the unilateral transform, even when the functions involved are one-sided. As has been stated, this is one important reason why the bilateral transform will be used in subsequent chapters of this book.

CHAPTER 6

STEP AND IMPULSE FUNCTIONS

6.1 Definitions

Reference has been made in earlier chapters to steps and impulses in the time functions considered. In this chapter we consider the definitions and some of the more important properties associated with these ideas. These can be introduced by considering a simple electrical example.

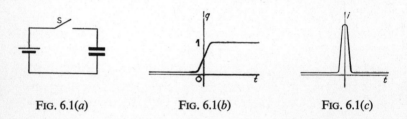

FIG. 6.1(*a*)   FIG. 6.1(*b*)   FIG. 6.1(*c*)

Consider the circuit in fig. 6.1(*a*) in which a cell of unit voltage is connected to a condenser of unit capacitance by leads of negligible impedance through a switch S. We assume that the condenser is initially uncharged and that the switch, initially open, is closed at time $t = 0$. For our present purpose we can regard the switch as an element in the circuit whose resistance diminishes continuously from infinity to zero during the very short time interval from $t = -\varepsilon$ to $t = \varepsilon$. Then the charge q on the condenser has a graph as shown in fig. 6.1(*b*) while the current i, which is the derivative of q, has a graph of the type shown in fig. 6.1(*c*). These two functions are in effect the unit step and impulse functions respectively.

In order to simplify the mathematical manipulation of such functions it is desirable to let ε tend to zero. Before this can be done however, we must define the functions in such a way that the limiting processes can be carried out. Consider therefore a function $h(x)$, shown in fig. 6.1(*d*), which has the following properties:

(*a*) $h(x) - \frac{1}{2}$ is an odd function of x,

(*b*) $h(x) \to 0$ as $x \to -\infty$ and $h(x) \to 1$ as $x \to \infty$,

(c) $h(x)$ is continuous and has derivatives of all orders which tend
to zero as $x \to \pm\infty$,

(d) $xh'(x) \to 0$ as $x \to \pm\infty.$†

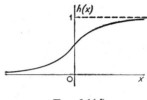

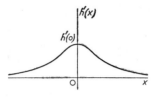

FIG. 6.1(d)   FIG. 6.1(e)

The precise form chosen for $h(x)$ is immaterial; two possibilities are
$\frac{1}{2} + (1/\pi)\tan^{-1}x$ and $\frac{1}{2}(1 + \tanh x)$. Then the derivative $h'(x)$ will have
a graph as shown in fig. 6.1(e), with maximum value $h'(0)$.

Consider now the function $H_\varepsilon(t) = h(t/\varepsilon)$. Graphs of this function
for different values of ε can be derived from fig. 6.1(d) by appropriate

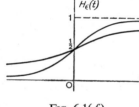

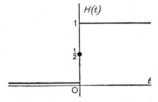

FIG. 6.1(f)   FIG. 6.1(g)

changes of scale for x, as in fig. 6.1(f). In particular, if ε is small the
graph will approximate to that of fig. 6.1(b). Now let $\varepsilon \to 0$. Then if
$t > 0$,

$$\lim H_\varepsilon(t) = \lim h(t/\varepsilon) = h(\infty) = 1,$$

while if $t < 0$,

$$\lim H_\varepsilon(t) = h(-\infty) = 0.$$

Also if $t = 0$, $H_\varepsilon(t) = h(0) = \frac{1}{2}$. In proceeding to the limit we have
therefore obtained the function $H(t)$ which has the value $\frac{1}{2}$ if $t = 0$
and otherwise the values 0 or 1 according as t is negative or positive.

† This condition will be found to be satisfied if, and only if, the lines $y = 0$
and $y = 1$ are true asymptotes (that is, the limiting positions of tangents at
points that tend to infinity) of the graph of $h(x)$. This can be proved if we
assume that $h'(x)$ always decreases as $|x|$ increases.

This is the strict definition of the *unit step function*. Its graph is shown in fig. 6.1(g).

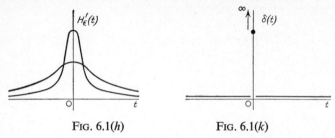

FIG. 6.1(h)   FIG. 6.1(k)

We turn now to the derivative $H_\varepsilon'(t)$ or $h'(t/\varepsilon)/\varepsilon$. When $t = 0$ this is equal to $h'(0)/\varepsilon$, which tends to infinity as $\varepsilon \to 0$. On the other hand if $t \neq 0$,

$$\lim_{\varepsilon \to 0} H_\varepsilon'(t) = \lim_{\varepsilon \to 0} \frac{1}{t}\frac{t}{\varepsilon}h'\left(\frac{t}{\varepsilon}\right) = 0,$$

using condition (d) above. Also if $t_1 < 0$ and $t_2 > 0$

$$\int_{t_1}^{t_2} H_\varepsilon'(t)\,dt = \left[H_\varepsilon(t) \right]_{t_1}^{t_2} = h(t_2/\varepsilon) - h(t_1/\varepsilon),$$

which tends to unity as $\varepsilon \to 0$, since $h(\infty) = 1$ and $h(-\infty) = 0$. We can therefore define the unit impulse function $\delta(t)$ formally as the function which is zero for all values of t except at $t = 0$, at which value it is infinite, with the additional condition

$$\int_{t_1}^{t_2} \delta(t)\,dt = 1. \tag{1}$$

Figs. 6.1(h) and (k) show graphs of $H_\varepsilon'(t)$ and of the limit $\delta(t)$. Notice that in fig. 6.1(h) the areas under the graphs for different values of ε are all unity.

More generally we can define the step and impulse functions $aH(t)$ and $b\delta(t)$. We call a and b the *amplitudes* of these functions. Notice that b is the *area* under the graph of the corresponding function $bh'(t/\varepsilon)/\varepsilon$ and not its maximum ordinate.

Two difficulties associated with the limiting functions $H(t)$ and $\delta(t)$ should be mentioned here. First, $\delta(t)$ as defined in the last section is strictly not a proper function at all. In describing it as we have done, we have in effect only stated what happens to the function $H_\varepsilon'(t)$ as $\varepsilon \to 0$. Even if this objection is overlooked there is the further point that both $H(t)$ and $\delta(t)$ are discontinuous when $t = 0$. Now when functions of this type actually arise in practice they are necessarily proper and usually continuous, as in the example given at the beginning of this section. They should properly be represented by $H_\varepsilon(t)$ and $H_\varepsilon'(t)$ respectively, with a very small value of ε, so that their graphs are as in figs. 6.1(b) and (c). Even though we actually use $H(t)$ and $\delta(t)$ in order to simplify manipulation we should therefore regard these functions as continuous. However, in the majority of applications, $H(t)$ and $\delta(t)$ are hypothetical functions, and we are interested not so much in the functions themselves as in certain derived functions, such as their Laplace transforms or the responses of systems which have $H(t)$ or $\delta(t)$ as inputs. These transforms and responses are usually straightforward functions of p and t respectively, and are the same as those derived from $H_\varepsilon(t)$ and $H_\varepsilon'(t)$ when the limit is taken as $\varepsilon \to 0$.

EXERCISE   Verify by differentiation that $\lim_{\varepsilon \to 0} (1/\varepsilon)f'(t/\varepsilon) = \delta(t)$ when $f(x) = \frac{1}{2}+(1/\pi) \tan^{-1}x$ and when $f(x) = \frac{1}{2}(1+\tanh x)$.

6.2   Laplace transforms

The transform of $H(t)$ can be evaluated directly as follows.

$$\mathfrak{L}H(t) = \int_{-\infty}^{\infty} H(t)\,e^{-pt}\,dt = \int_{0}^{\infty} e^{-pt}\,dt = \frac{1}{p}. \tag{1}$$

Taking $\delta(t)$ as the derivative of $H(t)$ and using property (V) of **5.4**,

$$\mathfrak{L}\,\delta(t) = p\mathfrak{L}H(t) = 1. \tag{2}$$

An alternative derivation of this important result is provided by the sifting theorem, which is proved later (see **6.3** (3)). For

$$\mathfrak{L}\,\delta(t) = \int_{-\infty}^{\infty} \delta(t)\,e^{-pt}\,dt = 1,$$

since $e^{-pt} = 1$ when $t = 0.$

These results can also be considered in relation to the limiting operations discussed in detail in the last section. Let $h_1(p)$ be the transform of $h'(x)$ so that

$$h_1(p) = \int_{-\infty}^{\infty} h'(x)\,e^{-px}\,dx.$$

Then $h_1(0) = \int_{-\infty}^{\infty} h'(x)\,dx = h(\infty)-h(-\infty) = 1.$

But, using property (III) of **5.4**,

$$\mathfrak{L}\frac{1}{\varepsilon}h'\left(\frac{t}{\varepsilon}\right) = h_1(\varepsilon p)$$

so that when $\varepsilon \to 0$ we obtain $\mathfrak{L}\delta(t) = h_1(0) = 1$, assuming that $h_1(p)$ is continuous at $p = 0$. In order to deduce the transform of $H(t)$ observe that, using property (V) of **5.4**, $\mathfrak{L}h(t/\varepsilon) = h_1(\varepsilon p)/p$, which tends to $1/p$ as $\varepsilon \to 0$. We have therefore confirmed (1) and (2).

6.3 Properties and applications

We have seen that the unit step function $H(t)$ has Laplace transform $1/p$. More generally, if the step occurs at time $t = t_1$, the corresponding function is $H(t-t_1)$. Using property (II) of **5.4**, its transform is $e^{-t_1 p}/p$. If now we take the difference of these functions we obtain a rectangular

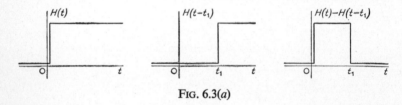

FIG. 6.3(a)

pulse of duration t_1 and of unit amplitude. This function, $H(t) - H(t-t_1)$ has transform $(1-e^{-pt_1})/p$. Graphs of these functions appear in fig. 6.3(a).

If the rectangular pulse function is divided by t_1 the integral of the pulse (which is measured by the area under its graph) becomes unity. If we now let $t_1 \to 0$ we obtain a definition of the unit impulse function which is simpler in some respects than that previously given; it does not, however, have the same flexibility; for example, it cannot be differentiated any further. Notice that the transform of this function is

$$\lim_{t_1 \to 0} \frac{1-e^{-pt_1}}{pt_1} = \lim_{t_1 \to 0} \frac{pt_1 - \frac{1}{2}p^2t_1^2 + \cdots}{pt_1} = 1,$$

thus providing further confirmation of a result obtained in the last section.

It has been seen how multiplication of any function $f(t)$ by $H(t)$ converts it into the corresponding one-sided function (see fig. 6.3(b)). For example, $H(t) \sin \omega t$ is a one-sided sinusoidal function, whose transform is $\omega/(p^2+\omega^2)$. Again, a single cycle of this function, that is a function which equals sin ωt for $0 < t < 2\pi/\omega$ and which is zero otherwise can be written

$$\{H(t) - H(t - 2\pi/\omega)\} \sin \omega t = H(t) \sin \omega t - H(t - 2\pi/\omega) \sin \omega(t - 2\pi/\omega).$$

This has transform

$$(1 - e^{-2\pi p/\omega})\omega/(p^2 + \omega^2).$$

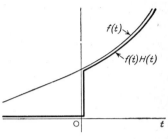

The way in which steps and impulses are taken care of automatically when transforms are used is shown by the following simple example. Consider the one-sided cosine function

$$f(t) = H(t) \cos \omega t,$$

FIG. 6.3(b)

whose transform is $p/(p^2 + \omega^2)$. Then this function has a unit step at the origin. Using property (V) of **5.4**, its derivative has transform

$$\frac{p^2}{p^2 + \omega^2} = 1 - \frac{\omega^2}{p^2 + \omega^2}.$$

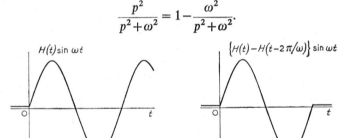

FIG. 6.3(c)

It follows that $f'(t) = \delta(t) - H(t)\,\omega \sin \omega t$, a relation that is immediately apparent from the graphs of $f(t)$ and $f'(t)$ (see fig. 6.3(d)).

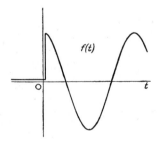
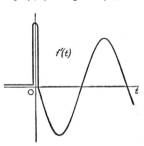

FIG. 6.3(d)

Consider now the unit impulse function $\delta(t)$. Condition (d) of **6.1** shows that $(t/\varepsilon)h'(t/\varepsilon) \to 0$ as $\varepsilon \to 0$. It follows that

$$t\delta(t) = 0 \qquad (1)$$

for all values of t. Now let $u(t)$ be any differentiable function of t. Applying Maclaurin's expansion to $u(t)$ we have

$$u(t)\,\delta(t) = u(0)\,\delta(t) + t\,\delta(t)\{u'(0) + \tfrac{1}{2}tu''(0) + \ldots\}.$$

Using (1) we deduce $u(t)\,\delta(t) = u(0)\,\delta(t)$, or more generally

$$u(t)\,\delta(t-t_1) = u(t_1)\,\delta(t-t_1). \qquad (2)$$

This result is important in the theory of sampling systems. Again, integrating (2),

$$\int_{-\infty}^{\infty} u(t)\,\delta(t-t_1)\,dt = u(t_1). \qquad (3)$$

This formula shows that if we are given a function $u(t)$ we can perform the operation of selecting the value of the function for a particular value t_1 of t by multiplying by $\delta(t-t_1)$ and integrating from $-\infty$ to ∞. Ths operation is sometimes called *sifting*. Notice that the infinite limits in the integral can be replaced by any pair of values provided the upper limit is greater and the lower limit less than t_1.

The unit impulse function has a wide range of applications of the following type. Consider a line along which mass is distributed continuously but not necessarily uniformly. Let $\rho(x)$ be the density (mass per unit length) at a distance x from the origin on the line. Then the mass of the segment of the line from $x = a$ to $x = b$ is

$$M = \int_a^b \rho(x)\,dx. \qquad (4)$$

If, however, the mass instead of being continuously distributed is concentrated or lumped into particles of finite masses $m_1, m_2, \ldots$ at the points $x_1, x_2, \ldots$, we can still express the total mass as an integral if we regard the density function as a series of impulses as in fig. 6.3(e). For if

$$\rho(x) = \sum_r m_r\,\delta(x-x_r), \qquad (5)$$

then $\qquad \displaystyle\int_a^b \rho(x)\,dx = \int_a^b \sum_r m_r\,\delta(x-x_r)\,dx = \sum m_r = M.$ (6)

This device can be employed with great effect whenever it is necessary to deal with some located quantity or characteristic that may be either continuously distributed or lumped. In the first case the appropriate theory will be expressed by means of integrals involving density functions while in the second case summations will be used. If now the lumped distributions are described by means of impulsive density functions, both cases can be represented by a common theory using integrals. Apart from the obvious economy of a single theory compared with two separate ones, advantage may be taken of the fact that integrals are frequently simpler to manipulate than summations.

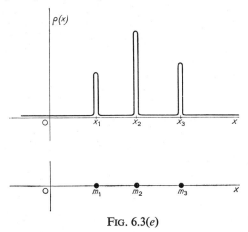

FIG. 6.3(e)

The various branches of mechanics and electromagnetic theory provide several instances in which this technique can be used. For example, it enables a theory based on the assumption of a continuous medium to take account of the granular nature of such a medium. Statistics is another subject that offers great scope for this idea.

An application of this process shows in another form the relations between Fourier series and integrals. Consider a function $f(t)$ expressed as a Fourier integral in the form

$$f(t) = \int_{-\infty}^{\infty} c(\omega)\, e^{j\omega t}\, d\omega. \tag{7}$$

Then $f(t)$ is thereby analysed into sinusoidal components with a continuously varying frequency ω. The coefficient function $c(\omega)$ is therefore a density function. If, however, $f(t)$ has period $2\pi/\Omega$ we know that the components have discrete frequencies $n\Omega$, where n is an integer. These components are in fact lumped, in the sense described above. To verify this write

$$c(\omega) = \sum_{n=-\infty}^{\infty} c_n \delta(\omega - n\Omega), \tag{8}$$

so that, using (3), (7) becomes

$$f(t) = \int_{-\infty}^{\infty} \sum c_n \delta(\omega - n\Omega) e^{j\omega t}\, d\omega = \sum c_n e^{jn\Omega t}, \tag{9}$$

which is the corresponding Fourier series. We see therefore that a Fourier series is a particular case of a Fourier integral in which the coefficient function is a train of impulses in the frequency domain.

Since the Fourier transform of $f(t)$ is $2\pi c(\omega)$, if $f(t)$ is a periodic function given by the Fourier series in (9) we deduce from (8)

$$f^*(j\omega) = 2\pi \sum_{n=-\infty}^{\infty} c_n \delta(\omega - n\Omega). \tag{10}$$

In particular, if $f(t) = \cos \Omega t = \frac{1}{2}(e^{j\Omega t} + e^{-j\Omega t})$, so that $c_1 = c_{-1} = \frac{1}{2}$,

$$f^*(j\omega) = \pi\{\delta(\omega - \Omega) + \delta(\omega + \Omega)\}. \tag{11}$$

Again, if $f(t)$ is a constant c_0,

$$f^*(j\omega) = 2\pi c_0 \delta(\omega). \tag{12}$$

These examples apparently contradict the condition that the Fourier transform of $f(t)$ can exist only if $f(t) \to 0$ as $t \to \pm\infty$. In order to explain this paradox we observe that the corresponding transform pairs $f(t)$ and $f^*(j\omega)$ satisfy **5.1** (4); they do not, however, satisfy **5.1** (3) since the integrals in the latter do not converge. They can nevertheless be made to satisfy the latter relation if we use a process for assigning a value to certain types of non-convergent integrals, known as Cesàro summation.†

If we put $j\omega = p$ in (12) and observe that $\delta(\omega)$ is an even function we have a formal expression for the bilateral Laplace transform of a constant. Thus

$$\mathcal{L}c_0 = 2\pi c_0 \delta(jp). \tag{13}$$

This concept has in reality no greater generality than the Fourier transform, since it is applicable only on the imaginary axis in the p-plane. It does, however, allow us to state a sifting theorem in the frequency domain analogous to (3). Thus

$$\int_{p-j\infty}^{p+j\infty} \delta(jp - jp_1)f^*(p_1)\,dp_1 = j\int_{-\infty}^{\infty} \delta(\omega)f^*(p+j\omega)\,d\omega = jf^*(p), \tag{14}$$

making the substitution $p_1 - p = j\omega$ and using (3).

It may be mentioned finally that the logical difficulties associated with impulse functions when they appear in integrals can be avoided by the use of *Stieltjes* integrals. A brief account of these is given in Appendix 8.

† See van der Pol and Bremmer, *op. cit.*, p. 49.

6.4   Analysis of arbitrary functions into step and impulse components

It will be seen in the next chapter that a fundamental characteristic of linear systems is that the response to an arbitrary input can be found by analysing the input into components of standard type and adding the responses to the individual components. The last two chapters have shown examples of this method of analysis, in which the standard functions were of the type e^{pt} multiplied by a suitable coefficient function depending on p. Different standard functions were given by different values of the parameter p. Thus when p took a series of discrete imaginary values a Fourier series was obtained, while if p was a continuously varying imaginary number, or complex number with constant real part, the given function $f(t)$ was expressed as a Fourier or Laplace integral. In both cases the coefficient function was a function of p. We now show how, in a similar way, $f(t)$ may be analysed into step or impulse components.

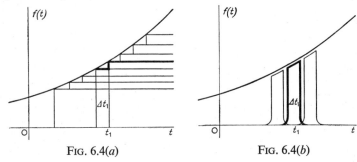

FIG. 6.4(a)   FIG. 6.4(b)

It is seen from fig. 6.4(a) how an approximation to $f(t)$ can be obtained by means of a series of steps of small amplitude. If a typical step occurs at time t_1 the amplitude of this component is easily seen to be $f'(t_1)\Delta t_1$ approximately, where Δt_1 is the interval between this step and the previous one. This typical component is therefore

$$f'(t_1)H(t-t_1)\Delta t_1.$$

Provided $f(t) \to 0$ as $t \to -\infty$ we then have

$$f(t) = \sum_{t_1} f'(t_1)H(t-t_1)\Delta t_1$$

approximately. The error of approximation can be removed by letting the individual increments Δt_1 tend to zero. When this is done the summation becomes an integral, thus

$$f(t) = \int_{-\infty}^{\infty} f'(t_1)H(t-t_1)\,dt_1. \tag{1}$$

We have thus achieved an analysis of $f(t)$ in terms of the standard functions $H(t-t_1)$ in which t_1 is the variable parameter. The coefficient function is $f'(t_1)$.

Again, referring to fig. 6.4(b), it is seen that $f(t)$ can be expressed as the sum of the functions whose graphs are shown under that of $f(t)$. A typical one of these can be regarded approximately as an impulse occurring at time t_1, whose amplitude is the area under the corresponding curve, namely $f(t_1)\Delta t_1$. Summing and taking the limit as $\Delta t_1 \rightarrow 0$ we have

$$f(t) = \int_{-\infty}^{\infty} f(t_1)\,\delta(t-t_1)\,dt_1. \tag{2}$$

This result could have been deduced from (1) by integration by parts or from **6.3** (3) by interchanging the variables t and t_1. Notice that $f(t_1)$ now takes on the role of a coefficient function, the standard function being the unit impulse $\delta(t-t_1)$ occurring at time t_1.

The part which these two rather artificial but very important formulae play in our subject will be developed in **8.4**.

6.5   Other associated functions

In this section we consider briefly the functions obtained by integrating $H(t)$ or differentiating $\delta(t)$ one or more times.

If $H(t)$ is integrated twice, taking each time the integral or primitive which vanishes when $t = -\infty$ we obtain successively the functions $R(t) = tH(t)$ and $P(t) = \frac{1}{2}t^2 H(t)$. These are called the *unit ramp function* and the *unit parabolic function* respectively. These graphs are shown in figs. 6.5(a) and (b) and their Laplace transforms are easily

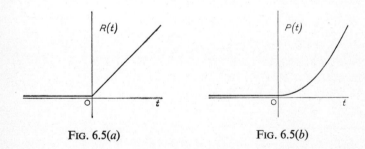

FIG. 6.5(a)   FIG. 6.5(b)

seen to be $1/p^2$ and $1/p^3$ respectively. In certain types of application, such as control systems in which the inputs have constant or substantially constant velocity or acceleration, it is convenient to use these as standard functions. A general function $f(t)$ can be analysed into components of this type by means of the formulae

$$f(t) = \int_{-\infty}^{\infty} f''(t_1)R(t-t_1)\,dt_1 \tag{1}$$

$$= \int_{-\infty}^{\infty} f'''(t_1)P(t-t_1)\,dt_1. \tag{2}$$

These can easily be derived using the methods of the last section. The general function of this type is defined as

$$\mathbf{D}^{-n}H(t) = \frac{t^n}{n!}H(t). \tag{3}$$

This has transform $1/p^{n+1}$.

The process of differentiating $\delta(t)$ is more difficult. Using the notation of **6.1**, if $H_\varepsilon(t) = h(t/\varepsilon)$ then $\delta(t) = \lim\limits_{\varepsilon \to 0} H_\varepsilon{}'(t)$. We can write formally

$$\delta'(t) = \lim_{\varepsilon \to 0} H_\varepsilon''(t) = \lim_{\varepsilon \to 0} h''(t/\varepsilon)/\varepsilon^2, \tag{4}$$

and call this the *unit impulse function of the second order*. Unfortunately, if we apply this definition strictly we obtain a function which is zero for *all* values of t. In order to obtain a realistic conception of this function it is necessary not to proceed to the limit but to take $H_\varepsilon''(t)$ with a small non-zero value of ε. The graph of such a function is shown in fig. 6.5(c). The transform of $H_\varepsilon''(t)$ will be a function which tends to p as $\varepsilon \to 0$. In this sense we can write

$$\mathfrak{L}\delta'(t) = p. \tag{5}$$

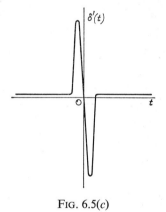

Functions of this type can arise in certain problems when certain combinations of circumstances occur. We shall not have occasion to use them in this book.

Fig. 6.5(c)

Impulse functions of higher order, which are defined as the higher derivatives of $\delta(t)$, can be introduced by extending the above process. An account of the properties of these is given by van der Pol and Bremmer.†

† *Op. cit.*, p. 49.

CHAPTER 7

LINEAR SYSTEMS

7.1 Definitions

We shall begin this chapter with a detailed explanation of the meaning of the two words which form its heading. Taking first the term "system", this refers in this context to a physical unit whose purpose is to convert a quantitative input u into a quantitative output x. Used in this sense this term includes mechanical or electrical devices used for automatic control or for communication purposes. It also includes computers, both analogue and digital. Such a system will frequently be made up of a number of elements each of which has the above characteristic. The analytical methods to be described will be applicable to these elements separately and, by combination, to the whole unit. We can therefore use the term "system" to refer to the individual elements as well as to the whole unit.

The elements of a system may be electrical or mechanical, or both. The former category includes passive networks, thermionic valves, electric motors and generators. In the latter are to be found hydraulic valves and motors, springs, elements making use of inertia and viscous damping, and devices whose operation depends basically on geometrical or kinematical principles. Either class may contain digital or analogue computing elements.

The input, or "forcing" function, and the output, or response, are usually functions of the continuous variable, time t. These may include steps or impulses. Alternatively, the input or the output or both may be sequences. Unlike functions of t, these have values defined only for isolated or discrete values of the independent variable. A full account of the theory of sequences and of their applications in linear system theory is given in Chapters 13 and 14. More generally a system may have several independent inputs or outputs (see **14.6**). When time is the independent variable the input and output will be represented by analogues such as voltages, currents, shaft rotations or linear displacements. Sequences can be represented in analogue or in digital form.

An essential feature of a system of this type is that the input function or sequence can be any one of a widely defined class. If it is necessary to impose restrictions at all these will be of the types that lay down, for example, that the input shall be continuous or that it shall have prescribed bounds. Thus a system should not have its input restricted say to exponential functions or polynomials. Taking an extreme case, any quantity, such as a power supply, that always has the same form should not be regarded as an input. For this reason electrical or mechanical oscillators are not normally regarded as systems within the present meaning of the term. The term, however, includes regulators and process controllers. In these important cases the inputs are taken to be the perturbations which it is the purpose of the system to eliminate.

The final requirement of a system is that the output x should be determined completely by the input and the characteristics of the system and in certain cases by an appropriate number of initial conditions. We can then represent the action of the system symbolically by

$$x = \mathbf{\Phi}u, \tag{1}$$

where $\mathbf{\Phi}$ is an operator representing the conversion of the input into the output. This operator will depend only on the lay-out of the system and not on the input. The system can therefore be shown in a block diagram as in fig. 7.1(a). If we have two systems in cascade, so that the

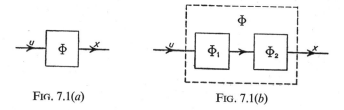

FIG. 7.1(a)   FIG. 7.1(b)

output of the first is the input to the second, as in fig. 7.1(b), the relation between the overall input and output can be written

$$x = \mathbf{\Phi}_2(\mathbf{\Phi}_1 u) = \mathbf{\Phi}_2 \cdot \mathbf{\Phi}_1 u = \mathbf{\Phi}u, \tag{2}$$

where the overall operator $\mathbf{\Phi} = \mathbf{\Phi}_2 \cdot \mathbf{\Phi}_1$. This equation provides the definition of the product of two operators of this type. A dot will always be used to indicate the combination or multiplication of operators in this way. Notice that such multiplication is not necessarily commutative, that is, $\mathbf{\Phi}_2 \cdot \mathbf{\Phi}_1$ is not necessarily the same as $\mathbf{\Phi}_1 \cdot \mathbf{\Phi}_2$.

This notation enables us to provide a compact but general definition of linearity as follows. An operator $\mathbf{\Phi}$ is linear if, and only if

$$\mathbf{\Phi}(u_1 + u_2) = \mathbf{\Phi}u_1 + \mathbf{\Phi}u_2, \tag{3}$$

for all admissible functions or sequences u_1 and u_2. A system is linear if its operator $\mathbf{\Phi}$ is linear. In other words if x_1 and x_2 are the outputs when the respective inputs u_1 and u_2 are applied separately, then the input $u_1 + u_2$ produces an output $x_1 + x_2$. This is called the *superposition principle*. As a corollary of (3),

$$\Phi(cu) = c\Phi u, \qquad (4)$$

where c is any constant.

Obvious examples of linear operators are **D** and $1/\mathbf{D}$, representing differentiation and indefinite integration. More generally it is shown in **2.6** (property (IIIc)) that the general rational fraction operator $F(\mathbf{D}) = P(\mathbf{D})/Q(\mathbf{D})$, where the polynomials $P(\mathbf{D})$ and $Q(\mathbf{D})$ have constant coefficients, is also linear. Thus the relation between the input

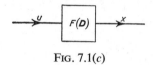

Fig. 7.1(c)

and output of the system shown in fig. 7.1(c) is a solution of the differential equation

$$Q(\mathbf{D})x = P(\mathbf{D})u. \qquad (5)$$

Most of the linear systems that arise in engineering problems are assumed to have operators of this type and we shall be concerned almost exclusively with these as far as the end of Chapter 12. There are, however, various classes of operator which although still linear are not of this type. Amongst these are the shift and difference operators **E** and Δ, and functions of these, applied to sequences and to functions of a continuous variable. These are considered in Chapter 13. Again, if the coefficients in the polynomials $P(\mathbf{D})$ and $Q(\mathbf{D})$ above are functions of t (but *not* of u or x) the differential equation and the operator $F(\mathbf{D})$ are still linear (see, for example, **1.2** (1)). Such an equation could represent a system with variable parameters, provided these are controlled by a clock, and are independent of the input and output. A simple but important operation on u is that of multiplication by a given function $f(t)$. Other linear operations are those of sampling and interpolation, which convert a function of continuous time into a sequence and vice versa. These will be discussed in Chapter 15.

It will be seen later that the superposition principle enables the characteristics of the response of a linear system to be determined in a general way for a wide range of input functions. It also allows conditions for stability to be prescribed and transients to be discussed independently of the input. The advantages of all this become apparent by contrast when non-linear systems come to be considered. Interest in the latter has increased greatly in recent years, and although many general techniques for studying them have been evolved, these have been of an *ad hoc* nature and have been based necessarily on special types of non-linearity and special input functions. While it is true that the introduction of non-linearity extends considerably the scope of automatic control, at the same time it greatly increases the difficulty of theoretical analysis.

7.2 General properties

The elementary operators $\mathbf{D}$ and $1/\mathbf{D}$ provide contrasting examples of an important general characteristic of a linear operator $\boldsymbol{\Phi}$, for if u is a given function $\mathbf{D}u$ is uniquely defined, while $(1/\mathbf{D})u$ defines an infinite number of functions. In general if $\boldsymbol{\Phi}u$ defines a unique function we say that the operator $\boldsymbol{\Phi}$ is *simple*, while if $\boldsymbol{\Phi}u$ represents more than one function the operator is *multiple*.

We have seen that if $x = \boldsymbol{\Phi}u$ where $\boldsymbol{\Phi} = P(\mathbf{D})/Q(\mathbf{D})$, then x is any solution of the differential equation $Q(\mathbf{D})x = P(\mathbf{D})u$. But the general solution of this equation takes the form $x = x_1 + x_0$, where x_1 is a particular integral and x_0 the complementary function, that is, the general solution of the equation $Q(\mathbf{D})x = 0$. Turning now to the more general operator $\boldsymbol{\Phi}$, in many cases this takes the form $\mathbf{P}/\mathbf{Q}$ where $\mathbf{P}$ and $\mathbf{Q}$ are simple operators, so that the output is given by the equation

$$\mathbf{Q}x = \mathbf{P}u. \tag{1}$$

This may be a differential equation with constant or variable coefficients, a difference equation or an integral equation; it may even reduce to a set of simultaneous algebraic equations. Let x_1 be one particular solution. Then

$$\mathbf{Q}x_1 = \mathbf{P}u. \tag{2}$$

If x denotes any other solution, subtracting (2) from (1) we have

$$\mathbf{Q}(x - x_1) = \mathbf{Q}x - \mathbf{Q}x_1 = \mathbf{P}u - \mathbf{P}u = 0,$$

using the linearity property 7.1 (3). Thus $x - x_1 = x_0$ where $\mathbf{Q}x_0 = 0$, so that

$$x = x_1 + x_0. \tag{3}$$

Thus the characteristic property of a linear constant coefficient differential equation that its general solution is the sum of a particular integral and the complementary function can be extended to cover any linear operator of this type. We call x_1 a *particular form* and x_0 the *complementary function* of $x = \boldsymbol{\Phi}u$.

It is easily verified that the general expression of the complementary function takes the form $C_1 v_1 + C_2 v_2 + \ldots$, where $v_1, v_2, \ldots$ constitute a complete set† of linearly independent solutions of $\mathbf{Q}v = 0$ and $C_1, C_2, \ldots$ are arbitrary constants. To show this observe that

$$\mathbf{Q}(C_1 v_1 + C_2 v_2 + \ldots) = C_1 \mathbf{Q}v_1 + C_2 \mathbf{Q}v_2 + \ldots = 0,$$

using **7.1** (3) and (4). We have finally that if $x = \mathbf{\Phi}u$ then

$$x = x_1 + \sum_r C_r v_r. \tag{4}$$

If $\mathbf{Q} = Q(\mathbf{D})$ the functions v_r take the form $t^k e^{\alpha t} \cos(\beta t + \gamma)$, but with more general operators other types of function will be obtained. The complementary function may contain a finite or an infinite number of terms. The arbitrary constants for any given run of the system will be determined by means of a number of initial conditions equal to the number of constants.

7.3 Stability, steady state and transients

Consider a linear system having a multiple operator $\mathbf{\Phi}$. Then the general output, whether it is a function of continuous time or a sequence, will take the form

$$x = x_1 + x_0 = x_1 + \sum C_r v_r. \tag{1}$$

If the system is such that $x_0 \to 0$ as $t \to \infty$ for all values of the arbitrary constants C_r, the output will tend to x_1 whatever the initial

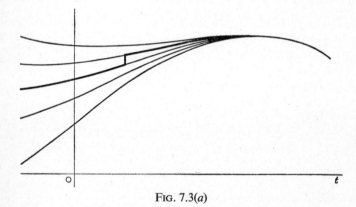

FIG. 7.3(a)

conditions may have been. Fig. 7.3(a) shows how the graphs of the outputs with the same input but with different initial conditions tend

† A complete set is by definition one with the property that *every* solution of $\mathbf{Q}v = 0$ can be expressed in the form $v = \Sigma C_r v_r$ (see **1.2** (3)).

to coincidence. Assume now that the output is following a particular curve when a small perturbation is applied. The effect of this will be to make the point tracing the curve jump on to an adjacent curve. Since this new curve tends to coincidence with the original curve as time proceeds, the effect of the perturbation is only temporary. For this reason we say that the system is *stable*. But x_0 tends to zero in all cases if and only if each function v_r tends to zero. We thus have as the *necessary and sufficient conditions for stability that each of these functions should tend to zero* as $t \to \infty$. Notice that these functions depend only on the operator $\mathbf{Q}$ and not on u, so that stability is determined completely by the system and does not depend in any way on the input. This is not necessarily the case for non-linear systems.

When $\mathbf{\Phi} = F(\mathbf{D})$ it was shown in **1.6** that the functions v_r take the form $t^k e^{\alpha t} \cos(\beta t + \gamma)$ where $\alpha \pm j\beta$ are roots of the equation $Q(\lambda) = 0$. We call this the *characteristic equation* of the system. Now this function will tend to zero as $t \to \infty$ if and only if $\alpha < 0$, for the factor $\cos(\beta t + \gamma)$, if it occurs, oscillates between 1 and -1, and although t^k tends to infinity it is well known that $t^k e^{\alpha t}$ tends to zero provided $\alpha < 0$. We thus have the fundamental result that *this system is stable if, and only if, all the roots of the characteristic equation have negative real parts*.

Returning now to the system whose response is given by (1), if this system is stable we call x_1 a *steady state* response, since this function represents the output ultimately, however it may have started. In fact, since x_1 could be any function satisfying the equation $\mathbf{Q}x = \mathbf{P}u$, and all these solutions have equal status, there is strictly no unique steady state response. However, in certain types of problem there is often some criterion which leads naturally to one particular function. This might be the solution which is purely sinusoidal or which remains finite as $t \to -\infty$ or which has the simplest form algebraically. As an example of the last of these conditions, if the general solution is say $3t + C_1 e^{-t} + C_2 e^{-2t}$ we would naturally say that the steady state response is $3t$.

Once we have fixed the steady state x_1 we define the *transient* response x_0 for a particular run x as the difference between x and x_1. Then, since the definitions of steady state and transient responses only apply to stable systems, the latter must tend to zero as $t \to \infty$. It often happens in practice that the output of a linear system becomes useful only when the transient has become inappreciable. The time taken by this process is called the *settling time*. It is clearly not possible to give a more precise general definition of the settling time, since the nature of the transients and the threshold level will vary from system to system. A typical example is however given in **8.1**.

7.4 Applications

If a voltage v is applied to a resistance R the current i is given by the equation $v = Ri$. If the resistance is replaced by a coil with inductance L or a condenser with capacitance C, the constant multiplier R must be replaced by an operator $L\mathbf{D}$ or $1/(C\mathbf{D})$. If these three elements are connected in series we have $v = Z(\mathbf{D})i$ where $Z(\mathbf{D}) = L\mathbf{D} + R + 1/(C\mathbf{D})$. We call $Z(\mathbf{D})$ the *impedance operator*. Proceeding now to the case of a general two-terminal network, the relations between the various voltages and currents are obtained from Kirchoff's laws as a set of simultaneous linear differential equations. If we eliminate from these equations all the voltages and currents except v, the voltage applied to the terminals, and i, the current flowing through them, we again obtain a relation $v = Z(\mathbf{D})i$, where the impedance operator $Z(\mathbf{D})$ is a rational fraction in $\mathbf{D}$. Such a network could be regarded as a linear system in which v is the input and i the output.

Consider the circuit shown in fig. 7.4(*a*). If the input u and the

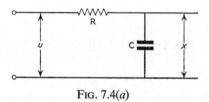

FIG. 7.4(*a*)

output x are the voltages across the input terminals and across the condenser as shown,

$$u = \left(R + \frac{1}{C\mathbf{D}}\right)i, \qquad x = \frac{1}{C\mathbf{D}}i,\dagger$$

so that

$$x = \frac{1/(C\mathbf{D})}{R + 1/(C\mathbf{D})}u = \frac{1}{1 + T\mathbf{D}}u, \tag{1}$$

where $T = RC$ is the time constant (see **2.4**). This circuit provides one of the simplest devices for smoothing the input u (see **8.2** and **8.3**). On the other hand, if the voltage across the resistance is taken as output y, then

$$y = \frac{T\mathbf{D}}{1 + T\mathbf{D}}u. \tag{2}$$

† The practice of writing an expression of this type as $\dfrac{i}{C\mathbf{D}}$ is to be deprecated. To avoid confusion the function operated on should always *follow* and not be absorbed into the operator,

If T is small we have $y = T\mathbf{D}u$ approximately. This circuit can therefore be used for differentiation. A fuller analysis of both these circuits is given in the next chapter.

In our next example a low-power input signal u is amplified and processed to form the armature current of a motor whose shaft rotation is to be the output x. Taking the motor torque T to be proportional to the armature current, assume that the amplifier is such that

$$T = k\frac{1+T_1\mathbf{D}}{1+T_2\mathbf{D}}u$$

where k, T_1 and T_2 are constants (the last two having the dimensions of time). If J is the inertia of the motor load, and if there is no friction, we have also $T = J\mathbf{D}^2 x$, or

$$x = \frac{1}{J\mathbf{D}^2}T.$$

Eliminating T,

$$x = \frac{k(1+T_1\mathbf{D})}{J\mathbf{D}^2(1+T_2\mathbf{D})}u. \tag{3}$$

A block diagram of this system is shown in fig. 7.4(b). This is an

FIG. 7.4(b)   FIG. 7.4(c)

example of the important general principle that if two systems with operators $F_1(\mathbf{D})$ and $F_2(\mathbf{D})$ are in cascade, as in fig. 7.4(c), the combined operator is formed by algebraic multiplication of these operators. This is proved formally in Appendix 6. Using the dot notation as in **7.1** (2), it can be written

$$F_2(\mathbf{D}).F_1(\mathbf{D}) = F_2(\mathbf{D})F_1(\mathbf{D}). \tag{4}$$

This property can only be applied if the two systems do not react on one another, so that, for example, the operator of two four-terminal networks in cascade is not the product of their separate operators.

Another useful general formula concerns systems with feed-back, as in fig. 7.4(d). The governing equation in this case is $x = F(\mathbf{D})(u-x)$, or

$$x = \frac{F(\mathbf{D})}{1+F(\mathbf{D})}u. \tag{5}$$

An interesting special case is when the element represented by $F(\mathbf{D})$ is an integrator. This may be of any type, but the manner in which it operates becomes clearly evident if we show it as a roller, ball and disc variable-speed gear. The complete circuit is shown in fig. 7.4(e). In

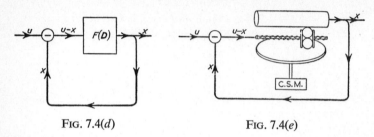

FIG. 7.4(d)   FIG. 7.4(e)

this, the disc is driven by a constant-speed motor so that the roller rotates at a rate proportional to the displacement of the ball cage from the centre of the disc. In other words, the *rate* of rotation of the roller is proportional to the *angle* of rotation of the shaft which positions the ball cage. The constant of proportionality depends on the rate of rotation of the disc, the radius of the roller and the pitch of the lead screw positioning the ball cage. This constant has dimensions of the reciprocal of time and can be written $1/T$, where T is a time constant. It follows that $F(\mathbf{D}) = 1/(T\mathbf{D})$. It is evident that, if the input shaft rotates at a substantially constant rate, the ball cage will set itself so that the roller follows the input rotation. However, any perturbation in the input is not immediately reproduced in the roller position. The latter can therefore be regarded as a smoothed version of the input. Also, when the system has settled, the displacement of the ball cage represents approximately the rate of rotation of the input shaft. This circuit therefore performs the two operations of smoothing and differentiation. In order to examine the operation of the system analytically we substitute $F(\mathbf{D}) = 1/(T\mathbf{D})$ in (5). This gives

$$x = \frac{1}{1+T\mathbf{D}}u \tag{6}$$

and
$$y = u-x = \frac{T\mathbf{D}}{1+T\mathbf{D}}u. \tag{7}$$

We observe that these equations are identical with (1) and (2). It can be inferred therefore that the systems of figs. 7.4(a) and (e) are mathematically equivalent and can be made to perform the same operations.

Finally, if we take the element $F(\mathbf{D})$ in fig. 7.4(d) to be the system shown in fig. 7.4(*b*) we obtain a typical servo system. In this case, after a little reduction, it is seen that

$$x = \frac{k(1+T_1\mathbf{D})}{k(1+T_1\mathbf{D})+J\mathbf{D}^2(1+T_2\mathbf{D})}u,\tag{8}$$

and that the error is

$$y = u-x = \frac{J\mathbf{D}^2(1+T_2\mathbf{D})}{k(1+T_1\mathbf{D})+J\mathbf{D}^2(1+T_2\mathbf{D})}u.\tag{9}$$

The analysis of all these operational equations will be considered in detail in the next chapter.

CHAPTER 8

ANALYSIS OF LINEAR SYSTEMS

8.1 Use of the differential equation

In the next three chapters we shall be concerned exclusively with systems whose operator is a rational fraction $F(\mathbf{D}) = P(\mathbf{D})/Q(\mathbf{D})$, in which the numerator and denominator both have constant coefficients. Then $x = F(\mathbf{D})u$, so that the output is given in terms of the input by the differential equation

$$Q(\mathbf{D})x = P(\mathbf{D})u. \tag{1}$$

Following 7.3 we can say immediately that the system is stable if and only if the roots of the characteristic equation

$$Q(\lambda) = 0 \tag{2}$$

all have negative real parts. The practical interpretation of this condition will be considered fully in the next chapter.

If the system is stable, a steady state response to a given input can often be found as a particular integral by one of the operational methods given in Chapter 2. With an unspecified input a particularly appropriate method is that of expansion of the operator $F(\mathbf{D})$ in ascending powers of $\mathbf{D}$, the theory of which is discussed in Appendix 7. In many applications $F(\mathbf{D})$ contains some power of $\mathbf{D}$ as a factor. Let

$$F(\mathbf{D}) = \mathbf{D}^s F_1(\mathbf{D}) = \mathbf{D}^s(f_0 + f_1\mathbf{D} + \ldots). \tag{3}$$

This expansion will normally be obtained by one of the algebraic processes described in Appendix 4. Compact expressions for the coefficients are, however, given by means of Maclaurin's theorem. Thus

$$f_0 = F_1(0), \qquad f_1 = F_1{}'(0), \qquad f_2 = \tfrac{1}{2}F_1{}''(0), \ldots. \tag{4}$$

A steady state response x_{ss} is therefore

$$x_{ss} = f_0\mathbf{D}^s u + f_1\mathbf{D}^{s+1}u + \ldots. \tag{5}$$

This expression is general, and, provided u and, its derivatives vary steadily, a useful convergent or asymptotic expansion is usually obtained (see Appendix 7). In practice the number of terms used is one, two or at most three.

If $\mathbf{D}^s u$ is constant all higher derivatives will vanish, so that (5) becomes

$$x_{ss} = f_0 \mathbf{D}^s u = F_1(0)\mathbf{D}^s u. \tag{6}$$

If, more generally, $\mathbf{D}^s u$ is not constant but is not changing rapidly, (6) can be regarded as a first approximation. A better approximation will be

$$x_{ss} = f_0 \mathbf{D}^s u + f_1 \mathbf{D}^{s+1} u, \tag{7}$$

and so on.

We take as our first example the circuit or mechanical system discussed in **7.4** for which $F(\mathbf{D}) = 1/(1 + T\mathbf{D})$. The characteristic equation is $1 + T\lambda = 0$. This has one root $\lambda = -1/T$, so that the system is stable provided $T > 0$. Since the transient is $C e^{-t/T}$ the system will settle exponentially. More specifically, when $t = T, 2T, 3T, \ldots$ the transient takes the values $0.37C, 0.14C, 0.05C, \ldots$ The settling time (see **7.3**) in this case might be defined as the time taken for the transient to be reduced to some specified fraction of its initial value. For example, if this fraction is 1 per cent, the settling time is between $4T$ and $5T$. It is clear that the smaller the time constant T, the shorter is the settling time.

The steady state is given by

$$x_{ss} = \frac{1}{1 + T\mathbf{D}} u = (1 - T\mathbf{D} + T^2\mathbf{D}^2 - \ldots) u, \tag{8}$$

using equation (11) of Appendix 4. It follows that, as a first approximation, the steady state output equals the input. The second approximation is $u - T\mathbf{D}u$. Now $T\mathbf{D}u$ is approximately the amount by which u changes in time T; we deduce that when the system has settled, the output follows the input with an approximate time lag T. Since this system is used primarily as a smoothing device we have here the simplest example of an important general principle which states that automatic smoothing necessarily introduces lag. We shall see later that the more effective the smoothing, the greater the lag.

If with the same system we take as output the voltage across the resistance or the displacement of the ball cage the operator becomes effectively $\mathbf{D}/(1 + T\mathbf{D})$. It follows that the transient is again exponential but that the steady state output is $\mathbf{D}u - T\mathbf{D}^2 u + \ldots$. We deduce that the output measures the derivative of the input, again with an approximate time lag T.

Consider now the servo represented by fig. 7.4(d) with $F(\mathbf{D})$ taking the form of the combined operator of the units shown in fig. 7.4(b). We see from **7.4** (9) that the operator which gives the error is

$$\frac{J\mathbf{D}^2(1+T_2\mathbf{D})}{k(1+T_1\mathbf{D})+J\mathbf{D}^2(1+T_2\mathbf{D})}. \tag{9}$$

The characteristic equation is the cubic

$$k(1+T_1\lambda)+J\lambda^2(1+T_2\lambda) = 0. \tag{10}$$

It can be shown, using a formula (**9.3** (6)) derived in the next chapter, that this represents a stable system if all the constants are positive and if $T_1 > T_2$. The operator (9) is a special case of (3) in which $s = 2$. It is easily seen that $F_1(0)$, which is obtained by removing the factor $\mathbf{D}^2$ and replacing $\mathbf{D}$ in the resulting operator by zero, is J/k. The steady state output is therefore $(J/k)\mathbf{D}^2u + \dots$. It follows that if u or its first derivative is constant there is no steady state error. In other cases the error is approximately proportional to $\mathbf{D}^2u$. The task of a designer of such a servo is to choose the parameters k, T_1 and T_2 of the amplifier so that the constant of proportionality J/k is sufficiently small and the transient performance is satisfactory. A knowledge of the roots of (10) is usually sufficient to enable the transient behaviour to be assessed.

For example, if the constants are such that (10) becomes

$$\lambda^3 T^3 + 4\lambda^2 T^2 + 6\lambda T + 4 = 0,$$

where T is a time constant, this can be factorised in the form

$$(\lambda T+2)(\lambda^2 T^2+2\lambda T+2) = 0,$$

so that the roots are $\lambda = -2/T$ or $(-1\pm j)/T$. The transient will therefore be of the form

$$e^{-t/T}\{A\cos(t/T)+B\sin(t/T)\}+C\,e^{-2t/T}.$$

The first of these terms is more significant than the second, partly because it is oscillatory and partly because it settles more slowly.

This operational method of analysing a linear system is frequently adequate for the purpose of giving a general indication of its performance. Compared with the other methods described in the following sections, which are based on particular inputs and which are more commonly used by engineers, it has the advantage of generality. Since it is based on simple general operational rules it is easy to apply. In order to extract the same information using the harmonic response

(8.2) devious reasoning involving phase shift and zero frequency response must be introduced, while if the Laplace transform method **(8.3)** is used special theorems are required. Also in the latter case the additional labour of finding partial fractions is necessary. The operational method can therefore usually be recommended, at any rate in a preliminary examination of a given system.

Expansion of the operator, even if only the first term is taken, should not be used to obtain the output in time intervals in which u has steps or impulses, for in this case successive terms of the series and the corresponding remainders will contain impulses of increasing order. Large errors will therefore occur with the steps or impulses in u. The proper method in this case is to use the Laplace transform, as explained in **8.3**.

8.2 Harmonic response

The methods of analysis to be described in this and the following sections are based on input functions of special types, for example sinusoidal or impulse or step functions. Extensions to more general input functions are then achieved by analysis into components of these respective types. The output is found by obtaining the response to these components separately and then adding, making use of the super-position principle.

If we have a sinusoidal input $U_1 \cos(\omega t + \varepsilon)$ it is convenient to regard this as the real part of a complex exponential function. In fact, even though we are only using the real part we shall write

$$u = U_1 e^{j(\omega t + \varepsilon)} = U e^{j\omega t}, \tag{1}$$

where
$$U = U_1 e^{j\varepsilon}. \tag{2}$$

This is equivalent to introducing a *complex amplitude U* whose modulus is the actual amplitude U_1 and whose angle is the initial phase ε. Then, provided $Q(j\omega) \neq 0$, the corresponding steady state output is given by

$$x = F(j\omega)U e^{j\omega t} = X e^{j\omega t}, \tag{3}$$

where
$$X = F(j\omega)U. \tag{4}$$

We have used here a special case of the general result $F(\mathbf{D}) e^{\alpha t} = F(\alpha) e^{\alpha t}$ (see **2.6**, property (Ic)). *It follows that the steady state output is also sinusoidal, with the same frequency as the input. Also the ratio of the amplitudes and the difference of the phases of the output and input are respectively the modulus and angle of $F(j\omega)$* (see Appendix 1 (17)).

We call $F(j\omega)$ the *harmonic response multiplier* of the system. It is a complex number which varies with ω. If we plot on an Argand diagram the points which represent this number for different values of ω we obtain a curve called the *harmonic response locus*. For example, with the circuit shown in fig. 7.4(a), $F(j\omega) = 1/(1+j\omega T)$. It is easily proved that

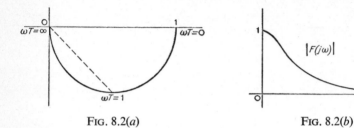

FIG. 8.2(a)   FIG. 8.2(b)

the locus in this case is the semicircle shown in fig. 8.2(a). As an example of the interpretation of this locus, if $\omega = 1/T$, $|F(j\omega)| = 1/\sqrt{2}$ and ang $F(j\omega) = -\frac{1}{4}\pi$. It follows that for this frequency the output has a phase lag of 45° compared with the input and that the ratio of their amplitudes is $1/\sqrt{2}$.

The fact that $|F(j\omega)| = 1/\sqrt{(1+\omega^2 T^2)} \to 0$ as $\omega \to \infty$ demonstrates in one way the smoothing property of this circuit, for if we assume that the input has a sinusoidal perturbation of frequency ω, this is multiplied on passing through the circuit by a factor which decreases as the frequency increases. The graph of this factor is shown in fig. 8.2(b). Notice that in this reasoning we have made use of the linearity of the circuit in order to discuss the effect of the perturbation independently of the rest of the input.

This circuit is the simplest non-trivial type of filter that can be devised. It is of course possible by using more complex types of networks to design filters which are frequency-selective in a variety of ways.

If an input or signal u is passed through two filters in cascade, their respective operators being $F_1(\mathbf{D})$ and $F_2(\mathbf{D})$, the combined operator $F(\mathbf{D})$ is $F_1(\mathbf{D})F_2(\mathbf{D})$. Since

$$|F(j\omega)| = |F_1(j\omega)||F_2(j\omega)|$$

and $$\text{ang } F(j\omega) = \text{ang } F_1(j\omega) + \text{ang } F_2(j\omega),$$

if we are given loci for $F_1(j\omega)$ and $F_2(j\omega)$ separately we can construct the locus of $F(j\omega)$ point by point from these by multiplying the corresponding moduli and adding the corresponding arguments.

More general inputs can be considered by the harmonic response technique by analysing them into sinusoidal components. Thus if

$$u = \sum_r U_r e^{j\omega_r t} \tag{5}$$

then

$$x = \sum_r X_r e^{j\omega_r t}, \tag{6}$$

where

$$X_r = F(j\omega_r)U_r. \tag{7}$$

In these expressions the numbers ω_r can be any set of frequencies. In the particular case where they are multiples of a fundamental frequency Ω, the expressions (5) and (6) for the input and output are Fourier series (see **4.3** (1)) whose coefficients are related by (7). This method of analysis can be extended to the case where the frequency varies continuously, in which case the expressions (5) and (6) become Fourier integrals (see **4.4** (3)), and (7) becomes a relation between Fourier transforms. This process is considered again in the next section.

The harmonic response method is particularly appropriate in communication systems, where the representation of signals in the frequency domain is usually more important than their representation in the time domain. It is also useful for control systems when the input can be analysed into sinusoidal components which fall mainly in clearly defined frequency bands, or when sinusoidal inputs can be used for testing purposes. If the relation between input and output can be obtained experimentally for all frequencies it is possible theoretically to deduce the nature of the operator $F(\mathbf{D})$, if the form of this is not known in the first place. Harmonic response loci can be used in these cases to indicate modifications necessary in a system to produce desired characteristics in its performance.

8.3   Use of Laplace transforms

Other special functions widely used in the analysis of linear systems are those which have Laplace transforms. These are usually, but not always one-sided functions. If the input $u(t)$ and the output $x(t)$ have transforms $u^*(p)$ and $x^*(p)$ it follows from property (VI) of **5.4** that

$$x^*(p) = F(p)u^*(p). \tag{1}$$

It was shown in that section that if, with a given input, the output $x(t)$ given by this expression exists at all, it must be unique. In particular, if $u(t)$ is one-sided it is easily seen that $x(t)$ is the particular integral that also is one-sided. If $F(\mathbf{D})$ and $u(t)$ are given, the standard method for evaluating $x(t)$ is to express $x^*(p)$, given by (1), in partial fractions. These are then interpreted term by term by means of a table of transforms, such as table 3.2(A). The multiplier $F(p)$, which is the ratio of the transforms of the output and the input, is called the *transfer function* of the system.

This method is frequently used to find the response to the unit step function $H(t)$ and the unit impulse function $\delta(t)$. Since the transforms of these functions are $1/p$ and 1, the corresponding responses are the functions whose transforms are $F(p)/p$ and $F(p)$ respectively. Taking yet again the example $F(\mathbf{D}) = 1/(1+T\mathbf{D})$, if $u(t) = H(t)$

$$x^*(p) = \frac{1}{p(1+Tp)} = \frac{1}{p} - \frac{T}{1+Tp},$$

so that
$$x(t) = (1-e^{-t/T})H(t). \tag{2}$$

On the other hand, if $u(t) = \delta(t)$, $x^*(p) = 1/(1+Tp)$, so that

$$x(t) = \frac{1}{T}H(t)\,e^{-t/T}. \tag{3}$$

Graphs of these two functions are shown in figs. 8.3(*a*) and (*b*).

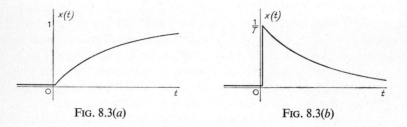

FIG. 8.3(*a*)   FIG. 8.3(*b*)

As a more general example, let the input be a rectangular pulse of duration τ. Then

$$u(t) = H(t) - H(t-\tau),$$

$$u^*(p) = \frac{1}{p}(1-e^{-\tau p}),$$

$$x^*(p) = \frac{1-e^{-\tau p}}{p(1+Tp)},$$

so that
$$x(t) = (1-e^{-t/T})H(t) - (1-e^{-(t-\tau)/T})H(t-\tau).$$

This is equivalent to

$$x(t) = 1-e^{-t/T} \quad \text{if } 0 < t < \tau,$$
$$= (1-e^{-\tau/T})e^{-(t-\tau)/T} \quad \text{if } t > \tau.$$

Graphs of $u(t)$ and $x(t)$ are shown in fig. 8.3(c).

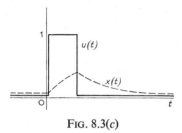

FIG. 8.3(c)

Once again the smoothing and delaying effect of a system with this operator is demonstrated. If the input is a unit step, fig. 8.3(a) shows that the output gradually takes up the new value of the input. On the other hand if the pulse in fig. 8.3(c) is regarded as a perturbation, the corresponding output is seen to be attenuated and spread out in comparison with the disturbance.

If we replace p by $j\omega$ in (1) we have

$$x^*(j\omega) = F(j\omega)u^*(j\omega). \tag{4}$$

This shows that if output and input both have Fourier transforms the ratio of these is $F(j\omega)$, the harmonic response multiplier. This equation provides the most general form of **8.2** (7).

8.4 Weighting function

Let the one-sided response to the unit impulse function $\delta(t)$ of a system whose operator is $F(\mathbf{D})$ be $W(t)$. Then it is easily proved that the response to an impulse $\delta(t-t_1)$ occurring at time t_1 is $W(t-t_1)$. More generally, if the input consists of a series of impulses of different amplitudes $c_1, c_2, \ldots$ occurring at different times $t_1, t_2, \ldots$, so that

$$u(t) = \sum_r c_r \delta(t-t_r), \tag{1}$$

then
$$x(t) = \sum_r c_r W(t-t_r), \tag{2}$$

using the superposition rule. It is shown in figs. 8.4(a) to (d) how if $W(t)$ is given, (2) can be used to construct $x(t)$ graphically. Thus if $W(t)$ is as in fig. 8.4(a) and $u(t)$ as in fig. 8.4(b), the responses to the separate impulses are shown in fig. 8.4(c). The output is formed by adding these, as in fig. 8.4(d).

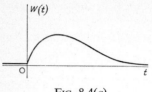

FIG. 8.4(a)

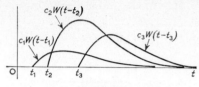

FIG. 8.4(c)

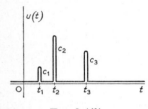

FIG. 8.4(b)

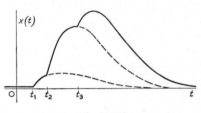

FIG. 8.4(d)

Proceeding now to the general input $u(t)$, we saw in **6.4** (2) that this could be analysed into impulsive components by writing

$$u(t) = \int_{-\infty}^{\infty} u(t_1)\,\delta(t-t_1)\,dt_1. \qquad (3)$$

Generalising (2), the corresponding output is therefore

$$x(t) = \int_{-\infty}^{\infty} u(t_1)W(t-t_1)\,dt_1. \qquad (4)$$

An alternative and equally useful form, obtained by a change of variable to $\tau = t-t_1$, is

$$x(t) = \int_{-\infty}^{\infty} u(t-\tau)W(\tau)\,d\tau. \qquad (5)$$

In the present case $W(t)$ vanishes when $t < 0$, so that $W(t-t_1)$ vanishes when $t_1 > t$. The upper limit in the integral can therefore be replaced by t, giving

$$x(t) = \int_{-\infty}^{t} u(t_1)W(t-t_1)\,dt_1. \qquad (6)$$

This equation represents in its most direct form the relation between the input $u(t)$ and the output $x(t)$. It shows that at any time t the output depends linearly on the values of the input at all previous times t_1, with a weighting factor $W(t-t_1)$ depending only on the time difference $t-t_1$. For this reason $W(t)$ is called the *weighting function* of the system.

This process can be demonstrated graphically by fig. 8.4(e) as follows. In order to evaluate $x(t)$ for a particular time t, we first draw the graph of $W(t-t_1)$ for fixed t and variable t_1. This graph is obtained from that of $W(t)$ by reversing it and displacing it to the right a distance corresponding to time t. For each t_1, $u(t_1)$ is multiplied by the intercept on the corresponding ordinate of the graph of $W(t-t_1)$. Integration of the product then gives $x(t)$. As t increases, the graph of $W(t-t_1)$ moves steadily to the right, as indicated by the arrow.

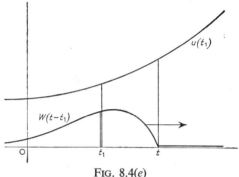

FIG. 8.4(e)

The weighting function $W(t)$, which, as was shown in the last section, is given by

$$W(t) = \mathfrak{L}^{-1}F(p),\tag{7}$$

provides a complete representation of the system and can be used as an alternative to the operator $F(\mathbf{D})$.

To take an example, if $F(\mathbf{D}) = 1/(1+T\mathbf{D})$ it was shown in **8.3** (3) that $W(t) = (1/T)H(t)e^{-t/T}$. The graph of this function appears in fig. 8.3(b). Again if $F(\mathbf{D}) = 1/(\mathbf{D}+\alpha)(\mathbf{D}+\beta)$ then

$$F(p) = \frac{1}{(p+\alpha)(p+\beta)} = \frac{1}{\beta-\alpha}\left(\frac{1}{p+\alpha} - \frac{1}{p+\beta}\right)$$

so that

$$W(t) = \frac{1}{\beta-\alpha}H(t)(e^{-\alpha t} - e^{-\beta t}).$$

This function has a graph of the type shown in fig. 8.4(a). In the first example, (6) becomes

$$x(t) = \frac{1}{T}\int_{-\infty}^{t} e^{-(t-t_1)/T} u(t_1)\, dt_1,$$

a form that has been derived previously by direct solution of the differential equation (see **2.5** (4)).

The fundamental relation (4) of this approach to the problem used in this section can be looked at in yet another way. Using Laplace transforms, as in the last section, we have

$$x^*(p) = F(p)u^*(p). \qquad (8)$$

Using property (IV) of **5.4**, (4) follows immediately. In other words, *the output is formed by convolution of the input and the weighting function.*

If two systems with operators $F_1(\mathbf{D})$ and $F_2(\mathbf{D})$ and weighting functions $W_1(t)$, $W_2(t)$ are in cascade the combined operator $F(\mathbf{D})$ is $F_2(\mathbf{D})F_1(\mathbf{D})$, so that

$$x^*(p) = F_2(p)F_1(p)u^*(p). \qquad (9)$$

It follows that $F(p) = F_1(p)F_2(p)$. The overall weighting function $W(t)$ is therefore formed by convolution of $W_1(t)$ and $W_2(t)$, that is,

$$W(t) = \int_{-\infty}^{\infty} W_1(t_1)W_2(t-t_1)\, dt_1. \qquad (10)$$

A slight modification, first used by Carson,† of the general method described in this section is to analyse $u(t)$ into step functions as in **6.4** (1). Then if $A(t)$ is the response to the unit step function we have

$$u(t) = \int_{-\infty}^{\infty} u'(t_1)H(t-t_1)\, dt_1, \qquad (11)$$

hence $$x(t) = \int_{-\infty}^{\infty} u'(t_1)A(t-t_1)\, dt_1. \qquad (12)$$

The function $A(t)$ is called by Carson the *indicial admittance* of the system. It has the property

$$A'(t) = W(t). \qquad (13)$$

Using this and integrating by parts, (12) can be shown to be identical with (4).

8.5 Summary

In this section we summarise the five main ways of representing analytically the relation between the input and output of a linear system. At the same time we shall recapitulate the particular advantages and disadvantages of each.

The operational equation

$$x(t) = F(\mathbf{D})u(t) \qquad (1)$$

† Carson, J. R., *Electric Circuit Theory and the Operational Calculus.* McGraw-Hill (New York).

represents the relation in its most general form and is applicable to all systems of the type considered in this chapter, and to all inputs. Using the operational methods developed in Chapter 2 the responses of the system to particular inputs of elementary types can, in most cases, be calculated more quickly than by any other method, particularly if the order of the differential equation is low. With more general inputs the operator $F(\mathbf{D})$ yields immediately, by its denominator, the characteristic equation $Q(\lambda) = 0$, from which the stability and transient behaviour is determined. This operator also enables information about the steady state response to be inferred by inspection. The most common cases where operational *methods* are not appropriate are those in which step and impulse functions are involved. Even in these, however, the operational *notation* is still applicable.

The equation

$$X = F(j\omega)U \tag{2}$$

and its various extensions derived in **8.2**, which determine the harmonic response of the system, are particularly appropriate in applications in which the frequency domain is of primary importance. It is also useful for analysis and synthesis of systems of other types in which sinusoidal functions can be used as test inputs. Another advantage of this method is that use can be made of the various harmonic response loci.

In the same way, the relation between the Laplace transforms of input and output,

$$x^*(p) = F(p)u^*(p), \tag{3}$$

arises naturally when working with one-sided functions and with functions involving steps and impulses. It is particularly useful for representing and determining the response to impulse, step or ramp functions.

Both (2) and (3) have the advantage that the conversion performed by the system is represented by multiplication by a factor $F(j\omega)$ or $F(p)$. In other words the system is represented by a function, the harmonic response multiplier or the transfer function, which is the ratio of the complex amplitudes or the Laplace transforms of the output and the input. In either case therefore analysis can be carried out by algebraic methods.

Equations (2) and (3) lack the generality of (1) since they are based essentially on special types of functions. In some respects they can be considered as complementary special cases of (1). Notice that the relation between the Fourier transforms

$$x^*(j\omega) = F(j\omega)u^*(j\omega) \tag{4}$$

can be considered as a generalisation of (2) and a special case of (3).

Finally, if the weighting function is used,

$$x(t) = \int_{-\infty}^{\infty} W(t-t_1)u(t_1)\,dt_1. \tag{5}$$

This formula can, as was shown in the last section, be obtained directly using the linearity or superposition principle. This fundamental approach, which will be the basis of later generalisations, is useful in solving certain theoretical problems. It is not in general so convenient for particular systems and inputs, since the basic relationships are all expressed in terms of integrals, each of which has to be evaluated.

Fig. 8.5(a) shows diagrammatically the connections between the above five alternative formulae.

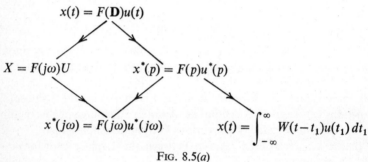

FIG. 8.5(a)

CHAPTER 9

STABILITY

9.1 The characteristic equation

The output x of a linear system whose operator is

$$F(\mathbf{D}) = P(\mathbf{D})/Q(\mathbf{D})$$

is the solution of the differential equation

$$Q(\mathbf{D})x = P(\mathbf{D})u. \qquad (1)$$

The complementary function in this solution takes the form $\sum\limits_{r=1}^{n} C_r e^{\lambda_r t}$
where $\lambda_1, \lambda_2, \ldots \lambda_n$ are the roots of the characteristic equation

$$Q(\lambda) = 0. \qquad (2)$$

This form has to be modified when some or all of these roots are complex or multiple. It was shown in **7.3** that this complementary function tends to zero as $t \to \infty$ whatever the initial conditions, if, and only if, the real parts of all the numbers λ_r are negative. These are therefore the necessary and sufficient conditions for stability. We call these numbers the *zeros* of the function $Q(\lambda)$. The corresponding complementary function terms are called the *natural modes* of the system. These of course do not depend on the input.

Information about not only the stability of the system but also the nature of the transient response can be displayed effectively if the zeros of $Q(\lambda)$ are shown in an Argand diagram of the complex number λ. This is

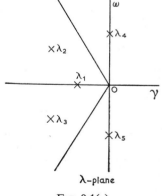

Fig. 9.1(a)

called the λ-plane and is shown in fig. 9.1(a). Then for stability all the zeros must lie in the half-plane to the left of the imaginary axis.

Put $\lambda = \gamma + j\omega$. Then a negative real zero such as λ_1 will give a natural mode proportional to $e^{\lambda_1 t}$. This dies away aperiodically, that is to say without oscillation. Also the larger the magnitude of λ_1 the sooner this mode becomes negligible. On the other hand a pair of conjugate complex zeros such as λ_2 and λ_3, which are represented by points which are images in the real axis, will give rise to modes of the forms $e^{\gamma t} \cos \omega t$ and $e^{\gamma t} \sin \omega t$, where $\lambda_2, \lambda_3 = \gamma \pm j\omega$. The combination of these is a damped oscillation with frequency ω and attenuation measured by $|\gamma|$. As a special case of this, if λ_4 and λ_5 are conjugate imaginary zeros $\pm j\omega$ on the imaginary axis, the corresponding modes form an undamped oscillation of frequency ω. In this case we say the system is critically stable.

Assuming that the system is stable, if all the zeros of $Q(\lambda)$ are shown in the λ-plane the most significant ones are usually those nearest to the imaginary axis. These represent the modes of the transient that settle most slowly, and their distance from this axis gives an indication of the settling time of the system. In fact, the greater this distance the less the settling time.

Another characteristic which may be desirable in certain systems is that no mode, however damped, should have a high oscillation frequency. In this case none of the zeros should be far from the real axis. Again it may be necessary that oscillatory modes, of whatever frequency, should be so damped that their oscillations become insignificant within a single cycle. This condition can be stated analytically by prescribing an upper limit for the *logarithmic decrement* $-2\pi\gamma/\omega$, which is by definition the logarithm of the ratio of successive maxima of the mode. In this case the zeros of $Q(\lambda)$ will have to lie to the left of a pair of inclined lines like those shown in fig. 9.1(*a*).

Before an examination of the stability and the transient response can be undertaken in this way the equation $Q(\lambda) = 0$ must be solved. This can be done easily in general only if $n = 1$ or 2 or, to a lesser extent, if $n = 3$ or 4. For higher order equations methods of successive approximation must be used. These are usually quite manageable for real roots, but complex roots almost invariably involve lengthy numerical processes. A brief account of some of these methods is given in Appendix 9.

The difficulties associated with the numerical computation of the zeros of $Q(\lambda)$, particularly if it is desired to examine the effect of varying one or more of the parameters of the system, has led to the development of indirect methods of studying the stability and the transient response without actually solving the characteristic equation. The remainder of this chapter is devoted to a discussion of these. They are based primarily on an investigation of the variation of $Q(\lambda)$, or more generally of $F(\lambda)$, for a selected range of values of the complex variable λ.

9.2 Mapping

Let
$$Q(\lambda) \equiv a_0\lambda^n + a_1\lambda^{n-1} + \dots + a_n. \tag{1}$$

When λ is an arbitrary complex number, $Q(\lambda)$ will in general also be complex. Its value can be represented on an Argand diagram which we shall call the Q-plane, to distinguish it from the λ-plane. Then if P represents λ in the latter and P' the corresponding value of Q in the former, a correspondence is set up between points in the two planes. This graphical process is called a *mapping*. In particular, since a given value of λ determines a unique value of Q, each point P maps into a single point P'. On the other hand, since the equation $Q(\lambda) = Q_1$ has n roots in λ, each point P' maps into n points P. In particular, the origin O' in the Q-plane maps into the n zeros $\lambda_1, \lambda_2, \dots \lambda_n$ of $Q(\lambda)$.

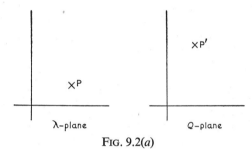

FIG. 9.2(*a*)

Now if λ varies continuously $Q(\lambda)$ will also vary continuously. It follows that a continuous curve in the λ-plane will map on to a continuous curve in the Q-plane. Further, if P describes a closed curve C

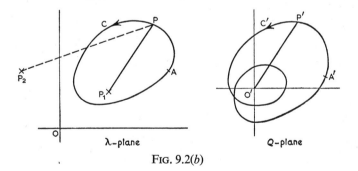

FIG. 9.2(*b*)

beginning and ending at a point A, P' will describe a curve C' which must end at the point A' at which it begins, since this is the only point corresponding to A. Thus the curve C' also is closed.

We now derive a simple rule for determining the number Z_C of zeros of $Q(\lambda)$ inside C. Since $\lambda_1, \ldots \lambda_n$ are the roots of $Q(\lambda) = 0$, (1) can be written

$$Q(\lambda) = a_0(\lambda - \lambda_1)(\lambda - \lambda_2) \ldots (\lambda - \lambda_n). \tag{2}$$

Equating the angles of both sides of this equation and using equation (16) of Appendix (1) we have

$$\text{ang } Q(\lambda) = \sum_{r=1}^{n} \text{ang}(\lambda - \lambda_r).$$

Assume for the sake of argument that λ_1, represented by P_1, lies inside C (see fig. 9.2(b)). Then as P describes C in a counter-clockwise sense $P_1 P$ describes a complete revolution, so that $\text{ang}(\lambda - \lambda_1)$ increases by 2π. On the other hand, for a zero λ_2 outside C the total rotation of $P_2 P$ as P moves round C is zero. If, therefore, $[\text{ang } Q(\lambda)]_C$ denotes the change in ang $Q(\lambda)$ as P describes C we have

$$[\text{ang } Q(\lambda)]_C = 2\pi Z_C. \tag{3}$$

But $[\text{ang } Q(\lambda)]_C$ can be determined immediately by inspection of C', since it is the angle through which $O'P'$ turns as P' describes C' in the Q-plane. We deduce that the number of zeros of $Q(\lambda)$ inside C in the λ-plane is equal to the number of times its map C' in the Q-plane circles the origin O'. With a curve like that in fig. 9.2(b), $Q(\lambda)$ would have two zeros inside C.

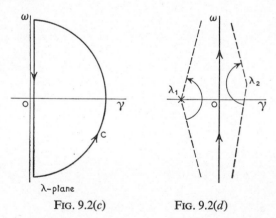

FIG. 9.2(c)   FIG. 9.2(d)

In using the angle of a complex number to detect the presence of complex zeros we are generalising the process of locating real zeros of a continuous function $f(x)$ in a given interval by its changes of sign. In fact, in many applications the angle of a complex number plays the part of, and can be regarded as a generalisation of the positive or negative sign of a real number.

In particular, if C is a semicircle with sufficiently large radius with the imaginary axis as diameter, as in fig. 9.2(c), Z_C is the number of zeros with positive real parts. We shall find more useful a modified form of this result wherein, instead of a closed curve C, we describe the imaginary axis from $\lambda = -j\infty$ to $\lambda = j\infty$. Then, if λ_1 is a zero with a negative real part, fig. 9.2(d) shows that $\text{ang}(\lambda - \lambda_1)$ increases by π whereas if λ_2 has a positive real part $\text{ang}(\lambda - \lambda_2)$ decreases by π. Let Z_+ and Z_- be the numbers of zeros with positive and negative real parts respectively. Since $\lambda = j\omega$ on the imaginary axis it follows that

$$\left[\, \text{ang}\, Q(j\omega) \,\right]_{\omega=-\infty}^{\infty} = \pi(Z_- - Z_+). \tag{4}$$

Since the coefficients of $Q(\lambda)$ are all real, $Q(-j\omega)$ and $Q(j\omega)$ are conjugate complex numbers, so that $\text{ang}\, Q(-j\omega) = -\text{ang}\, Q(j\omega)$. We deduce that

$$\left[\, \text{ang}\, Q(j\omega) \,\right]_{0}^{\infty} = \tfrac{1}{2}\pi(Z_- - Z_+). \tag{5}$$

9.3   Conditions for stability

Let λ_1 be a negative real zero $-\mu_1$ and λ_2 and λ_3 conjugate complex zeros $-\mu_2 \pm j\nu_2$ with negative real parts. Then the corresponding factors of $Q(\lambda)$ are $\lambda + \mu_1$, and $\lambda^2 + 2\mu_2\lambda + \mu_2^2 + \nu_2^2$. The coefficients of the terms in both these factors are all positive, and if the system is stable this must be the case for all the real factors of $Q(\lambda)$. When these factors are multiplied together the coefficients of the product must likewise all be positive. Assuming that a_0, the coefficient of λ^n is positive, we thus have as necessary conditions for stability,

$$a_1, a_2, \ldots a_n > 0. \tag{1}$$

When $n = 2$ it is easily seen that these conditions are sufficient, for in this case $Q(\lambda) \equiv a_0\lambda^2 + a_1\lambda + a_2$, so that

$$\lambda_1, \lambda_2 = \frac{-a_1 \pm \sqrt{(a_1^2 - 4a_0a_2)}}{2a_0}.$$

If these numbers are real they are both negative since $\sqrt{(a_1^2 - 4a_0a_2)} < a_1$, while if they are complex their real part is $-a_1/(2a_0)$. If, however, $n \geq 3$ the conditions (1) are no longer sufficient. To show this we need only produce an example to the contrary, such as

$$Q(\lambda) \equiv \lambda^3 + \lambda^2 + 4\lambda + 30 \equiv (\lambda + 3)(\lambda^2 - 2\lambda + 10) = 0. \tag{2}$$

The quadratic factor gives the conjugate complex zeros $1 \pm 3j$.

We now apply the method of the last section to determine sufficient conditions for stability. It will be assumed that all the coefficients of

$Q(\lambda)$ are positive and that there are no zeros on the imaginary axis. Then

$$Z_- + Z_+ = n. \tag{3}$$

Now $\left[\operatorname{ang} Q(j\omega)\right]_0^\infty = \tfrac{1}{2}\pi L$, where L is the number of right angles through which the line $O'P'$ in the Q-plane turns as P' moves along the curve C' from the point corresponding to $\omega = 0$ to $\omega = \infty$, so that, using **9.2** (5),

$$Z_- - Z_+ = L. \tag{4}$$

But for stability $Z_+ = 0$. In this case

$$L = n. \tag{5}$$

Let $$Q(j\omega) = X(\omega) + jY(\omega).$$

If $n = 2$, $$Q(j\omega) = -a_0\omega^2 + a_1 j\omega + a_2.$$

Equating real and imaginary parts,

$$X(\omega) = a_2 - a_0\omega^2, \qquad Y(\omega) = a_1\omega.$$

These are the parametric equations of a parabola. As ω increases from 0 to ∞, P' describes the upper half of this curve in the sense shown by the arrow in fig. 9.3(a). Since $Y(\omega)/X(\omega) \to 0$ as $\omega \to \infty$, $O'P'$ turns

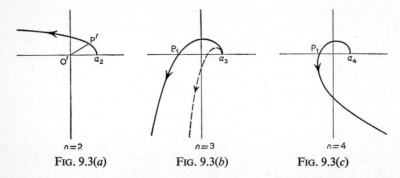

$n=2$ $n=3$ $n=4$

Fig. 9.3(a)   Fig. 9.3(b)   Fig. 9.3(c)

through two right angles in a counter-clockwise sense, so that $L = 2$. The system is therefore always stable, provided a_0, a_1 and a_2 are all positive. It is easily seen that if one or more of these constants is negative, differently orientated parabolic arcs are obtained. These will give other values of L such as zero and -2. The system is unstable with both of these values.

If $n = 3$, $$X(\omega) = a_3 - a_1\omega^2, \qquad Y(\omega) = a_2\omega - a_0\omega^3.$$

The corresponding locus must begin in the first and finish in the third quadrants. Two types of curve are possible. These are shown in fig. 9.3(b) by full and dotted lines, for which $L = 3$ and $L = -1$ respectively. The first therefore represents a stable and the second an unstable system. If the curve cuts the real axis in P_1 this point is given by $Y(\omega) = 0$, or $\omega^2 = a_2/a_0$. The system is stable if and only if $X(\omega)$ is negative for this value. A sufficient additional condition for stability is therefore $a_3 - a_1 a_2/a_0 < 0$, that is

$$a_1 a_2 - a_0 a_3 > 0. \tag{6}$$

It is easily verified that this condition is not satisfied by a system with (2) as characteristic equation.

If $n = 4$, $\quad X(\omega) = a_4 - a_2\omega^2 + a_0\omega^4, \quad Y(\omega) = a_3\omega - a_1\omega^3,$

giving a locus beginning in the first and ending in the fourth quadrants. Reference to fig. 9.3(c) shows that $L = 4$ only if the locus passes round the origin. Using again the conditions that at P_1, $Y(\omega) = 0$ and $X(\omega) < 0$ we deduce $\omega^2 = a_3/a_1$ and $a_4 - a_2 a_3/a_1 + a_0 a_3^2/a_1^2 < 0$ or

$$a_1 a_2 a_3 - a_0 a_3^2 - a_1^2 a_4 > 0. \tag{7}$$

As an example, if $Q(\lambda) = \lambda^4 + 3\lambda^3 + 5\lambda^2 + 4\lambda + a_4$ it is easily verified that the system is stable if $a_4 = 2$ and unstable if $a_4 = 6$.

This method can be extended to the general equation $Q(\lambda) = 0$ of degree n. It is evident that for stability $X(\omega)$ and $Y(\omega)$ must together have $n-1$ positive zeros and that these must alternate. This property can be used to derive criteria for the general case. These are stated in the next section and proved in Appendix 10.

9.4 The criteria of Routh and Hurwitz

The conditions for stability of a system whose characteristic equation is

$$a_0\lambda^n + a_1\lambda^{n-1} + \ldots + a_n = 0 \tag{1}$$

are stated most simply in a general form by means of the criteria of Hurwitz. Let Δ_r be the rth order determinant

$$\begin{vmatrix} a_1 & a_3 & a_5 & \ldots & a_{2r-1} \\ a_0 & a_2 & a_4 & \ldots & a_{2r-2} \\ 0 & a_1 & a_3 & \ldots & a_{2r-3} \\ 0 & a_0 & a_2 & \ldots & a_{2r-4} \\ \cdot & \cdot & \cdot & \ldots & \cdot \\ \cdot & \cdot & \cdot & \ldots & \cdot \\ 0 & \cdot & \cdot & \ldots & a_r \end{vmatrix} .$$

This is formed by starting with a_1 and increasing successive suffixes in each row by two and decreasing successive suffixes in each column by one, with the convention that $a_k = 0$ if $k > n$ or if $k < 0$. Then, assuming $a_0 > 0$, as will be done throughout this section, the system is stable if and only if

$$\Delta_1 > 0, \Delta_2 > 0, \ldots, \Delta_n > 0. \qquad (2)$$

If $n = 3$ this gives the conditions

$$a_1 > 0, \quad \begin{vmatrix} a_1 & a_3 \\ a_0 & a_2 \end{vmatrix} > 0, \quad \begin{vmatrix} a_1 & a_3 & 0 \\ a_0 & a_2 & 0 \\ 0 & a_1 & a_3 \end{vmatrix} > 0, \qquad (3)$$

or, $a_1 > 0, \Delta_2 > 0, a_3\Delta_2 > 0$. It follows that $a_3 > 0$. Since

$$\Delta_2 = a_1a_2 - a_0a_3 > 0$$

and $a_0, a_1, a_3, > 0$, it follows that $a_2 > 0$, so that the system is stable

if, and only if,

$$a_1, a_2, a_3, \Delta_2 > 0, \qquad (4)$$

confirming **9.3** (6).

If $n = 4$ the conditions become

$$a_1 > 0, \quad \begin{vmatrix} a_1 & a_3 \\ a_0 & a_2 \end{vmatrix} > 0, \quad \begin{vmatrix} a_1 & a_3 & 0 \\ a_0 & a_2 & a_4 \\ 0 & a_1 & a_3 \end{vmatrix} > 0, \quad \begin{vmatrix} a_1 & a_3 & 0 & 0 \\ a_0 & a_2 & a_4 & 0 \\ 0 & a_1 & a_3 & 0 \\ 0 & a_0 & a_2 & a_4 \end{vmatrix} > 0. \qquad (5)$$

Here $\Delta_4 = a_4\Delta_3$ and $\Delta_3 = a_1a_2a_3 - a_0a_3{}^2 - a_1{}^2a_4$ and it can be shewn as above that the conditions are equivalent to

$$a_1, a_2, a_3, a_4, \Delta_3 > 0, \qquad (6)$$

again confirming a result of the last section.

The conditions when $n > 4$ can be written down in the same way but they cannot be reduced to the simple forms of (4) and (6). For although all the coefficients $a_1, \ldots a_n$ must be positive, more than one auxiliary condition will now be necessary.

Although the names of Routh and Hurwitz are frequently given jointly as the originators of the above criteria, Routh, whose work was published first, stated the conditions in a different form. He gave two rules which we now reproduce. In his first rule the coefficients are arranged alternatively in two rows and a third row is formed from these as shown below.

$$a_0 \qquad a_2 \qquad a_4 \qquad a_6 \qquad \cdots$$

$$a_1 \qquad a_3 \qquad a_5 \qquad a_7 \qquad \cdots$$

$$a_2 - \frac{a_0}{a_1}a_3 \quad a_4 - \frac{a_0}{a_1}a_5 \quad a_6 - \frac{a_0}{a_1}a_7 \quad \cdots$$

A fourth row is then formed in exactly the same way from the second and third rows. This process is continued as far as the $(n+1)$th row, which will consist of a single term. Then the system is stable if, and only if, the first term of each row is positive.

Routh's second rule tells us how to write down these first terms directly in terms of the original coefficients. It is as follows. Starting with a_1 form a sequence of expressions, each from the preceding one, by the substitutions given in table 9.4(A). Thus from a_1 we obtain

Replace	a_0	a_1	a_2	a_3	a_4	$\cdots$
by	a_1	$a_2 - \dfrac{a_0}{a_1}a_3$	a_3	$a_4 - \dfrac{a_0}{a_1}a_5$	a_5	$\cdots$

TABLE 9.4(A)

$a_2 - a_0 a_3 / a_1$. This in turn gives

$$a_3 - \frac{a_1\left(a_4 - \dfrac{a_0}{a_1}a_5\right)}{a_2 - \dfrac{a_0}{a_1}a_3} = \frac{a_3(a_1 a_2 - a_0 a_3) - a_1(a_1 a_4 - a_0 a_5)}{a_1 a_2 - a_0 a_3},$$

and so on. It can be verified that these are the required expressions. It can also be shown that this sequence is equivalent to

$$\Delta_1, \quad \frac{\Delta_2}{\Delta_1}, \quad \frac{\Delta_3}{\Delta_2}, \quad \frac{\Delta_4}{\Delta_3}, \quad \cdots, \quad \frac{\Delta_n}{\Delta_{n-1}},$$

thus providing the link between the rules of Routh and of Hurwitz. Formal proofs of all these results are given in Appendix 10.

When numerical values for the coefficients are given, evaluation of the Hurwitz determinants can be formidable. In this case direct application of Routh's first rule is preferable. Thus for the quintic equation

$$\lambda^5 + 4\lambda^4 + 8\lambda^3 + 9\lambda^2 + 5\lambda + 2 = 0$$

the working is as follows.

$$
\begin{array}{cccccc}
1 & & 8 & & 5 & \\
& 4 & & 9 & & 2 \\
& & \frac{23}{4} & & \frac{9}{2} & \\
& & & \frac{135}{23} & & 2 \\
& & & & \frac{343}{135}. &
\end{array}
$$

This system is therefore stable. This method has the advantage that if any term (whether first of its row or not) is negative, the system is unstable. The working can then be terminated as soon as a negative term appears, thus saving needless further computation. For example, if in the above equation the constant term were 24 instead of 2 the third row would become $\frac{23}{4}$, -1, indicating instability immediately.

EXERCISES　Using any of the methods described in this section or the last, determine the stability of systems whose characteristic equations are:

1. $\lambda^4 + 4\lambda^3 + 6\lambda^2 + 5\lambda + 1 = 0$,
2. $\lambda^5 + \lambda^4 + 3\lambda^3 + 2\lambda^2 + 5\lambda + 1 = 0$.

CHAPTER 10

LINEAR SYSTEMS WITH FEED-BACK

10.1 Operational representation

A feature of many linear systems, particularly those incorporating some form of automatic control, is the existence of a feed-back loop. In such cases the form of the operator introduces certain characteristics into the steady state response and allows special methods to be used for investigating the stability of the system.

To illustrate these we shall consider the general properties of linear error-controlled servo systems in which the various elements have operators which are rational functions of **D** with constant coefficients. The basic elements of such a system are usually as shown in fig. 10.1(*a*).

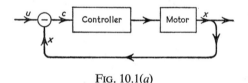

FIG. 10.1(*a*)

Briefly, the input *u*, which is a low-power signal, is fed into a differencing element. The output *x* is fed back and subtracted from *u* in this element to form the *error* or *correction* signal *c*. This correction signal is processed and amplified in the *controller* to produce a signal which activates the *motor* or power source. This generates the output.

The characteristics of the motor are usually determined by external considerations such as availability and the load on the output. On the other hand, the layout of the controller is usually at the disposal of the designer. Taking into account the nature of expected input functions and the motor and load characteristics, his task is to ensure stability and to arrange that the output satisfies certain requirements. These requirements are usually related to the transient and steady state or harmonic responses.

A typical system of this class was discussed briefly in **7.4**. The flow diagram of this is reproduced in fig. 10.1(*b*). Here *T* denotes the torque generated by the motor. The operators of the controller and motor can be combined to form a single operator $A(\mathbf{D})$, given in this case by

$$A(\mathbf{D}) = \frac{k(1+T_1\mathbf{D})}{J\mathbf{D}^2(1+T_2\mathbf{D})}. \tag{1}$$

The operator $A(\mathbf{D})$, which would transform the input into the output if there were no feed-back of the output, is called the *open-loop operator*.

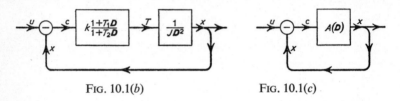

FIG. 10.1(*b*)   FIG. 10.1(*c*)

The flow diagram can now be shown in the simplified form of fig. 10.1(*c*). The governing equations of the system are then

$$x = A(\mathbf{D})c, \qquad c = u - x,$$

so that, eliminating x, $\{1 + A(\mathbf{D})\}c = u$. The error and the output can therefore be expressed in terms of the input by the equations

$$c = \frac{1}{1 + A(\mathbf{D})}u, \tag{2}$$

$$x = \frac{A(\mathbf{D})}{1 + A(\mathbf{D})}u. \tag{3}$$

The operator $A(\mathbf{D})/\{1 + A(\mathbf{D})\}$ is the *closed-loop operator* of the system.

This example represents one of the simplest practicable types of servo. Both the motor and controller operators can be and frequently are considerably more complicated. Nevertheless, however complex they may be, the operator $A(\mathbf{D})$ has two special characteristics. First, it usually contains some positive integral power of $\mathbf{D}$ as a factor of the denominator. We shall see in **10.2** that this condition is necessary if the servo is not to have a static error. In the above example this power is two. Higher values will occur if the controller contains integrating elements.

The second property is that the degree of the denominator of $A(\mathbf{D})$ always exceeds that of the numerator. This follows firstly from the fact that it is impossible to devise a network or automatically operating physical element the numerator of whose operator has a degree exceeding that of the denominator. For example, in **7.4** a circuit and a mechanical system for automatic differentiation were described. These both had operator $\mathbf{D}/(1+T\mathbf{D})$ instead of $\mathbf{D}$. It was shown in **8.1** that this operator represents differentiation with a time lag T. Although this lag can be made arbitrarily small it cannot be eliminated entirely. To put this in another way, an input can only be differentiated as it is generated by comparing its present value with some past value. This necessarily causes a lag in the derivative obtained. This lag is normally represented by a factor $1+T\mathbf{D}$ in the denominator of the operator. This line of reasoning can be extended to more complex direct operations. Secondly we observe that the motor will always have an operator whose denominator exceeds the numerator in degree, so that $A(\mathbf{D})$ also has this property.

When $A(\mathbf{D})$ has been simplified it can be written in the form

$$A(\mathbf{D}) = \frac{KP(\mathbf{D})}{\mathbf{D}^s R(\mathbf{D})}, \tag{4}$$

where
$$P(\mathbf{D}) = 1 + p_1\mathbf{D} + p_2\mathbf{D}^2 + \ldots, \tag{5}$$
and
$$R(\mathbf{D}) = 1 + r_1\mathbf{D} + r_2\mathbf{D}^2 + \ldots. \tag{6}$$

The constant K, called the *gain*, is the ratio of the constant term in the numerator to the coefficient of $\mathbf{D}^s$ in the denominator. Substituting in (2) and (3) and simplifying we have

$$c = \frac{\mathbf{D}^s R(\mathbf{D})}{Q(\mathbf{D})} u, \tag{7}$$

$$x = \frac{KP(\mathbf{D})}{Q(\mathbf{D})} u, \tag{8}$$

where
$$Q(\mathbf{D}) = KP(\mathbf{D}) + \mathbf{D}^s R(\mathbf{D}). \tag{9}$$

It is seen that the error c and the output x are both solutions of differential equations with the same characteristic equation,

$$Q(\lambda) = 0.$$

10.2   Stability and steady state

Using the notation of the last section, the error of the servo is given in terms of the input by the differential equation

$$Q(\mathbf{D})c = \mathbf{D}^s R(\mathbf{D})u. \tag{1}$$

The characteristic equation is

$$Q(\lambda) \equiv KP(\lambda) + \lambda^s R(\lambda) = 0. \tag{2}$$

The system is stable if, and only if, all the roots of this equation have negative real parts. Stability can be determined in a particular case by applying the criteria given in the last chapter. Better still, when the equation can be solved easily its roots provide information about the transient behaviour of the system.

As in 7.3, we can regard the error as made up of two components, a transient error and a steady state error. The latter can be obtained directly by expanding the operator in ascending powers of $\mathbf{D}$. Thus,

$$c_{ss} = \frac{\mathbf{D}^s R(\mathbf{D})}{Q(\mathbf{D})} u = \frac{\mathbf{D}^s(1 + r_1 \mathbf{D} + \ldots)}{K(1 + p_1 \mathbf{D} + \ldots) + \mathbf{D}^s(1 + r_1 \mathbf{D} + \ldots)} u$$

$$= \frac{\mathbf{D}^s}{K}\{1 + (r_1 - p_1)\mathbf{D} + \ldots\} u, \tag{3}$$

provided $s \geqq 2$. In many cases a sufficient approximation is given by the first term of this series, so that

$$c_{ss} = \frac{1}{K}\mathbf{D}^s u. \tag{4}$$

Thus the error is approximately proportional to the sth derivative of the input. If a derivative of u of lower order is constant there is no steady state error. For example, with the system shown in fig. 10.1(b), $s = 2$. If the input has a constant velocity there is no steady state error. On the other hand, if u has a constant acceleration there is a constant error $J\mathbf{D}^2 u/k$. This result is still true approximately for more general inputs provided the acceleration is not changing rapidly. Going one step further, if the servo is to have zero error with constant acceleration input it must have $s \geqq 3$. This can be effected by including a term proportional to the integral of the error in the signal generated by the controller. This important parameter s is called the *order* or *class*† of servo. It is equal to the number of integrations between the error and the output.

If $s = 0$ we have a *zero-order system*. In this case (4) becomes $c_{ss} = u/K$, so that there will be a steady state error even when the input is static.

10.3   Response to step inputs

Valuable information about the characteristics of a servo is sometimes revealed by the response to a step input function. This can often be determined experimentally for an existing system. On the other hand,

---

† If s is called the *class* of the system the term *order* can be used for the order of the characteristic equation.

if $A(\mathbf{D})$ is given it can be computed conveniently using the Laplace transform. If $x = A(\mathbf{D})c$ then

$$x = \frac{A(\mathbf{D})}{1+A(\mathbf{D})}u = \frac{KP(\mathbf{D})}{Q(\mathbf{D})}u,$$

using **10.1** (8). Taking transforms,

$$x^* = \frac{KP(p)}{Q(p)}u^*. \tag{1}$$

If $u = H(t)$, the unit step function, $u^* = 1/p$, so that

$$x^* = \frac{KP(p)}{pQ(p)}. \tag{2}$$

By expressing the right-hand side in partial fractions and interpreting term by term in the usual way, the corresponding output is determined.

Likewise if the input is the unit ramp function $tH(t)$, whose transform is $1/p^2$, the output is given by

$$x^* = \frac{KP(p)}{p^2Q(p)}. \tag{3}$$

As an example, consider the system of fig. 10.1(b). Let $k/J = \omega_n^2$, so that ω_n is the undamped natural frequency of the system. Assume further that $T_2 = 1/(6\omega_n)$ and $T_1 = 11/(6\omega_n)$. We can write

$$A(\mathbf{D}) = \frac{\omega_n^2(11\mathbf{D}+6\omega_n)}{\mathbf{D}^2(\mathbf{D}+6\omega_n)}.$$

Using (2), the response to a unit step input is given by

$$\begin{aligned}
x^* &= \frac{\omega_n^2(11p+6\omega_n)}{p\{\omega_n^2(11p+6\omega_n)+p^2(p+6\omega_n)\}} \\
&= \frac{\omega_n^2(11p+6\omega_n)}{p^4+6p^3\omega_n+11p^2\omega_n^2+6p\omega_n^3} \\
&= \frac{\omega_n^2(11p+6\omega_n)}{p(p+\omega_n)(p+2\omega_n)(p+3\omega_n)}.
\end{aligned}$$

Expressing this in partial fractions by standard methods gives

$$x^* = \frac{1}{p}+\frac{5}{2(p+\omega_n)}-\frac{8}{p+2\omega_n}+\frac{9}{2(p+3\omega_n)},$$

so that $x = (1+2 \cdot 5\,e^{-\omega_n t}-8\,e^{-2\omega_n t}+4 \cdot 5\,e^{-3\omega_n t})H(t).$ (4)

Similarly, using (3), the response to the ramp input $\omega_n t H(t)$ is given by

$$x^* = \frac{\omega_n^3(11p+6\omega_n)}{p^2(p+\omega_n)(p+2\omega_n)(p+3\omega_n)},$$

whence $x = (\omega_n t - 2 \cdot 5 e^{-\omega_n t} + 4 e^{-2\omega_n t} - 1 \cdot 5 e^{-3\omega_n t})H(t).$ (5)

Graphs of input and output in these two cases are shown in figs. 10.3(a) and (b) respectively.

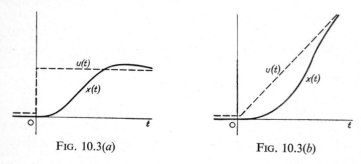

FIG. 10.3(a)   FIG. 10.3(b)

10.4   The Nyquist diagram

The methods described so far in this chapter enable the performance of a particular system to be analysed, provided the operator $A(\mathbf{D})$ is known completely. It happens frequently, however, that it is desired to study a system over a range of values of one or more of its parameters, or to suggest modifications in the controller or motor in order to improve the performance. Alternatively, it may happen that $A(\mathbf{D})$ is not known completely, so that a theoretical investigation must be supplemented by experimental tests. In both of these cases harmonic response methods of analysis can be effective, particularly if graphical representations are used.

Assume that the output feed-back is disconnected and that a sinusoidal signal of frequency ω representing the error c is fed into the controller. Then the output x will have a steady state response which is also sinusoidal with the same frequency ω. The amplitude ratio and phase difference of output and error are the modulus and angle of the complex number $A(j\omega)$. Then the *Nyquist diagram* is the locus of the point representing this number as ω varies from zero to infinity. It is in fact the harmonic response locus (see **8.2**) giving the output in terms of the error.

Since, if λ is any complex number,

$$A(\lambda) = \frac{KP(\lambda)}{\lambda^s R(\lambda)},$$ (1)

a fraction whose numerator has a degree less than that of the denominator, $A(\lambda) \to 0$ as $|\lambda| \to \infty$. It follows that the point $\omega = \infty$ on the locus is at the origin. To find the form of the locus as $\omega \to 0$, we see from **10.1** (5) and (6) that $P(0) = R(0) = 1$. Thus for small values of ω we have

$$A(j\omega) = \frac{K}{(j\omega)^s} = (-j)^s \frac{K}{\omega^s} \tag{2}$$

approximately. As $\omega \to 0$ with $s > 0$, the locus therefore tends to infinity in a direction depending on the value of s. In particular, if $s = 1, 2$ or 3 the locus tends to become parallel to the negative imaginary axis, the negative real axis or the positive imaginary axis respectively. Typical loci in these cases are shown in fig. 10.4(a).

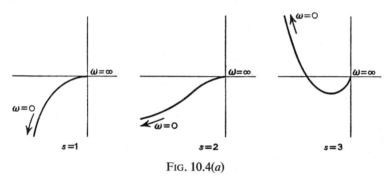

FIG. 10.4(a)

With a zero order system, that is one for which $s = 0$, $A(0) = K$. In this case, therefore, the locus remains finite. It can still, however, be used for the examination of stability by the methods to be described in the next section.

This property provides one method of determining experimentally the order s of a servo and hence, using **10.2** (4), the nature of its steady state lag. For if a low-frequency signal is applied to the controller the phase lag of the output will be approximately s right angles.

10.5   Stability from the Nyquist diagram

Let
$$F(\lambda) = 1 + A(\lambda) = \frac{\lambda^s R(\lambda) + K P(\lambda)}{\lambda^s R(\lambda)} = \frac{Q(\lambda)}{\lambda^s R(\lambda)}. \tag{1}$$

Then $F(\lambda)$ is a rational fraction whose numerator and denominator have the same degree n. Now $F(\lambda)$ is zero if and only if $Q(\lambda)$ is zero. The zeros of $F(\lambda)$ are therefore the same as the zeros of $Q(\lambda)$, which of course determine the stability and transient response of the closed-loop system. Let Z_+ and Z_- be the numbers of these zeros with positive and negative real parts respectively. Turning to the denominator of $F(\lambda)$, this vanishes when $\lambda = 0$ and when $R(\lambda) = 0$. For these values of λ, $F(\lambda)$ is infinite. They are called *poles* of $F(\lambda)$. Let P_+ and P_- be the numbers of these poles (that is, the numbers of zeros of $R(\lambda)$) which have positive and negative real parts respectively. Then

$$Z_+ + Z_- = P_+ + P_- + s = n, \tag{2}$$

since the numerator and denominator both have degree n.

Another relation between these quantities can be obtained by inspection from the Argand diagram, for if the vector OP in fig. 10.5(a) represents $A(j\omega)$ and if I is the point -1, then IP will represent

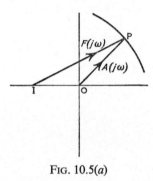

Fig. 10.5(a)

$F(j\omega)$, since $F(j\omega) = 1 + A(j\omega)$. Also the angle PIO is equal to ang $F(j\omega)$. We now extend to the rational fraction $F(\lambda)$ the method applied in **9.2** to the polynomial $Q(\lambda)$.

Since
$$F(j\omega) = \frac{Q(j\omega)}{(j\omega)^s R(j\omega)},$$

$$\text{ang } F(j\omega) = \text{ang } Q(j\omega) - \text{ang } R(j\omega) - s \text{ ang } j\omega.$$

Taking the change in the individual terms of this equation as ω increases from zero to infinity, as in **9.2**, $[\text{ang } Q(j\omega)] = \frac{1}{2}\pi(Z_- - Z_+)$ and $[\text{ang } R(j\omega)] = \frac{1}{2}\pi(P_- - P_+)$. Also ang $j\omega$ remains constant at $\frac{1}{2}\pi$. It follows that if L is the number of right angles described by the vector IP in a counter-clockwise sense as ω goes from zero to infinity, then

$$L = Z_- - Z_+ - P_- + P_+. \tag{3}$$

Adding (2) and (3),
$$L = s + 2P_+ - 2Z_+. \tag{4}$$

If the closed-loop system is stable $Z_+ = 0$ so that

$$L = s + 2P_+. \tag{5}$$

It usually happens that P_+, the number of positive zeros of $R(\lambda)$, is also zero. Since

$$x = \frac{KP(\mathbf{D})}{\mathbf{D}^s R(\mathbf{D})}c$$

it follows that in this case, except for the integrations represented by the factor $\mathbf{D}^s$, the *open-loop* system is stable. If we make this assumption we have

$$L = s. \tag{6}$$

If $P_+ = 0$ and the closed-loop system is unstable, (4) shows that $L < s$.

If the Nyquist diagram of a system has been drawn, both L and s are apparent by inspection so that the stability is determined immediately, using (6). If it is known that the open-loop system is unstable, (5) will be used instead of (6).

Example 1   If the controller is a pure amplifier with gain k and the output is damped, the damping factor being β, the equations of motion are

$$T = kc = (J\mathbf{D}^2 + \beta\mathbf{D})x,$$

so that

$$A(\mathbf{D}) = \frac{k}{J\mathbf{D}^2 + \beta\mathbf{D}}.$$

Expressing $A(j\omega)$ in real and imaginary parts for plotting,

$$A(j\omega) = \frac{k}{-J\omega^2 + j\beta\omega} = -\frac{kJ}{J^2\omega^2 + \beta^2} - j\frac{k\beta}{\omega(J^2\omega^2 + \beta^2)}.$$

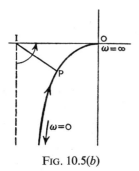

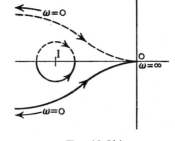

FIG. 10.5(*b*)   FIG. 10.5(*c*)

This locus lies entirely in the third quadrant and is shown in fig. 10.5(*b*). It is evident that $L = s = 1$, so that the system is stable.

Example 2   If the servo is stabilised by first derivative of error instead of output damping we obtain the system of fig. 10.1(*b*). In this case

$$A(j\omega) = \frac{k(1+j\omega T_1)}{-J\omega^2(1+j\omega T_2)} = -\frac{k(1+\omega^2 T_1 T_2)}{J\omega^2(1+\omega^2 T_2{}^2)} - j\frac{T_1 - T_2}{J\omega(1+\omega^2 T_2{}^2)}.$$

If $T_1 > T_2$ the locus again lies entirely in the third quadrant, as in fig. 10.5(*c*). It is clear that $L = s = 2$, so that the system is stable. If, however, $T_1 < T_2$ the imaginary part of $A(j\omega)$ is positive, so that the locus lies in the second quadrant. This is shown by the dotted line in fig. 10.5(*c*), and in this case we see that $L = -2$. The system is therefore unstable. This condition for instability can be confirmed using **9.3** (6).

Example 3   If the servo of example 2 has a component proportional to the integral of the error in the controlling signal,

$$A(\mathbf{D}) = \frac{k}{J\mathbf{D}^2}\left(\frac{1+T_1\mathbf{D}}{1+T_2\mathbf{D}} + \frac{1}{T_3\mathbf{D}}\right).$$

This is a third order servo, and it is found that the locus is of the type shown in fig. 10.5(*d*). It is clear that stability depends on which side of I

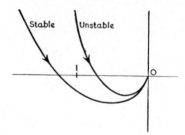

Fig. 10.5(*d*)

the locus passes, for in one case $L = 3$ while in the other $L = -1$. The stability can in fact be varied by changing the values of the time constants T_1, T_2 and T_3 or of the gain k.

10.6   Applications of the Nyquist diagram

In this section and the next we give a summary of the various ways in which the Nyquist diagram and other graphical methods can be applied to the design of linear feed-back systems. Full accounts of these, together with numerous worked examples, are to be found in most of the standard engineering textbooks on this subject; the discussion here is therefore limited to a brief statement of the mathematical principles involved.

The main applications of the Nyquist diagram occur in the synthesis of linear feed-back systems. The method can be applied to systems at the design stage or to systems after construction. The responses of the open-loop system to given sinusoidal error signals of different frequencies are obtained, in the first case by calculation and in the second by trial. The Nyquist locus is then obtained by plotting on a polar diagram points representing the amplitude and phase of the output relative to those of the error input.

If the locus passes through I there is a frequency ω for which $A(j\omega) = -1$ or $Q(j\omega) = 0$. The system is at best only critically stable. The examples given in the last section show that for stable systems the point I lies to the *left* of the locus as seen by an observer facing along the curve in the sense of increasing ω. This rule is not universal, but it applies to most of the simpler types of system which are met in practice. Furthermore, the degree of stability is represented approximately by the shortest distance of I from the locus, provided this distance is reasonably small.

To obtain a quantitative measure of this stability, draw a line IP perpendicular to the locus and mark off a length PQ along the curve in the sense of increasing ω, equal to IP (see fig. 10.6(a)). Let ω_P and ω_Q be the frequencies corresponding to the points P and Q and let λ_P, λ_Q

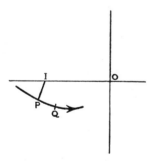

FIG. 10.6(a)

and λ_I be the values of λ corresponding to P, Q and I when $A(\lambda)$ is mapped. Then $\lambda_P = j\omega_P$ and $\lambda_Q = j\omega_Q$. Let $\lambda_Q - \lambda_P = \delta\lambda_Q$ and $\lambda_I - \lambda_P = \delta\lambda_I$. Assuming that $\delta\lambda_Q$ and $\delta\lambda_I$ are sufficiently small we have the following first order approximations:

$$\delta A_I = A(\lambda_I) - A(\lambda_P) = A'(\lambda_P)\,\delta\lambda_I,$$
$$\delta A_Q = A(\lambda_Q) - A(\lambda_P) = A'(\lambda_P)\,\delta\lambda_Q.$$

These complex increments in $A(\lambda)$ are represented respectively by PI and PQ. Since these lines are perpendicular and equal in length, $\delta A_I = j \delta A_Q$. It follows that

$$\delta \lambda_I = j \, \delta \lambda_Q = -\delta \omega_Q = -(\omega_Q - \omega_P),$$

so that $\qquad\qquad \lambda_I = -\delta \omega_Q + j \omega_P.$

Now λ_I will normally be the zero of $Q(\lambda)$ with the smallest negative real part. This zero defines the transient mode with the least damping, so that its real part $-\delta \omega_Q$ gives an indication of the settling time, or alternatively the rapidity of response of the system.

An alternative method of describing the degree of stability makes use of the concepts of gain and phase margins. We have pointed out that for a critically stable system there is a frequency ω for which $A(j\omega) = -1$, in other words the gain $|A(j\omega)| = 1$ and the phase ang $A(j\omega) = \pi$. Let the locus for a stable system cut a circle with centre O and unit radius in P_1 and the real axis in P_2, as in fig. 10.6(b). Let ω_1

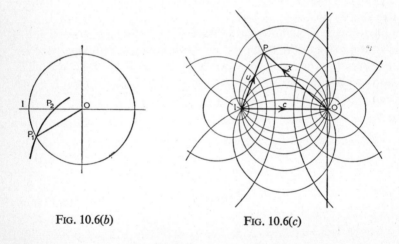

FIG. 10.6(b)   FIG. 10.6(c)

and ω_2 be the frequencies corresponding to P_1 and P_2. Then $|A(j\omega_1)| = 1$ and ang $A(j\omega_1) > \pi$. The amount by which ang $A(j\omega_1)$ exceeds π is called the *phase margin*. Similarly at P_2, ang $A(j\omega_2) = \pi$. The difference between $|A(j\omega_2)|$ and unity is the *gain margin*. Either of these can be used as a measure of stability.

Another way of interpreting the Nyquist diagram is based on the fact that if P is the point on the locus corresponding to frequency ω, the vector IP represents the input in amplitude and phase compared with the error IO and the output OP. The phase difference ϕ between input and output is therefore the angle *IPO* and the amplitude ratio *M* is *OP/IP*. The loci of constant ϕ are circles through *I* and *O* (see fig. 10.6(*c*)). The loci of constant *M* are also circles (Appollonius' circles) which are orthogonal to the first family. If a diagram showing these circles is superposed on the Nyquist locus the values of *M* and ϕ for all frequencies are evident at a glance. For a servo system it is desirable that there should be no appreciable resonance in the frequency range in which the system is expected to operate. This means that an upper limit must be placed on the value of *M*. The diagram we have described briefly provides a ready method of ensuring this.

Let us assume now that an investigation on one of the above lines suggests that the performance of the system will be unsatisfactory. It will usually be evident how the curve must be reshaped in order to improve the response. One of the simplest modifications is to change the gain of the controller. This has the effect of changing the size but not the shape or orientation of the locus. Alternatively, extra elements can be introduced to produce phase lag or lead. These will be represented in $A(\mathbf{D})$ by extra factors in the numerator or denominator of the type $1 + T\mathbf{D}$. The new locus must be plotted point by point, but the necessary multiplication or division of $A(j\omega)$ by $1 + j\omega T$ can be facilitated by the use of the fundamental properties of the modulus and angle given by Appendix 1 (15), (16) and (17). These properties can be used with effect in the original plotting if, as is frequently the case, the numerator and denominator of $A(j\omega)$ are given in factorised form.

10.7 Other graphical methods

The Nyquist stability criterion which we derived in **10.5** is usually given in a form which is more general, but at the same time much more complicated to apply. Referring to **9.2**, if instead of the polynomial $Q(\lambda)$ we map the rational fraction $F(\lambda)$ and take λ counter-clockwise round a closed contour *C* not passing through any pole or zero of $F(\lambda)$, it is easily shown that **9.2**(3) generalises to

$$[\text{ang}\, F(\lambda)]_C = 2\pi(Z_C - P_C), \tag{1}$$

where P_C is the number of poles of $F(\lambda)$ inside *C*. This result is a special case of *Cauchy's theorem*.

In order that the stability of the system may be examined, *C* must embrace the positive half of the λ-plane. We accordingly take a semi-circle of large radius on the imaginary axis as diameter. Since, however, the origin is a pole of $A(\lambda)$, and therefore of $F(\lambda)$, it must be excluded. This is arranged by indenting *C* by means of the small semicircle *KLM* in fig. 10.7(*a*).

To illustrate the construction of the corresponding curve C' consider
example 2 of **10.5**, for which

$$A(\lambda) = \frac{k(1+\lambda T_1)}{J\lambda^2(1+\lambda T_2)}.$$

The required curve C' (see fig. 10.7(b)) is obtained by mapping separately
the different segments of the semicircle C. First we draw the portion
$H'K'$ corresponding to HK. This is the frequency response locus for the

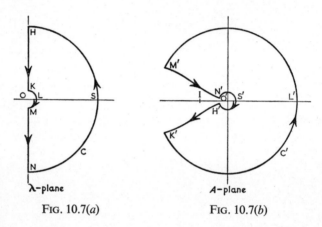

FIG. 10.7(a)   FIG. 10.7(b)

open-loop system, as shown in fig. 10.5(c). The portion $M'N'$ corresponding to the negative imaginary axis MN is then the reflection of
$H'K'$ in the real axis. Since for large $|\lambda|$, $A(\lambda) = kT_1/JT_2\lambda^2$ approximately, the large semicircle NSH maps into the small circle $N'S'H'$.
Finally, it is found that the small semicircle KLM transforms into a
large circle $K'L'M'$.

If we assume that $P_C = 0$, it follows from (1) that the system is stable
if and only if the point I is not enclosed by C'. This is easily seen to be so
for the above example, but with more complicated systems, for which
$s > 2$ or for which $H'K'$ cuts the negative real axis in one or more points,
this criterion is not so simple to apply. Thus for example 3 of **10.5** the
curve C' turns out to be as shown in fig. 10.7(c). If a point P is made to
describe C' in the sense indicated by the arrows it is found that the total
angle through which IP turns is zero. This indicates stability. On the
other hand, if the point P_1 falls to the right of I, IP must describe two
revolutions. In this case $Z_+ = 2$, so that the system is unstable. These
conclusions are in agreement with those of **10.5**.

It is evident that, compared with the above criterion, the rule given in
10.5 uses a diagram which is both simpler to construct and easier to

interpret. The existence of the simple rule, however, is due solely to the fact that the numerator and denominator of $F(\lambda) = 1 + A(\lambda)$ have the same degree; for without **10.5**(2), which expresses this property, **10.5**(3) is by itself insufficient to determine stability. The simple rule is thus available only for functions of this type. In other cases, for example when the system contains finite time delays (see **13.7**), the complete semicircle of fig. 10.7(a) must be mapped.

As an alternative to the Nyquist diagram, in which $A(j\omega)$ is plotted, we can use the locus of its reciprocal. Since

$$1 + \frac{1}{A(\lambda)} = \frac{Q(\lambda)}{KP(\lambda)}$$

has the same zeros as $Q(\lambda)$, the stability of the system is still determined by the position of the point I relative to the locus. In this case, however, the general rule requires the use of a closed curve, as in the method just described. Since the degree of $Q(\lambda)$ always exceeds that of $P(\lambda)$ there is no simplified rule available like that described in **10.5**.

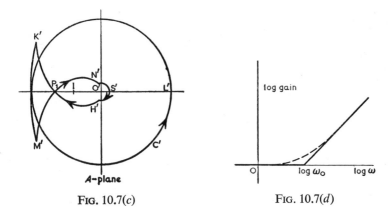

FIG. 10.7(c)   FIG. 10.7(d)

With the inverse locus the point corresponding to infinite frequency is at infinity. Provided $s > 0$, the point for which $\omega = 0$ is at the origin and the order of the servo is related to the direction of the tangent to the curve at this point. One advantage of this locus is that loci of constant M and ϕ, as defined in the last section, are circles with centre I and straight lines through I respectively. In fact, for any point on the curve, M and ϕ are immediately evident. Another advantage is that it is easier to observe the effect of modifying the feed-back.

The most widely used alternatives to the Nyquist diagram are, however, logarithmic plots. Fundamentally these are separate graphs of

$\log |A(j\omega)|$ and ang $A(j\omega)$ against $\log \omega$. One of the main advantages of this approach is that if $A(\lambda)$ is given in factorised form, both of these plots can be built up by addition from basic curves corresponding to the individual factors. In particular for a factor $1 + \lambda/\omega_0$,

$$\log \left| 1 + \frac{j\omega}{\omega_0} \right| = \tfrac{1}{2} \log \left(1 + \frac{\omega^2}{\omega_0{}^2} \right).$$

If ω tends to zero this also tends to zero, while if ω is large it is approximately $\log \omega - \log \omega_0$. The corresponding curve, shown in fig. 10.7(d), therefore has two asymptotes, one being the frequency axis and the other inclined at a definite angle to this axis and cutting it at the point corresponding to a frequency ω_0. For most of its length the curve can be represented by one or other of these asymptotes.

When several factors of this type are multiplied together it is evident that the resulting locus will approximate to a number of straight-line segments whose junction points occur at the different frequencies ω_0. This property, incidentally, offers a possible method of determining the operator $A(\mathbf{D})$ of a system whose harmonic response has been found experimentally.

The stability and the gain and phase margins of the system are clearly indicated by the relative positions of the log gain and phase loci in relation to the frequency axis when these are drawn on the same figure. The effect of altering the gain is immediately apparent, for this simply shifts the gain locus at right angles to the frequency axis.

If $\log |A(j\omega)|$ is plotted against ang $A(j\omega)$, the resulting curve being marked for values of ω, we obtain a map of $\log A(\lambda)$. It is possible to see how M and ϕ vary with frequency if a diagram showing curves of constants M and ϕ is superposed on the locus. Again the effect of a change of gain can easily be estimated.

Finally we mention very briefly a rather different approach, the so-called *root locus method*, devised by Evans†. If we write

$$A(\lambda) = K \frac{(\lambda - \lambda_1)(\lambda - \lambda_2)\ldots}{(\lambda - \lambda_1{}')(\lambda - \lambda_2{}')\ldots},$$

we see that $A(\lambda)$ can be represented completely by its zeros $\lambda_1, \lambda_2, \ldots$, its poles $\lambda_1{}', \lambda_2{}', \ldots$ and the gain K. The roots of the characteristic equation are given by $A(\lambda) = -1$, that is

$$|A(\lambda)| = 1, \tag{2}$$

$$\operatorname{ang} A(\lambda) = \pi. \tag{3}$$

† Evans, W. R., Control System Synthesis by the Root Locus Method. *Trans. I.E.E.* 1950.

If the zeros and poles of $A(\lambda)$ are marked in the λ-plane, the locus of points satisfying (3) is obtained by trial and error using the relation

$$\text{ang } A(\lambda) = \text{ang}(\lambda - \lambda_1) + \text{ang}(\lambda - \lambda_2) + \ldots - \text{ang}(\lambda - \lambda_1') - \ldots.$$

Now (2) can be written

$$\frac{|\lambda - \lambda_1||\lambda - \lambda_2| \ldots}{|\lambda - \lambda_1'||\lambda - \lambda_2'| \ldots} = \frac{1}{K},$$

so that for each point on the above locus a value of K can be calculated. If these values are marked on the locus, the stability and transient behaviour of the system for different values of K can be seen at a glance.

10.8 Generalisations

The theory developed so far in this chapter, although based on servo systems, is applicable to a wide range of linear error-actuated automatic control systems. In fact many of the techniques can be extended to cover feed-back systems of a more general type.

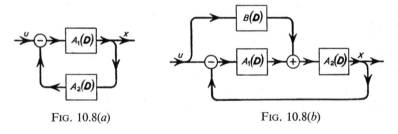

FIG. 10.8(a)   FIG. 10.8(b)

Consider for example the system shown in fig 10.8(a). Here the output x is modified by the operator $A_2(\mathbf{D})$ before it is subtracted from the input. Such an arrangement could be used when the desired output is not u but $\{A_2(\mathbf{D})\}u$; thus with $A_2(\mathbf{D})$ equal to $\mathbf{D}$ the system could be a velocity-controlled servo rather than a position-controlled one. The relation between the input and the output is easily seen to be

$$x = \frac{A_1(\mathbf{D})}{1 + A_1(\mathbf{D})A_2(\mathbf{D})} u. \tag{1}$$

The steady state response is deduced by expanding the operator, while the stability and the transient modes are determined from the zeros of $1 + A_1(\lambda)A_2(\lambda)$. The stability can be examined by means of a Nyquist diagram or one of the other graphical techniques described earlier in this chapter if the function $A_1(\lambda)A_2(\lambda)$ is used for plotting instead of $A(\lambda)$.

Another type of system is shown in fig. 10.8(*b*). Here the signal controlling the unit generating the output contains a component fed forward from the input as well as one depending on the error. The governing equation is

$$x = A_2(\mathbf{D})\{B(\mathbf{D})u + A_1(\mathbf{D})(u - x)\},$$

so that
$$x = \frac{A_2(\mathbf{D})\{B(\mathbf{D}) + A_1(\mathbf{D})\}}{1 + A_1(\mathbf{D})A_2(\mathbf{D})}u. \qquad (2)$$

Stability is again determined by the zeros of $1 + A_1(\lambda)A_2(\lambda)$, and is therefore independent of the operator $B(\mathbf{D})$. By suitable choice of this operator it is however possible to eliminate the steady state error for a wide range of input functions. Ideally, if $B(\mathbf{D}) = 1/A_2(\mathbf{D})$ this error is eliminated for all inputs. In this case the output feed-back serves only to remove errors due to initially incorrect settings of the output and to perturbations or instrumental inaccuracies. An example of the application of these principles to a more general type of linear system is given in **16.3**.

It emerges from the above examples that the stability of systems of these types depends only on the operators appearing in the closed-loop part of the system. It is not affected in general by the forms of the input and output nor by the stages at which they enter and leave the loop. Thus if the loop contains operators $A_1(\mathbf{D})$, $A_2(\mathbf{D})$, $A_3(\mathbf{D})$, ..., the stability depends only on the zeros of the function $1 + A_1(\lambda)A_2(\lambda)A_3(\lambda)$ . . ..

Another extension of the theory of this chapter is to multi-loop systems. Returning to the system shown in fig. 10.1(*c*), if the open-loop operator $A(\mathbf{D})$ takes the form $A_1(\mathbf{D})/\{1 + A_1(\mathbf{D})\}$, so that the corresponding element contains a subsidiary closed loop, a Nyquist diagram for the function $A_1(\lambda)$ can be used to determine P_+, the number of poles of $A(\lambda)$ with positive real parts. The stability of the whole system can then be determined from a second diagram for the function $A(\lambda)$ by applying the condition **10.5** (5).

CHAPTER 11

STATISTICAL METHODS

11.1 Introduction

The practical analysis and design of linear systems is usually based on the response to special types of input function, such as sinusoidal or unit step or velocity functions. Such functions often provide convenient test inputs for which the response can be calculated or observed. They are, however, artificial and are not usually representative of the type of signal to be expected in practice. It is true that, given say the response to a unit step input, a skilled designer may be able to judge whether a system will perform satisfactorily with a typical input. He will do this by mentally analysing the input into step components and estimating the effect of superposition of the outputs corresponding to these.

A more scientific approach to the problem of design or synthesis is to take account of the actual inputs to be expected and to specify a criterion or *norm* by which the performance of the system can be measured. Since a system will be designed to operate not on a single input but on a whole range of functions, it is logical to describe these in statistical terms. In order to measure the performance it is necessary to compare the actual output $x(t)$ with the desired output $x_d(t)$. If the error $\varepsilon(t)$ is defined as the difference between these, a reasonable norm might be the average value of $\varepsilon(t)$. Unfortunately both positive and negative errors can be expected in general. If a simple average is taken it is therefore possible for errors of large magnitude and opposite signs to cancel. To avoid this it is necessary to use an average to which $\varepsilon(t)$ makes a positive contribution whether it is in fact positive or negative. The simplest way of doing this is to take the average of $|\varepsilon(t)|$. It is, however, difficult to handle a norm of this type analytically. It will be seen that if we use instead the average value of $\{\varepsilon(t)\}^2$, the problem of determining the optimum system can be stated in a convenient form, and in many cases solved completely. The operator for the optimum system is then the one from a specified range that makes the mean squared error a minimum.

The definition of the optimum system by the minimum mean squared error criterion can be justified further on general statistical grounds, since it is a particular case of the principle of least squares. Objections to it have, however, been raised on the ground that it gives undue weight to large errors. Again, for example, if the system is concerned with controlling a weapon the actual magnitude of the error is significant only in so far as it must be small enough for the target to be destroyed. If the error is outside this limit it does not matter how large it is. Literally, a miss is as good as a mile. Nevertheless, a powerful if not absolute argument in favour of this norm is the fact that it yields an analytical solution. There are many instances in different branches of science where this consideration is used to justify mathematical assumptions that do not correspond completely with experience.

Turning now to possible inputs $u(t)$ to the system, a set of functions of this type is referred to as an *ensemble*. If the ensemble is defined in statistical or probability terms it represents a *random* or *stochastic process*. The statistical quantities used in the analysis of random processes are averages of $u(t)$ and of various functions of $u(t)$, such as its square. A particularly important function of this type, in fact the one with which we shall be mainly concerned, is the autocorrelation function. This will be introduced in the next section.

The averages may be taken over all functions of the ensemble for the same time t or they may be taken for a particular function $u(t)$ over all time from $-\infty$ to ∞. These two alternatives are referred to as *ensemble*

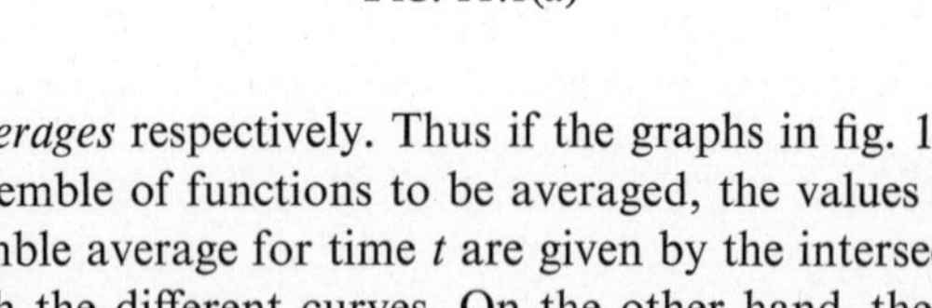

Fig. 11.1(a)

and *time averages* respectively. Thus if the graphs in fig. 11.1(a) represent the ensemble of functions to be averaged, the values contributing to the ensemble average for time t are given by the intersections of the line AB with the different curves. On the other hand, the values from which the time average for a particular function is obtained are represented by points on the heavy line CD which is the graph of this function.

If the various ensemble averages and in fact the detailed probability distributions are independent of t we say that the ensemble constitutes a *stationary random process*. To cover the case of averages such as the autocorrelation function which, as we shall see, depend on the values of the functions at different times, this definition should properly state that the distributions are invariant under a shift in time.

A stationary random process is *ergodic* if the various constant ensemble averages are equal to the corresponding time averages taken over almost all the individual functions $u(t)$. In statistical language this is equivalent to saying that the individual functions $u(t)$ of the ensemble have the statistical characteristics of large samples taken from a population whose distribution is that of the ensemble for any particular value of t.

The linear analysis given in the following sections is based on ensemble averages. These can often be derived by theoretical methods from the specification of the operating conditions of the system. In cases where this is not possible, an alternative is to calculate the time average from an observational record of a typical function of the ensemble. If it is assumed that the ensemble is ergodic, this time average can be used instead of an ensemble average. This method is particularly useful when dealing with unwanted and unpredictable perturbations, described by the generic term *noise*.

In order to give a complete quantitative description of the distribution of the functions in an ensemble a knowledge of the fundamentals of the theory of statistics and probability is required. This knowledge is not necessary for the application of linear analysis, and for this reason it is not assumed here. A short account is, however, given in Appendix 11.

11.2 Correlation functions

The averages which are used when analysing linear systems by statistical methods are those which represent or measure the degree of association between values of the same function of an ensemble or between the values of corresponding functions of different ensembles at times differing by a specified time interval τ. These averages are called *correlation functions*.

Consider an ensemble of functions $u(t)$ with zero mean.† If t and τ are such that there is little or no association between $u(t)$ and $u(t+\tau)$, then a particular value of $u(t)$ is just as likely to be associated with a positive value of $u(t+\tau)$ as with negative value. For this reason we can expect the average value of the product $u(t)u(t+\tau)$ to be near zero. On the other hand, the association between the two values may be such that both tend to have the same sign, either positive or negative. In this case the product will have an average which is definitely positive. Again, if $u(t)$ and $u(t+\tau)$ tend to have opposite signs the average of the product

† This restriction is not necessary for the theory developed in this chapter and it will not be assumed in general.

will be negative. This average is called the *autocorrelation function* of the ensemble of functions $u(t)$ and is denoted by $\phi_u(\tau)$.

If we take two extreme cases, on the one hand values of a function $u(t)$ of the ensemble at different times may be completely unrelated, however close the times may be. An ensemble of this type, which is called *white noise*, would in general have no continuity; it represents in fact the characteristic of erratic variation in the extreme. In this case $\phi_u(\tau) = 0$ for all values of τ except zero and $\phi_u(\tau)$ will usually be an impulse function (see Appendix 12). On the other hand, if each function $u(t)$ is a constant, $\phi_u(\tau)$ will be constant.

Usually the situation is intermediate between these extremes. Thus if τ is small, $u(t+\tau)$ can be expected to lie in a range of values that do not differ greatly from $u(t)$. On the other hand, if τ is large there will be very little association between $u(t)$ and $u(t+\tau)$. We may therefore expect $\phi_u(\tau)$ to decrease in magnitude as τ increases.

It follows from the theory given in Appendix 12 that if the functions of the ensemble are all periodic with the same frequency ω, then $\phi_u(\tau)$ is also periodic with frequency ω. Conversely and more generally, if $\phi_u(\tau)$ is oscillatory it can be inferred that the functions $u(t)$ of the ensemble contain periodic components.

In defining $\phi_u(\tau)$ the average may be taken with respect to the ensemble or with respect to time. It is remarkable that the theory of this chapter can be developed in terms of either. If the processes are stationary and ergodic the averages are the same, and it is immaterial which we choose. These conditions are, however, unnecessarily restrictive and moreover are not always satisfied. Most of the papers and books on this subject do in fact use time averages; for the typical optimisation problems, however, ensemble averages appear to be more appropriate and these will be used in this chapter and the next. They have the additional advantage of simplifying the presentation of the theory.

The time average is given by

$$T\{u(t)u(t+\tau)\} = \lim_{T_1 \to \infty} \frac{1}{2T_1} \int_{-T_1}^{T_1} u(t)u(t+\tau)\,dt. \tag{1}$$

In order to define the ensemble average we assume first that the ensemble consists of a finite number N of functions, $u_1(t), u_2(t) \ldots u_N(t)$. Then

$$\phi_u(t, \tau) = E\{u(t)u(t+\tau)\} = \frac{1}{N} \sum_{r=1}^{N} u_r(t)u_r(t+\tau). \tag{2}$$

This is, by definition, the *autocorrelation function*. The symbols E and T will be used in this book to denote ensemble and time averages respectively. In adopting this convenient notation we are following and extending the practice of most writers on statistics and probability whereby a statistical average or so-called expected value is indicated by the symbol E (see Appendix 11).

If, as is usually the case, there is an infinite number of functions in the ensemble, a relative frequency or probability distribution must be used. In this case the summation becomes an integral and the average takes the form

$$\phi_u(t, \tau) = E\{u(t)u(t+\tau)\} = \int u(t)u(t+\tau)\,dP. \tag{3}$$

This is a double integral taken with respect to two variables u_1 and u_2. The differential dP is the probability that $u(t)$ lies between u_1 and $u_1 + du_1$ and that, for the same member of the ensemble, $u(t+\tau)$ lies between u_2 and $u_2 + du_2$. A fuller explanation of this representation is given in Appendix 11. In view of its more compact form and its greater generality we shall use (3) rather than (2) in this chapter. Readers not familiar with the language and notation of statistics may, however, find the arguments clearer if mentally they replace integrals as used in (3) by summations as in (2).

More generally, if we have two ensembles related in such a way that each function $u(t)$ of the first is paired with a function $v(t)$ of the second and vice versa, we can define a *cross-correlation function*

$$\phi_{uv}(t, \tau) = \int u(t)v(t+\tau)\,dP \tag{4}$$

When, as often happens, $u(t)$ and $v(t)$ are statistically independent,

$$\phi_{uv}(t, \tau) \equiv 0. \tag{5}$$

The definitions given above do not necessarily require the various processes to be stationary. When they are so, however, the various auto- and cross-correlation functions are independent of t and can be written as $\phi_u(\tau)$ and $\phi_{uv}(\tau)$ respectively. We shall in fact assume from now on that random processes are stationary unless the contrary is stated.

We derive now some basic properties of the correlation functions. Observing that, if the process is stationary, (4) can be written in the form

$$\phi_{uv}(t_2 - t_1) = \int u(t_1)v(t_2)\,dP, \tag{5}$$

it follows that

$$\phi_{uv}(\tau) = \phi_{vu}(-\tau) \tag{6}$$

and

$$\phi_u(\tau) = \phi_u(-\tau), \tag{7}$$

so that $\phi_u(\tau)$ is always an even function. Again, if $w(t) = u(t) + v(t)$,

$$w(t)w(t+\tau) = u(t)u(t+\tau) + u(t)v(t+\tau) + v(t)u(t+\tau) + v(t)v(t+\tau).$$

Taking ensemble averages,

$$\phi_w(\tau) = \phi_u(\tau) + \phi_{uv}(\tau) + \phi_{vu}(\tau) + \phi_v(\tau). \tag{8}$$

As a very important special case, if $u(t)$ and $v(t)$ are independent,

$$\phi_w(\tau) = \phi_u(\tau) + \phi_v(\tau). \tag{9}$$

Putting $\tau = 0$ in (3),

$$\phi_u(0) = \int \{u(t)\}^2 \, dP, \tag{10}$$

which is of course the mean square value of $u(t)$.

It has been suggested above that $\phi_u(\tau)$ will usually decrease when $|\tau|$ increases. We can in fact prove that for any process,

$$|\phi_u(\tau)| \leqq \phi_u(0). \tag{11}$$

This is done by observing that

$$\{u(t)\}^2 + \{u(t+\tau)\}^2 \pm 2u(t)u(t+\tau) = \{u(t) \pm u(t+\tau)\}^2.$$

Averaging both sides and using the fact that the right-hand side is never negative,

$$2\phi_u(0) \pm 2\phi_u(\tau) \geqq 0,$$

whence (11) follows.

11.3 Spectral density

Although the problem of optimising a system can be stated and solved, at least partially, in terms of the correlation functions introduced in the last section, it is formulated and solved more directly if it is translated from these functions of the time difference τ into the frequency domain. Accordingly we introduce the Fourier transform of $\phi_u(\tau)$. Denoting this by $\Phi_u(j\omega)$ we have

$$\Phi_u(j\omega) = \int_{-\infty}^{\infty} \phi_u(\tau) e^{-j\omega\tau} \, d\tau. \tag{1}$$

It is shown in Appendix 12 that for certain types of ensemble this function represents the distribution of the harmonic components of the signals of the ensemble expressed in terms of average power. For this reason it is called the *power spectral density*, or more simply the *spectral density*.

Using **5.1** (4) for the inverse transform,

$$\phi_u(\tau) = \frac{1}{2\pi} \int_{-\infty}^{\infty} \Phi_u(j\omega) e^{j\omega\tau} d\omega. \tag{2}$$

Putting $\tau = 0$ in (2),

$$\phi_u(0) = \int \{u(t)\}^2 dP = E(u^2) = \frac{1}{2\pi} \int_{-\infty}^{\infty} \Phi_u(j\omega) d\omega. \tag{3}$$

This important formula allows the mean square value of the functions in an ensemble to be expressed directly in terms of the spectral density. Since $\phi_u(\tau) = \phi_u(-\tau)$

$$\Phi_u(j\omega) = \int_{-\infty}^{0} \phi_u(\tau) e^{-j\omega\tau} d\tau + \int_{0}^{\infty} \phi_u(\tau) e^{-j\omega\tau} d\tau$$

$$= 2 \int_{0}^{\infty} \phi_u(\tau) \cos \omega\tau \, d\tau, \tag{4}$$

replacing τ by $-\tau$ in the first integral and using equation (12) of Appendix 1. It follows that $\Phi_u(j\omega)$ is always real and is an even function of ω; also, when it represents power it cannot be negative.

By taking the bilateral Laplace transform rather than the Fourier transform a more general spectral density $\Phi_u(p)$ is formed. It is an even function of p, that is,

$$\Phi_u(-p) = \Phi_u(p). \tag{5}$$

The Fourier transform of $\phi_{uv}(\tau)$ is the *cross spectral density* $\Phi_{uv}(j\omega)$ of the ensembles represented by $u(t)$ and $v(t)$. Again, we can define it more generally by means of a Laplace transform. It follows from **11.2** (6) that

$$\Phi_{uv}(p) = \Phi_{vu}(-p). \tag{6}$$

Also if $w(t) = u(t) + v(t)$ then

$$\Phi_w(p) = \Phi_u(p) + \Phi_{uv}(p) + \Phi_{vu}(p) + \Phi_v(p). \tag{7}$$

If $u(t)$ and $v(t)$ are independent,

$$\Phi_w(p) = \Phi_u(p) + \Phi_v(p). \tag{8}$$

Unlike spectral densities, cross spectral densities are usually complex.

A typical expression for the autocorrelation function $\phi_u(\tau)$ is $e^{-\beta|\tau|}$. The derivation of this from suitable assumptions is given in Appendix 12 and its graph is shown in fig. 11.3(a). Then

$$\Phi_u(p) = \int_{-\infty}^{\infty} e^{-\beta|\tau|} e^{-p\tau} d\tau = \int_{-\infty}^{0} e^{(\beta-p)\tau} d\tau + \int_{0}^{\infty} e^{-(\beta+p)\tau} d\tau$$

$$= \frac{1}{\beta-p} + \frac{1}{\beta+p} = \frac{2\beta}{\beta^2-p^2}. \tag{9}$$

In particular $\Phi_u(j\omega) = 2\beta/(\omega^2+\beta^2)$. The graph of this spectral density is shown in fig. 11.3(b).

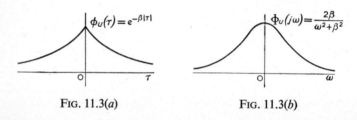

FIG. 11.3(a)   FIG. 11.3(b)

We now investigate the effect of a linear system or filter on the autocorrelation function and spectral density of an ensemble. With the usual notation let

$$x(t) = F(\mathbf{D})u(t) \tag{10}$$

Let the weighting function of the system be $W(t)$, the inverse transform of $F(p)$. Then from **8.4** (5),

$$x(t) = \int_{-\infty}^{\infty} W(\tau_1)u(t-\tau_1) d\tau_1.$$

Now if $v(t)$ is a function of an ensemble associated with those of $u(t)$ and $x(t)$,

$$\phi_{vx}(\tau) = \int v(t)x(t+\tau) dP$$

$$= \iint W(\tau_1)v(t)u(t+\tau-\tau_1) d\tau_1 dP$$

$$= \int W(\tau_1)\phi_{vu}(\tau-\tau_1) d\tau_1,$$

inverting the order of integration and assuming that the ensembles are stationary. Since this is a convolution integral we have, taking transforms of both sides and then using (6),

$$\Phi_{vx}(p) = F(p)\Phi_{vu}(p), \tag{11}$$

$$\Phi_{xv}(p) = F(-p)\Phi_{uv}(p). \tag{12}$$

If now we put $v = x$ in (11) and $v = u$ in (12) and eliminate $\Phi_{xu}(p)$, we have

$$\Phi_x(p) = F(p)F(-p)\Phi_u(p). \tag{13}$$

The relation between the actual spectral densities is given by putting $p = j\omega$. Since $F(-j\omega) = \overline{F(j\omega)}$, the bar denoting as usual the conjugate complex number, and since for any complex number z, $z\bar{z} = |z|^2$, we have

$$\Phi_x(j\omega) = |F(j\omega)|^2 \Phi_u(j\omega). \tag{14}$$

This fundamental relation can be compared with the formula

$$x^*(j\omega) = F(j\omega)u^*(j\omega)$$

connecting the Fourier transforms of the input and output. Since the autocorrelation functions are quadratic functions of the input and output it is not surprising that their spectral densities have as ratio a quadratic function of the system's transfer function.

It is seen from (13) that $\phi_x(\tau)$ can be expressed in terms of $\phi_u(\tau)$ by means of a weighting function $W_1(\tau)$ whose transform is $F(-p)F(p)$. Thus

$$\phi_x(\tau) = \int_{-\infty}^{\infty} \phi_u(\tau_1)W_1(\tau - \tau_1)\,d\tau_1, \tag{15}$$

where

$$W_1(\tau) = \int_{-\infty}^{\infty} W(\tau_2)W(\tau_2 + \tau)\,d\tau_2. \tag{16}$$

The relation between $\phi_u(\tau)$ and $\phi_x(\tau)$ can be expressed alternately in the form

$$\phi_x(\tau) = F(\mathbf{D})F(-\mathbf{D})\phi_u(\tau). \tag{17}$$

This can be deduced from (13) or it can be obtained directly from (10).

CHAPTER 12

DESIGN OF OPTIMUM SYSTEMS

12.1 Parameter optimisation

We now show how the optimisation problem in its simplest form can be solved. Consider a system whose operator is $F(\mathbf{D})$ and whose input consists of an effective signal $s(t)$ with a perturbation or noise $n(t)$ added. It is required that the system shall act purely as a filter, by removing $n(t)$ and leaving $s(t)$ unchanged. In general, these objectives will be incompatible. Our object will be to effect the best compromise on the basis of the minimum mean square error criterion.

The basic equations of the problem are

$$x(t) = F(\mathbf{D})u(t), \tag{1}$$

$$u(t) = s(t) + n(t), \tag{2}$$

$$\varepsilon(t) = x(t) - s(t) = \{F(\mathbf{D}) - 1\}s(t) + F(\mathbf{D})n(t). \tag{3}$$

If it is assumed that the signal and noise are independent, using **11.3** (8) and (14) their spectral densities and that of the error are related by the equations

$$\Phi_u(j\omega) = \Phi_s(j\omega) + \Phi_n(j\omega), \tag{4}$$

$$\Phi_\varepsilon(j\omega) = |F(j\omega) - 1|^2 \Phi_s(j\omega) + |F(j\omega)|^2 \Phi_n(j\omega). \tag{5}$$

The mean square error will be denoted by I. Also, where there is no possibility of confusion the argument $j\omega$ will be omitted from the functions F and the various spectral densities Φ. We then have from **11.3** (3),

$$I = E(\varepsilon^2) = \frac{1}{2\pi} \int_{-\infty}^{\infty} \Phi_\varepsilon(j\omega) \, d\omega,$$

or

$$I = \frac{1}{2\pi} \int_{-\infty}^{\infty} \{|F - 1|^2 \Phi_s + |F|^2 \Phi_n\} \, d\omega. \tag{6}$$

The problem then is to choose the operator $F(\mathbf{D})$ from a specified class so that I is a minimum. This process will now be demonstrated by means of an elementary example.

Assume that both the signal and the noise have spectral densities of the type shown in fig. 11.3(b). The constants β will be expressed as the reciprocals of time constants T_s and T_n. We can therefore write

$$\Phi_s = \frac{K_s}{1+\omega^2 T_s^2}, \qquad \Phi_n = \frac{K_n}{1+\omega^2 T_n^2}. \qquad (7)$$

In practice the constants K_s and K_n will represent the mean powers of the non-periodic components of the functions, so that the latter will be much smaller than the former. The reciprocals of the time constants give an indication of the cut-off frequencies of the two ensembles. Since

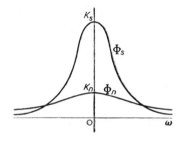

Fig. 12.1(a)

the noise will usually contain higher frequency components than the signal, T_n will be much smaller than T_s. In fact, T_n is often taken to be zero, so that Φ_n is a constant K_n. A perturbation of this type, having a flat spectrum, constitutes white noise (see Appendix 12). Graphs of the two spectral densities are shown in fig. 12.1(a).

We will assume that the filter is of the simplest possible type, that for which

$$F(\mathbf{D}) = \frac{1}{1+T\mathbf{D}}. \qquad (8)$$

Our problem is to find the optimum value of the smoothing time constant T, that is, the value that makes the mean square error I a minimum. Substituting in (5) and simplifying gives

$$\Phi_\varepsilon = \frac{1}{1+\omega^2 T^2}\left\{\frac{K_s\omega^2 T^2}{1+\omega^2 T_s^2}+\frac{K_n}{1+\omega^2 T_n^2}\right\}. \qquad (9)$$

Now
$$\int_{-\infty}^{\infty} \frac{d\omega}{1+\omega^2 T^2} = \left[\frac{1}{T}\tan^{-1}\omega T\right]_{-\infty}^{\infty} = \frac{\pi}{T}.$$

Using this and similar results, it can be shown by expressing (9) in partial fractions and then integrating and simplifying, that

$$2I = \frac{1}{\pi}\int_{-\infty}^{\infty}\Phi_\varepsilon\,d\omega = \frac{TK_s}{T_s(T+T_s)} + \frac{K_n}{T+T_n}$$
$$= \frac{K_s}{T_s} - \frac{K_s}{T+T_s} + \frac{K_n}{T+T_n}. \tag{10}$$

For different values of T, this is a minimum when $dI/dT = 0$, that is, when

$$\frac{K_s}{(T+T_s)^2} - \frac{K_n}{(T+T_n)^2} = 0.$$

Writing $K_n = m^2 K_s$ this gives

$$T = \frac{mT_s - T_n}{1-m}. \tag{11}$$

Substituting in (10), we have

$$I_{\min} = \tfrac{1}{2}K_s\left\{\frac{1}{T_s} - \frac{(1-m)^2}{T_s - T_n}\right\}. \tag{12}$$

This example is typical of the method of optimisation of a single parameter. It can be extended to apply to two or more adjustable parameters. Assume, for example, that the smoothing circuit has a gain K and that both K and T can be chosen arbitrarily, so that

$$F(\mathbf{D}) = \frac{K}{1+T\mathbf{D}}. \tag{13}$$

By the above method it can be shown that

$$2I = \frac{K_s}{T_s} - \frac{K_s}{T+T_s} + \frac{K_s(K-1)^2}{T+T_s} + \frac{K^2 K_n}{T+T_n}. \tag{14}$$

This is a minimum when $\partial I/\partial K = 0$ and $\partial I/\partial T = 0$. Carrying out this differentiation and solving the resulting equations it is found that

$$T = \frac{mT_s - \{\sqrt{(1+m^2)}+m\}T_n}{\sqrt{(1+m^2)}}, \tag{15}$$

and
$$K = 1 - \frac{m}{\sqrt{(1+m^2)}}. \tag{16}$$

Substituting these values in (14) and simplifying gives

$$I_{\min} = \tfrac{1}{2}K_s\left[\frac{1}{T_s} - \frac{\{\sqrt{(1+m^2)}-m\}^2}{T_s - T_n}\right]. \tag{17}$$

It is evident, as might have been expected, that the value for I_{min} given by (17) is less than that given by (12). To take a numerical example, let $T_n = 0$ and $K_n = \frac{1}{9}K_s$, so that $m = \frac{1}{3}$. The ratio of these values for I_{min} is found to be 0·865. This is a measure of the improvement that can be obtained by introducing an adjustable gain K into the system.

12.2 System optimisation

In this section we consider the more general problem of optimisation of a filter when no restrictions are placed on its type other than that of stability. For the present we restrict consideration to the problem of pure filtering, so that equations (1) to (6) of the last section still apply. Summarising these, we require to minimise I, where

$$I = \frac{1}{2\pi}\int_{-\infty}^{\infty} \Phi_\varepsilon(j\omega)\,d\omega$$

$$= \frac{1}{2\pi}\int_{-\infty}^{\infty} \{|F(j\omega)-1|^2\Phi_s(j\omega)+|F(j\omega)|^2\Phi_n(j\omega)\}\,d\omega. \tag{1}$$

Using **12.1** (4) and writing $F(-j\omega)$ as $\bar{F}$, the integrand can be re-arranged as follows.

$$\Phi_\varepsilon = |F-1|^2\Phi_s + |F|^2\Phi_n$$

$$= (F-1)(\bar{F}-1)\Phi_s + F\bar{F}\Phi_n$$

$$= F\bar{F}\Phi_u - (F+\bar{F})\Phi_s + \Phi_s$$

$$= \Phi_u\left(F-\frac{\Phi_s}{\Phi_u}\right)\left(\bar{F}-\frac{\Phi_s}{\Phi_u}\right)+\frac{\Phi_s\Phi_u-\Phi_s^2}{\Phi_u}$$

or $$I = \frac{1}{2\pi}\int_{-\infty}^{\infty}\left\{\Phi_u\left|F-\frac{\Phi_s}{\Phi_u}\right|^2+\frac{\Phi_s\Phi_n}{\Phi_u}\right\}\,d\omega, \tag{2}$$

since Φ_s and Φ_u are real.

Now both terms of the integrand are positive or zero, so that their separate contributions to the integral must be positive or zero. Since the second term is independent of F the problem of optimisation reduces to minimisation of the integral of the first term. An absolute minimum value of I would be obtained by taking $F(j\omega) = \Phi_s(j\omega)/\Phi_u(j\omega)$. The corresponding system operator is

$$F(\mathbf{D}) = \Phi_s(\mathbf{D})/\Phi_u(\mathbf{D}). \tag{3}$$

Unfortunately, $\Phi_s(p)$ and $\Phi_u(p)$ are both even functions of p, so that any pole of the corresponding $F(p)$ with a negative real part must be matched

T.L.S.—9

by a pole with a positive real part. Such a system must necessarily be unstable. We must therefore consider the problem of minimising

$$I_1 = \frac{1}{2\pi} \int_{-\infty}^{\infty} \Phi_u |F - \Phi_s/\Phi_u|^2 \, d\omega, \tag{4}$$

subject to the condition that $F(p)$ is to have no poles with positive real parts.

Since $\Phi_u(p)$ is even, if it is rational its numerator and denominator can both be expressed as the product of factors of the type $q_r - p^2$. Let p_r be the square root of q_r with a *negative* real part so that

$$q_r - p^2 = p_r{}^2 - p^{2l} = (p_r - p)(p_r + p).$$

By collecting together all the first and all the second factors of these pairs we can write

$$\Phi_u(p) = \Psi(p)\Psi(-p), \tag{5}$$

where $\Psi(p)$ has no zero or pole with a positive real part. Then since

$$\Phi_u(j\omega) = \Psi(j\omega)\Psi(-j\omega) = |\Psi(j\omega)|^2,$$

the integrand of I_1 becomes

$$|\Psi|^2 |F - \Phi_s/\Phi_u|^2 = |\Psi F - \Psi \Phi_s/\Phi_u|^2$$
$$= |\Psi F - \Phi_s/\overline{\Psi}|^2.$$

Denoting $\Psi(p)F(p) - \Phi_s(p)/\Psi(-p)$ by $f^*(p)$, let $f(t)$ be the inverse transform of this function. If we apply the convolution theorem to the functions $f(t)$ and $f(-t)$ and then put $\tau = 0$, we have

$$\int_{-\infty}^{\infty} f(t)f(t-\tau) \, dt = \mathfrak{L}^{-1} f^*(p)f^*(-p) = \mathfrak{F}^{-1}|f^*(j\omega)|^2$$
$$= \frac{1}{2\pi} \int_{-\infty}^{\infty} |f^*(j\omega)|^2 e^{j\omega\tau} \, d\omega;$$

$$\int_{-\infty}^{\infty} \{f(t)\}^2 \, dt = \frac{1}{2\pi} \int_{-\infty}^{\infty} |f^*(j\omega)|^2 \, d\omega. \tag{6}$$

This important result is known as *Parseval's theorem*.

We now put $f(t) = f_+(t) + f_-(t)$ where $f_+(t) = f(t)H(t)$ and $f_-(t) = f(t)H(-t)$, $H(t)$ being the unit step function. Let $f_+^*(p)$ and $f_-^*(p)$ be the transforms of these two functions. Then

$$f_+^*(p) = \int_0^{\infty} f(t) e^{-pt} \, dt.$$

Since $f(t)$ has a Fourier transform, this integral converges when $\mathscr{R}p = 0$. It must therefore converge for all values of p which have positive real parts (see **5.3**). It follows that $f_+^*(p)$ can have no poles with positive real parts. Similarly, $f_-^*(p)$ can have no poles with negative real parts.

If $g^*(p) = \Phi_s(p)/\Psi(-p)$, a similar process can be used to split $g^*(p)$ into components $g_+^*(p)$ and $g_-^*(p)$. Also, since by hypothesis neither $\Psi(p)$ nor $F(p)$ can have poles with positive real parts, we have

$$f_+^*(p) = \Psi(p)F(p) - g_+^*(p), \tag{7}$$

$$f_-^*(p) = -g_-^*(p). \tag{8}$$

But, using (6),

$$I_1 = \int_{-\infty}^{\infty} \{f(t)\}^2 \, dt = \int_{-\infty}^{\infty} \{f_+(t)\}^2 \, dt + \int_{-\infty}^{\infty} \{f_-(t)\}^2 \, dt$$

$$= \frac{1}{2\pi} \int_{-\infty}^{\infty} |f_+^*(j\omega)|^2 \, d\omega + \frac{1}{2\pi} \int_{-\infty}^{\infty} |f_-^*(j\omega)|^2 \, d\omega. \tag{9}$$

Neither of these two integrals can be negative, and (8) shows that the second is independent of F. The first integral will be zero if $f_+^*(p) = 0$ and (7) shows that this will be so if

$$F(\mathbf{D}) = \frac{g_+^*(\mathbf{D})}{\Psi(\mathbf{D})}. \tag{10}$$

Since $g_+^*(p)$ has no poles and $\Psi(p)$ no zeros with positive real parts, this operator corresponds to a stable system and is therefore the required operator. The minimum mean square error is then

$$I_{\min} = \frac{1}{2\pi} \int_{-\infty}^{\infty} \{|g_-^*(j\omega)|^2 + \Phi_s(j\omega)\Phi_n(j\omega)/\Phi_u(j\omega)\} \, d\omega. \tag{11}$$

Provided $g^*(p)$ is a proper rational fraction, $g_+^*(p)$ can be found directly by expressing $g^*(p)$ in partial fractions and picking out and adding those with poles with negative real parts. The remaining terms give $g_-^*(p)$. As is shown in the example of the next section, terms corresponding to a pole at the origin or on the imaginary axis must be included with $g_+^*(p)$.

Taking once again the example of the last section, with Φ_s and Φ_n as given by **12.1** (7),

$$\Phi_u = K_s \left\{ \frac{1}{1+\omega^2 T_s^2} + \frac{m^2}{1+\omega^2 T_n^2} \right\} = \frac{k^2(1+\omega^2 T_1^2)}{(1+\omega^2 T_s^2)(1+\omega^2 T_n^2)},$$

where $\quad k^2 = K_s(1+m^2) \quad$ and $\quad T_1^2 = (m^2 T_s^2 + T_n^2)/(1+m^2).$

Then $\quad\quad\quad\quad \Phi_u(p) = \dfrac{k^2(1-p^2 T_1^2)}{(1-p^2 T_s^2)(1-p^2 T_n^2)},$

so that $$\Phi_u(p) = \Psi(p)\Psi(-p),$$

where $$\Psi(p) = \frac{k(1+pT_1)}{(1+pT_s)(1+pT_n)}.$$

Thus $$g^*(p) = \frac{\Phi_s(p)}{\Psi(-p)} = \frac{K_s(1-pT_s)(1-pT_n)}{k(1-p^2T_s^2)(1-pT_1)} = \frac{K_s(1-pT_n)}{k(1+pT_s)(1-pT_1)}.$$

Taking partial fractions and separating as above,

$$g^*_+(p) = \frac{K_s(T_s+T_n)}{k(T_s+T_1)(1+pT_s)}, \qquad g^*_-(p) = \frac{K_s(T_1-T_n)}{k(T_1+T_s)(1-pT_1)}.$$

From (10), the optimum operator is therefore

$$F(\mathbf{D}) = \frac{(T_s+T_n)(1+T_n\mathbf{D})}{(1+m^2)(T_s+T_1)(1+T_1\mathbf{D})}. \tag{12}$$

If $T_n = 0$, this result is found to agree with **12.1** (15) and (16).

12.3   Inputs with no autocorrelation function

The assumption that the input to a system belongs to a stationary ensemble can be taken to imply that this function varies in some manner within a restricted range about some mean value, often zero. This characteristic is not applicable to the inputs of many linear systems which have to be designed in practice. For instance, many servos have to be designed for inputs, the signal components of which increase or decrease more or less steadily during a given run. However, it may happen that, even though the input is not stationary or has no auto-correlation function, the methods of this chapter can still be applied. This is possible if the first or second derivative or some such associated function $r(t)$ has a fixed autocorrelation function. Such cases can be covered by the general equation

$$s(t) = F_r(\mathbf{D})r(t), \tag{1}$$

where $r(t)$ is stationary and has a spectral density $\Phi_r(j\omega)$, and $F_r(\mathbf{D})$ is an operator such as $1/\mathbf{D}$ or $1/\mathbf{D}^2$. The error is then given by

$$\varepsilon(t) = \{F(\mathbf{D})-1\}F_r(\mathbf{D})r(t) + F(\mathbf{D})n(t). \tag{2}$$

Now the system operator $F(\mathbf{D})$ will naturally be chosen to keep the error small for all t. We can therefore expect the error to be stationary. Its spectral density will then be given by

$$\Phi_\varepsilon = |F-1|^2|F_r|^2\Phi_r + |F|^2\Phi_n. \tag{3}$$

If we write

$$\Phi_s(j\omega) = |F_r(j\omega)|^2\Phi_r(j\omega), \tag{4}$$

(3) becomes

$$\Phi_\varepsilon = |F-1|^2\Phi_s + |F|^2\Phi_n. \tag{5}$$

This is identical with **12.1** (5), and the optimum operator $F(\mathbf{D})$ can be determined as in either of the last two sections.

Equation (4) can be regarded as *defining* the spectral density for ensembles of the present type, which have no autocorrelation function and to which, therefore, the definition of **11.3** cannot be applied. As examples, if $s'(t)$ and $s''(t)$ are stationary with spectral densities of the type given by **11.3** (9), we have respectively

$$\Phi_s(j\omega) = \frac{K_1}{\omega^2(1+\omega^2 T_1^{\,2})}, \tag{6}$$

$$\Phi_s(j\omega) = \frac{K_2}{\omega^4(1+\omega^2 T_2^{\,2})}. \tag{7}$$

As an example we will find the optimum open-loop operator $A(\mathbf{D})$ for a servo whose input consists of a signal with stationary first derivative together with white noise. Let Φ_s be given by (6) and let

$$\Phi_n = K_n = m^2 K_1.$$

Then

$$\Phi_s(p) = \frac{K_1}{-p^2(1-p^2 T_1^{\,2})}, \tag{8}$$

$$\Phi_u(p) = \Phi_s(p)+\Phi_n(p) = K_1\frac{1-m^2 p^2 + m^2 T_1^{\,2} p^4}{-p^2(1-T_1^{\,2}p^2)} = \Psi(p)\Psi(-p),$$

where

$$\Psi(p) = k\frac{1+\alpha p+\beta p^2}{p(1+T_1 p)},$$

and $k^2 = K_1$, $\beta = mT_1$ and $\alpha^2 = m^2 + 2\beta$. Using the notation of the last section it is easily seen that

$$g^*(p) = \frac{\Phi_s(p)}{\Psi(-p)} = \frac{k}{p(1+T_1 p)(1-\alpha p+\beta p^2)}. \tag{9}$$

The second and third factors clearly give poles with negative and positive real parts respectively, assuming that $\alpha > 0$. The corresponding partial fractions contribute therefore to $g_+^*(p)$ and $g_-^*(p)$. The remaining partial fraction, corresponding to the pole at the origin, must be included with $g_+^*(p)$; if this were not done $I_{\min}$ given by **12.2** (11) would be infinite. By taking these partial fractions and recombining them it is found that

$$g_+^*(p) = \frac{k(1+\gamma p)}{p(1+T_1 p)},\tag{10}$$

where $\gamma = T_1(\alpha T_1 + \beta)/(T_1{}^2 + \alpha T_1 + \beta)$. The overall operator $F(\mathbf{D})$ is then given by

$$F(\mathbf{D}) = \frac{g_+^*(\mathbf{D})}{\Psi(\mathbf{D})} = \frac{1+\gamma\mathbf{D}}{1+\alpha\mathbf{D}+\beta\mathbf{D}^2}.\tag{11}$$

But, from **10.1** (3),

$$F(\mathbf{D}) = \frac{A(\mathbf{D})}{1+A(\mathbf{D})}.$$

Solving for $A(\mathbf{D})$ it follows that

$$A(\mathbf{D}) = \frac{1+\gamma\mathbf{D}}{\mathbf{D}(\alpha-\gamma+\beta\mathbf{D})}.\tag{12}$$

Since this has $\mathbf{D}$ as a factor of the denominator the required servo must be of the first order.

12.4   Optimisation with constraints

Linear systems are built up from physical elements which must of necessity have finite working ranges. In many cases this is of no practical significance; on the other hand, occasions do arise when the possibility of saturation of a system at some stage is an important factor in its design. If such saturation is undesirable the solution of the optimisation problem becomes subject to one or more constraints. A typical example is that of a servo system whose motor has a limited power or torque output.

In order that linear analysis may be extended to cover conditions of this type, the constraints must be expressed quantitatively by prescribing suitable mean square values of the functions $y(t)$ that must be limited, these functions being linearly dependent on the signal and noise. A restriction of this type will not in general impose a limit on the *maximum* value of $y(t)$. If, however, it is assumed that $y(t)$ has a particular probability distribution, such as the Gaussian distribution, the mean square value can be chosen so that there is a definite probability, say 95 per cent, that a given saturation value is not exceeded at any particular time.

If we assume that $y(t)$ belongs to a stationary process, using our previous notation, the mean square value of $y(t)$ is $E(y^2)$ and, like the mean square error, is given by an integral in terms of its spectral density. Thus

$$I = E(\varepsilon^2) = \frac{1}{2\pi}\int_{-\infty}^{\infty} \Phi_\varepsilon(j\omega)\,d\omega, \tag{1}$$

$$J = E(y^2) = \frac{1}{2\pi}\int_{-\infty}^{\infty} \Phi_y(j\omega)\,d\omega. \tag{2}$$

The optimisation problem is to find the operator $F(\mathbf{D})$ which minimises I and for which J, which also depends on $F(\mathbf{D})$, has a specified value J_0. To make this clearer, assume that the system to be designed is a servo whose motor torque must be restricted. Since the torque is proportional to $\mathbf{D}^2 x$, the output x being given by $F(\mathbf{D})u$, (1) and (2) become

$$I = \frac{1}{2\pi}\int_{-\infty}^{\infty} \{|F-1|^2\Phi_s + |F|^2\Phi_n\}\,d\omega, \tag{3}$$

$$J = \frac{1}{2\pi}\int_{-\infty}^{\infty} \omega^4\Phi_x\,d\omega = \frac{1}{2\pi}\int_{-\infty}^{\infty} \omega^4|F|^2\Phi_u\,d\omega. \tag{4}$$

The method of solution we use is that of undetermined multipliers, due originally to Lagrange. If λ is any constant,

$$I+\lambda J = \frac{1}{2\pi}\int_{-\infty}^{\infty} \{|F-1|^2\Phi_s + |F|^2(\Phi_n + \lambda\omega^4\Phi_u)\}\,d\omega. \tag{5}$$

The process of **12.1** or of **12.2** can now be used to find the operator $F_\lambda(\mathbf{D})$ which makes $I+\lambda J$ a minimum. Let $I = I_\lambda$ and $J = J_\lambda$ when $F = F_\lambda$. Then if F_1 is any other operator for which $J = J_\lambda$, let $I = I_1$ when $F = F_1$. Since $I_\lambda + \lambda J_\lambda$ is the minimum,

$$I_1 + \lambda J_\lambda \geqq I_\lambda + \lambda J_\lambda,$$

so that $I_1 \geqq I_\lambda$. It has been proved therefore that I_λ is the minimum value of I for operators F for which $J = J_\lambda$. Also, by substituting in (4) the expression obtained for F_λ and evaluating the integral, we obtain a formula for J_λ in terms of λ. If this is equated to the required value J_0 an equation for λ is obtained. If this is solved, the value of λ obtained can be substituted in $F_\lambda(\mathbf{D})$ to give the required optimum operator.

To illustrate this process we make the above example more specific by assuming that there is no noise and that the second derivative of the input is stationary, so that

$$\Phi_s = \Phi_u = \frac{K_2}{\omega^4(1+T_2^2\omega^2)}. \tag{6}$$

Then

$$I + \lambda J = \frac{1}{2\pi} \int_{-\infty}^{\infty} \left(|F-1|^2 + \lambda \omega^4 |F|^2 \right) \Phi_s \, d\omega$$

$$= \frac{1}{2\pi} \int_{-\infty}^{\infty} \frac{K_2(1+\lambda\omega^4)}{\omega^4(1+T_2^2\omega^2)} \left\{ \left| F - \frac{1}{1+\lambda\omega^4} \right|^2 + \frac{\lambda\omega^4}{(1+\lambda\omega^4)^2} \right\} d\omega, \qquad (7)$$

after some rearrangement. The next step involves factorisation of $1 + \lambda p^4$. This is facilitated if we put $\lambda = 4\mu^4$, since

$$1 + 4\mu^4 p^4 = (1 + 2\mu p + 2\mu^2 p^2)(1 - 2\mu p + 2\mu^2 p^2). \qquad (8)$$

Then if $K_2 = k^2$, with the usual notation it is found that

$$\Psi(p) = \frac{k(1+2\mu p + 2\mu^2 p^2)}{p^2(1+T_2 p)},$$

$$g^*(p) = \frac{k}{p^2(1+T_2 p)(1-2\mu p + 2\mu^2 p^2)}.$$

Extracting and recombining the partial fractions for the poles at the origin and at the point $-1/T_2$, we deduce

$$g_+^*(p) = \frac{k(1+2\mu p + \gamma p^2)}{p^2(1+T_2 p)}, \qquad (9)$$

where

$$\gamma = \frac{2\mu^2 T_2(T_2 + 2\mu)}{T_2^2 + 2\mu T_2 + 2\mu^2}. \qquad (10)$$

Equating $g_+^*(p)$ to $\Psi(p)F(p)$ gives the optimum operator as

$$F_\lambda(\mathbf{D}) = \frac{1 + 2\mu\mathbf{D} + \gamma\mathbf{D}^2}{1 + 2\mu\mathbf{D} + 2\mu^2\mathbf{D}^2}. \qquad (11)$$

If this form is substituted for F in (4) we have

$$J_\lambda = \frac{1}{2\pi} \int_{-\infty}^{\infty} \frac{K_2}{1+T_2^2\omega^2} |F_\lambda(j\omega)|^2 \, d\omega$$

$$= \frac{K_2}{2\pi} \int_{-\infty}^{\infty} \frac{1 + 2\beta\omega^2 + \gamma^2\omega^4}{(1+4\mu^4\omega^4)(1+T_2^2\omega^2)} \, d\omega, \qquad (12)$$

where $\beta = 2\mu^2 - \gamma$. Evaluation of this integral is straightforward but rather tedious. Partial fractions or the method of residues can be used. Alternatively tables for integrals of this type are available.† It is found that

$$J_\lambda = K_2 \frac{\gamma^2(2\mu + T_2) - 4\gamma\mu^2 T_2 + 4\mu^3 T_2(3\mu + T_2)}{8\mu^3 T_2(T_2^2 + 2\mu T_2 + 2\mu^2)}.$$

† James, H. M., Nichols, M. B. and Phillips, R. S., *Theory of Servomechanisms*. McGraw-Hill (New York, 1947).

Newton, G. C., Gould, L. A. and Kaiser, J. F., *Analytical Design of Linear Feedback Controls*. Wiley (New York, 1957).

This expression can be simplified by putting $\mu/T_2 = v$ and substituting for γ. This gives finally

$$J_\lambda = \frac{K_2}{2T_2}\left\{\frac{3v+1}{2v^2+2v+1} - \frac{v(2v+1)}{(2v^2+2v+1)^3}\right\}. \tag{13}$$

To apply this formula, J_λ is equated to the specified value J_0 and the resulting equation is solved for v, using graphical or iterative methods. The corresponding values of γ and μ are then substituted in (11) to give the required operator.

An alternative and more informative procedure is to calculate the minimum mean square error I_λ as a function of v and to plot I_λ and J_λ against λ or v or against each other. It is found that for the above example

$$I_\lambda = \frac{8K_2T_2{}^3v^8(v+1)}{(2v^2+2v+1)^3}. \tag{14}$$

Fig. 12.4(a) shows the form of the corresponding graphs. If these are plotted more or less accurately it is possible to see at a glance the price

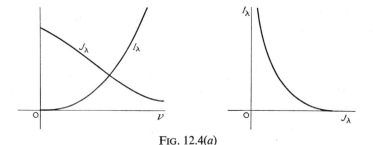

Fig. 12.4(a)

in terms of mean square error that has to be paid for output torque limitation at different levels.

It appears from the above example, as might have been expected, that I_λ increases as J_λ decreases. It follows that if λ and F_λ are chosen so that J_λ has a specified value J_0, it is not possible to obtain a better response from any system for which J_λ is less than J_0.

12.5 Further generalisations

So far we have confined our attention to systems such as servos or filters whose purpose is to reproduce the signal part of the input as nearly as possible, subject to specified conditions. We now consider cases where some linear operation, such as differentiation or prediction, has to be performed on the signal $s(t)$. In these cases the desired outputs are $\mathbf{D}s(t)$ and $s(t+T_p)$ respectively, the constant T_p being the prediction time. Using a result to be proved later (see **13.6** (3)), $s(t+T_p)$ can be written $e^{T_p\mathbf{D}}s(t)$. Thus these two examples, as well as others, are covered if the desired output is written as $F_d(\mathbf{D})s(t)$, where $F_d(\mathbf{D})$ is a specified operator. The error is then

$$\varepsilon(t) = x(t) - F_d(\mathbf{D})s(t). \tag{1}$$

If this formula is used instead of **12.1** (3) it is easily verified that **12.1** (5) becomes

$$\Phi_\varepsilon = |F - F_d|^2\Phi_s + |F|^2\Phi_n. \tag{2}$$

As in earlier sections we can write this in the form

$$\Phi_\varepsilon = |\Psi F - g^*|^2 + h^*, \tag{3}$$

where

$$\Phi_u(p) = \Psi(p)\Psi(-p), \tag{4}$$

$$g^*(p) = F_d(p)\Phi_s(p)/\Psi(-p), \tag{5}$$

and

$$h^*(p) = F_d(p)F_d(-p)\Phi_s(p)\Phi_n(p)/\Phi_u(p). \tag{6}$$

We then split $g^*(p)$ into two parts $g_+^*(p)$ and $g_-^*(p)$ and derive the optimum operator from the former as

$$F(\mathbf{D}) = g_+^*(\mathbf{D})/\Psi(\mathbf{D}). \tag{7}$$

If the various spectral densities and operators are rational, $\Psi(p)$ and $g_+^*(p)$ and hence $F(\mathbf{D})$ can be found as in **12.2**, by using partial fractions. If, however, other functions are used, as for example when $F_d(\mathbf{D}) = e^{T_p\mathbf{D}}$, $g_+^*(p)$ must be determined from $g_+(t)$. Thus

$$g_+^*(p) = \mathfrak{L}\{H(t)\mathfrak{F}^{-1}g^*(j\omega)\}. \tag{8}$$

To illustrate this process consider the problem of predicting at a time T_p ahead, an input without noise whose second derivative is stationary. Then

$$\Phi_s(j\omega) = \Phi_u(j\omega) = \frac{K_2}{\omega^4(1+T_2{}^2\omega^2)},$$

so that

$$\Phi_u(p) = \frac{k^2}{p^4(1-T_2{}^2p^2)}, \qquad \Psi(p) = \frac{k}{p^2(1+T_2p)},$$

where $K_2 = k^2$. It follows from (5) that

$$g^*(p) = \frac{k\,e^{T_p p}}{p^2(1+T_2p)}. \tag{9}$$

Now it is easily proved that

$$\frac{k}{p^2(1+T_2p)} = \mathfrak{L}H(t)k(t - T_2 + T_2\,e^{-t/T_2}).$$

Applying property (II) of **5.4**,

$$g(t) = H(t + T_p)k(t + T_p - T_2 + T_2 e^{-(t + T_p)/T_2}).$$

This function vanishes if $t < -T_p$, but not in general for other values. We form $g_+(t)$ by making $g(t)$ zero for $-T_p < t < 0$, leaving other values unchanged. Thus

$$g_+(t) = H(t)k(t + T_p - T_2 + T_2 e^{-T_p/T_2} e^{-t/T_2}).$$

Taking the transform,

$$g_+^*(p) = k\left(\frac{1}{p^2} + \frac{T_p - T_2}{p} + \frac{T_2^2 e^{-T_p/T_2}}{1 + T_2 p}\right)$$

$$= k\frac{1 + T_p p + \frac{1}{2}T^2 p^2}{p^2(1 + T_2 p)}$$

where $\quad \frac{1}{2}T^2 = T_2(T_p - T_2) + T_2^2 e^{-T_p/T_2}.$

From (7) it follows that

$$F(\mathbf{D}) = 1 + T_p \mathbf{D} + \frac{1}{2}T^2 \mathbf{D}^2. \tag{10}$$

This operator does not satisfy the condition that the denominator must be of degree at least equal to that of the numerator and is therefore technically unrealisable. It is, however, possible to find arbitrarily close approximations to it.

It can be verified that when T_p/T_2 is small, T is approximately equal to T_p. In this case it appears that prediction is effected simply by taking the first three terms of the Taylor series for $s(t + T_p)$. We may thus regard the general case given by (10) as the use of this form with a modified third term.

The other generalisation we consider allows the signal and noise to enter the system at different points instead of being added to form a single input. Consider, for example, the system with feed-back shown in fig. 12.5(a). The governing equation is

$$x(t) = F_2(\mathbf{D})[n(t) + F_1(\mathbf{D})\{s(t) - F_3(\mathbf{D})x(t)\}],$$

or $\qquad x(t) = F_1(\mathbf{D})F(\mathbf{D})s(t) + F(\mathbf{D})n(t) \tag{11}$

where $\qquad F(\mathbf{D}) = \dfrac{F_2(\mathbf{D})}{1 + F_1(\mathbf{D})F_2(\mathbf{D})F_3(\mathbf{D})}. \tag{12}$

Instead of (2) we now have

$$\Phi_\varepsilon = |F_1 F - F_d|^2 \Phi_s + |F|^2 \Phi_n. \tag{13}$$

Provided $F_1(\mathbf{D})$ is given, the optimum operator $F(\mathbf{D})$ can be deduced by the usual methods.

When $F(\mathbf{D})$ has been found it can be substituted in (12). Now although we have assumed $F_1(\mathbf{D})$ to be given, no restrictions have been placed on $F_2(\mathbf{D})$ or $F_3(\mathbf{D})$. Either of these can be specified arbitrarily; the optimum system is then obtained by choosing the other so that (12) is satisfied.

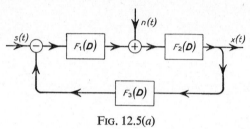

FIG. 12.5(a)

The treatment given in this chapter and the last to this important branch of the theory of linear systems has necessarily been brief. A reader seeking further information about the background of the subject and about its applications is referred to textbooks in which a fuller account is given. Among these can be mentioned books by Wiener,† who pioneered this approach to linear system design, and by Truxal,‡ in addition to those referred to on p. 136.

† Wiener, N., *The Extrapolation, Interpolation and Smoothing of Stationary Time Series*. Wiley (New York, 1948).
‡ Truxal, J. G., *Control System Synthesis*. McGraw-Hill (New York, 1955).

CHAPTER 13

DIFFERENCE OPERATORS

13.1 Sequences and differences

The introduction in relatively recent times into automatic control systems and into electronic engineering generally of such features as discrete pulses, intermittent operation and automatic digital computation has brought with it the need for a systematic technique for handling the associated problems of analysis and design. Much of this technique is already available in classical mathematical theory, particularly in the calculus of finite differences. It is our purpose to give in this chapter a brief account of the necessary parts of this subject.

With continuously operating systems, of the type with which we have been concerned exclusively so far in this book, the various signals have been represented by functions, such as $u(t)$, of the continuous variable t. With intermittent operation, however, the signals take the form of sequences, such as

$$\ldots u_{-2}, u_{-1}, u_0, u_1, u_2, \ldots. \tag{1}$$

The calculus of finite differences introduces processes and operations on sequences analogous to the processes of differentiation and integration and of solution of differential equations for functions of a continuous independent variable.

If the general term of the sequence (1) is denoted by u_r, the suffix r becomes the independent variable and, as such, corresponds to t in $u(t)$. For example we might have a sequence of terms for which $u_r = r(r+1)$. The corresponding values enumerated in (1) would then become

$$\ldots 2, 0, 0, 2, 6, \ldots. \tag{2}$$

The variation of such a sequence can be represented in the first instance by the sequence of *first differences* formed by subtracting each member of the original sequence from the following member. Thus from the sequence (2) we derive the sequence of differences

$$\ldots -2, 0, 2, 4, \ldots.$$

In general we denote $u_{r+1} - u_r$ by Δu_r. The sequence Δu_r corresponds to the derivative of $u(t)$. Again, we can take differences of the sequence

Δu_r to form the sequence $\Delta^2 u_r$ of *second differences* of u_r, corresponding to the second derivative of $u(t)$. For the sequence (1) the second differences are seen to have the constant value 2.

Proceeding to the general case, we can define differences of any order k by the formula

$$\Delta^k u_r = \Delta^{k-1} u_{r+1} - \Delta^{k-1} u_r. \tag{3}$$

To take another example, if $u_r = r^3$ then

$$\Delta u_r = (r+1)^3 - r^3 = 3r^2 + 3r + 1,$$

$$\Delta^2 u_r = 3(r+1)^2 + 3(r+1) + 1 - (3r^2 + 3r + 1) = 6r + 6,$$

$$\Delta^3 u_r = 6.$$

Differences of higher orders all vanish in this case.

It is apparent from this example that if u_r is a polynomial in r of degree n then Δu_r is a polynomial of degree $n-1$. More generally, if $k \leq n$, $\Delta^k u_r$ is of degree $n-k$, while if $k > n$ then $\Delta^k u_n = 0$.

The process of differencing polynomials is facilitated if these are expressed in terms of factorial functions $r^{(m)}$ defined by

$$r^{(m)} = r(r-1)(r-2)\ldots(r-m+1). \tag{4}$$

Then it is easily verified that

$$\Delta r^{(m)} = mr(r-1)\ldots(r-m+2) = mr^{(m-1)}. \tag{5}$$

This is analogous to the formula $\mathbf{D}t^m = mt^{m-1}$. In order to express a given polynomial in terms of factorials let

$$u_r = a_0 r^n + a_1 r^{n-1} + \ldots + a_n. \tag{6}$$

Then if

$$u_r = b_0 r^{(n)} + b_1 r^{(n-1)} + \ldots + b_n \tag{7}$$

it is seen that division of u_r by r gives a remainder b_n and a quotient $b_0(r-1)^{(n-1)} + b_1(r-1)^{(n-2)} + \ldots + b_{n-1}$. Division of this quotient by $r-1$ then leaves a remainder b_{n-1}, and so on. Thus the coefficients b_n, $b_{n-1}, \ldots b_1$, are obtained as the remainders when u_r, as given in (6), and the successive quotients are divided in turn by r, $r-1$, $\ldots r-n+1$, leaving the final identity $b_0 = a_0$. For example, if

$$u_r = r^3 - 2r^2 + 4r - 5,$$

$$u_r = r(r^2 - 2r + 4) - 5$$

$$= r\{(r-1)(r-1) + 3\} - 5$$

$$= r[(r-1)\{(r-2) + 1\} + 3] - 5,$$

so that

$$u_r = r^{(3)} + r^{(2)} + 3r^{(1)} - 5.$$

It follows from (5) that

$$\Delta u_r = b_0 n r^{(n-1)} + b_1(n-1)r^{(n-2)} + \ldots + b_{n-1}. \tag{8}$$

Higher order differences of u_r can be written down immediately if required.

A formula even simpler than (5) is obtained if $r^{(m)}$ is divided by $m!$ The quotient is the coefficient of x^m in the binomial expansion of $(1+x)^r$. Using the usual notation for these coefficients (see Appendix 4) we deduce from (5)

$$\Delta \binom{r}{m} = \binom{r}{m-1}. \tag{9}$$

Differences of different orders of a given sequence are usually displayed in vertical columns as in table 13.1(A). In such a table any

u_{-2}		$\Delta^2 u_{-3}$			u_{-2}		$\nabla^2 u_{-1}$	
	Δu_{-2}		$\Delta^3 u_{-3}$			∇u_{-1}		$\nabla^3 u_0$
u_{-1}		$\Delta^2 u_{-2}$			u_{-1}		$\nabla^2 u_0$	
	Δu_{-1}		$\Delta^3 u_{-2}$			∇u_0		$\nabla^3 u_1$
u_0		$\Delta^2 u_{-1}$			u_0		$\nabla^2 u_1$	
	Δu_0		$\Delta^3 u_{-1}$			∇u_1		$\nabla^3 u_2$
u_1		$\Delta^2 u_0$			u_1		$\nabla^2 u_2$	
	Δu_1		$\Delta^3 u_0$			∇u_2		$\nabla^3 u_3$
u_2		$\Delta^2 u_1$			u_2		$\nabla^2 u_3$	

Forward Differences   *Backward Differences*
TABLE 13.1 (A)   TABLE 13.1 (B)

element is the difference between the two nearest elements in the previous column, the upper element being subtracted from the lower. It is seen that differences of different orders but with the same suffix r lie on a falling diagonal. Differences expressed in this notation are usually called *forward differences*.

Since in analysing linear systems we tend to make use of past rather than future values of a given sequence an alternative notation is frequently preferable. This makes use of *backward differences* defined by the formula

$$\nabla u_r = u_r - u_{r-1}, \tag{10}$$

or, more generally,

$$\nabla^k u_r = \nabla^{k-1} u_r - \nabla^{k-1} u_{r-1}. \tag{11}$$

This formula should be compared carefully with (3). Backward differences are shown in table 13.1(B) where, once again, any element is the difference between the two nearest elements in the previous column. We see that in this case the same suffixes appear on *rising* diagonals in the table. It must be emphasised that for the same sequence u_r, differences appearing in the same positions in the two tables are always equal. For example, $\Delta^2 u_0 = \nabla^2 u_2$. We are in fact only using different notations for the same quantity.

Finally, the existence of a third notation, that of *central differences*, must be mentioned. This is used widely in computation, but since it is not particularly suitable for linear system analysis it will not be introduced in this book.

13.2   Use of operators

The symbols Δ and ∇ introduced in the last section can be regarded as operators which convert any sequence into the sequence formed by its first differences. It is clear that we can write

$$\Delta^m \Delta^n u_r = \Delta^m(\Delta^n u_r) = \Delta^{m+n} u_r, \tag{1}$$

with a similar relation for ∇. In fact, both these operators bear a very close resemblance to the operator $\mathbf{D}$. It is easily verified that they have properties analogous to **1.3** (2), (3) and (4), so that they may be manipulated algebraically in a very similar manner.

Another useful operator on sequences is $\mathbf{E}$, defined by the relation $u_{r+1} = \mathbf{E} u_r$. Then $u_{r+2} = \mathbf{E} u_{r+1} = \mathbf{E}^2 u_r$. In general,

$$\mathbf{E}^n u_r = u_{r+n}. \tag{2}$$

This definition holds for all integer values of n, positive and negative. Then

$$\Delta u_r = u_{r+1} - u_r = (\mathbf{E}-1)u_r, \tag{3}$$

so that
$$\Delta = \mathbf{E} - 1. \tag{4}$$

Similarly
$$\nabla = 1 - \mathbf{E}^{-1} = \mathbf{E}^{-1}(\mathbf{E}-1) = \mathbf{E}^{-1}\Delta. \tag{5}$$

Also
$$\mathbf{E} = 1 + \Delta \tag{6}$$

and
$$\mathbf{E}^{-1} = 1 - \nabla. \tag{7}$$

By using (4) it is possible to express a difference of any order directly in terms of members of the original sequence u_r. Thus

$$\Delta^n = (\mathbf{E}-1)^n = \mathbf{E}^n - n\mathbf{E}^{n-1} + \binom{n}{2}\mathbf{E}^{n-2} - \ldots + (-1)^n,$$

expanding by the binomial theorem. It follows that

$$\Delta^n u_r = u_{r+n} - n u_{r+n-1} + \binom{n}{2} u_{r+n-2} - \ldots + (-)^n u_r. \tag{8}$$

Again, using (6) or (7) any number of the sequence can be expressed in terms of the differences on a higher falling or a lower rising diagonal. Thus

$$\mathbf{E}^n = (1 + \Delta)^n = 1 + n\Delta + \binom{n}{2} \Delta^2 + \ldots + \Delta^n,$$

so that

$$u_{r+n} = u_r + n\Delta u_r + \binom{n}{2} \Delta^2 u_r + \ldots + \Delta^n u_r. \tag{9}$$

This important formula is called *Gregory's theorem*. Alternatively,

$$u_{r-n} = \mathbf{E}^{-n} u_r = (1 - \nabla)^n u_r,$$

or

$$u_{r-n} = u_r - n\nabla u_r + \binom{n}{2} \nabla^2 u_r - \ldots + (-)^n \nabla^n u_r. \tag{10}$$

If $a_0, \ldots a_n$ are constants, an expression of the type

$$a_0 u_{r+n} + a_1 u_{r+n-1} + \ldots + a_n u_r \tag{11}$$

can be written $Q(\mathbf{E}) u_r$, where the operator $Q(\mathbf{E})$ is given by

$$Q(\mathbf{E}) = a_0 \mathbf{E}^n + a_1 \mathbf{E}^{n-1} + \ldots + a_n. \tag{12}$$

Using (6), this operator can be written $Q(1 + \Delta)$, thereby enabling the form (11) to be expressed in terms of differences.

An important special case arises when $u_r = \kappa^r$, where κ is a constant. Then $\mathbf{E}^n u_r = \kappa^{r+n} = \kappa^n u_r$, so that

$$Q(\mathbf{E}) \kappa^r = Q(\kappa) \kappa^r. \tag{13}$$

Again, with a general sequence u_r,

$$\mathbf{E}^n (\kappa^r u_r) = \kappa^{r+n} u_{r+n} = \kappa^r (\kappa \mathbf{E})^n u_r,$$

so that

$$Q(\mathbf{E})(\kappa^r u_r) = \kappa^r Q(\kappa \mathbf{E}) u_r. \tag{14}$$

Equations (13) and (14) may be compared with properties (Ia) and (IIa) of **2.2**. In fact, the sequence κ^r will be found to play the same part in the calculus of differences as the exponential function does in the differential calculus.

13.3   Difference equations

If x_r is a sequence, a relation

$$F(x_r, x_{r+1}, \ldots, x_{r+n}) = 0 \tag{1}$$

which is satisfied for all values of r is called a *recurrence relation* or *difference equation* of the nth order. Then if we are given say

$x_0, x_1, \ldots x_{n-1}$, substitution of these values in (1) with $r = 0$ gives an equation for x_n. If this is solved we can now substitute for $x_1, \ldots x_n$ in (1) with $r = 1$ to give an equation for x_{n+1}. Proceeding in this way, as many more members of the sequence as may be desired can be calculated successively.

This process is usually laborious and one is naturally led to seek an explicit expression in terms of the independent variable r for the general term x_r of the sequence. Such an expression is called a *solution* of (1). The general solution of this equation will usually contain n arbitrary constants. These can for example be the n given initial values $x_0, \ldots x_{n-1}$.

The difference equation is the analogue in the calculus of finite differences of the differential equation. We shall be concerned only with the *linear difference equation*

$$a_0 x_{r+n} + a_1 x_{r+n-1} + \ldots + a_n x_r = u_r, \qquad (2)$$

where u_r is a given sequence. The coefficients $a_0, \ldots a_n$ can be functions of r. We will, however, confine our attention to the case where they are all constant. We shall assume also that neither a_0 nor a_n is zero. Using the notation of **13.2** (12), (2) can be written

$$Q(\mathbf{E})x_r = u_r. \qquad (3)$$

As in the linear differential equation, if $u_r = 0$ the equation is *homogeneous*.

The simplest type of equation is that which is homogeneous and of the first order, that is,

$$(\mathbf{E} - \kappa_1)x_r = 0. \qquad (4)$$

This is easily solved, since

$$x_r = \mathbf{E}x_{r-1} = \kappa_1 x_{r-1} = \kappa_1^2 x_{r-2} = \ldots = \kappa_1^r x_0.$$

Thus $$x_r = C\kappa_1^r, \qquad (5)$$

where C is an arbitrary constant.

To solve the general homogeneous equation

$$Q(\mathbf{E})x_r = 0 \qquad (6)$$

we must first solve an auxiliary or characteristic equation

$$Q(\kappa) = 0. \qquad (7)$$

If the roots of this are $\kappa_1, \kappa_2, \ldots \kappa_n$ then it is easily verified by substitution using **13.2** (13) that

$$x_r = C_1 \kappa_1^r + C_2 \kappa_2^r + \ldots + C_n \kappa_n^r \qquad (8)$$

is a solution. Moreover, if the roots are all different this is the general solution. For pairs of conjugate complex roots $\rho e^{\pm j\gamma}$ the corresponding terms in (8) can be written in the equivalent purely real form

$$\rho^r(A \cos r\gamma + B \sin r\gamma), \tag{9}$$

as in **1.5**. Repeated roots are dealt with as in **1.5** and **1.6**. For example, if the root κ_1 appears k times, the corresponding terms in (8) consist of $\kappa_1{}^r$ multiplied by an arbitrary polynomial in r of degree $k-1$. This polynomial can if desired be expressed in terms of factorials, as in **13.1**.

Following **2.2**, the general solution of the non-homogeneous equation (3) for x_r can be expressed in terms of an inverse operator thus:

$$x_r = \frac{1}{Q(E)} u_r. \tag{10}$$

At the same time, as in **2.6**, we can define the general rational fraction operator $F(E) = P(E)/Q(E)$ by the equations

$$x_r = F(E)u_r \tag{11}$$

or $$Q(E)x_r = P(E)u_r. \tag{12}$$

One of the simplest inverse operators is $1/\Delta$. Then $x_r = (1/\Delta)u_r$ if $\Delta x_r = u_r$, or $x_r = x_{r-1} + u_{r-1}$. Since $x_{r-1} = x_{r-2} + u_{r-2}$ and so on, it follows by repeated substitution that

$$x_r = u_{r-1} + u_{r-2} + \ldots + u_1 + u_0 + x_0 = \sum_{s=0}^{r-1} u_s + C,$$

where x_0 or C can be regarded as an arbitrary constant. Thus

$$\frac{1}{\Delta} u_r \equiv \sum^{s=r-1} u_s + C. \tag{13}$$

The inverse of the operation of differencing is therefore summation. This corresponds to the fact that the inverse of differentiation is indefinite integration. Notice that the lower limit of the summation is arbitrary. An alternative form which is sometimes more convenient uses the backward difference operator. This gives

$$\frac{1}{\nabla} u_r = \sum^{s=r} u_s + C. \tag{14}$$

The solution of the general equation (3) can be obtained formally by factorising the operator and following a process parallel to that used in **1.4**, **1.5** and **1.6**. However, since (3) is a special case of the general linear equation **7.2**(2), by applying a result proved in that section it follows that the general solution for x_r is formed by adding to a *particular solution* another sequence called the *complementary solution*. The latter is the general solution (8) of the corresponding homogeneous equation (6). The same is true of course for (12). In both cases the complementary solution can be denoted by $\{1/Q(\mathbf{E})\}0$.

The complementary solution can be written down once the characteristic equation has been solved. Particular solutions can be found by a range of operational processes analogous to those described in Chapter 2. In particular, corresponding to properties (Ic) and (IIc) of **2.6** we have

$$F(\mathbf{E})\kappa^r = F(\kappa)\kappa^r + \frac{1}{Q(\mathbf{E})}0, \tag{15}$$

$$F(\mathbf{E})(\kappa^r u_r) = \kappa^r F(\kappa\mathbf{E})u_r. \tag{16}$$

These follow from **13.2** (13) and (14). In addition, the operator $F(\mathbf{E})$ can be expanded in ascending powers of Δ or ∇ or in ascending or descending powers of $\mathbf{E}$. The choice between these will be determined by the conditions of the particular problem being solved and, in particular, by the nature of the given sequence u_r.

Example 1 $x_{r+2} - 2x_{r+1} + 2x_r = 2^r,$

or $x_r = \dfrac{1}{\mathbf{E}^2 - 2\mathbf{E} + 2}2^r.$

The characteristic equation is $\kappa^2 - 2\kappa + 2 = 0$ with roots $1 \pm j$, or $\sqrt{2}\,e^{\pm j\pi/4}$. The particular solution is

$$\frac{1}{2^2 - 2.2 + 2}2^r = 2^{r-1},$$

using (15). The complementary function is given by (9), so that

$$x_r = 2^{r-1} + 2^{\frac{1}{2}r}(A\cos\tfrac{1}{4}r\pi + B\sin\tfrac{1}{4}r\pi).$$

Example 2 $x_{r+2} - \tfrac{5}{2}x_{r+1} + x_r = u_r.$

Then $x_r = \dfrac{1}{\mathbf{E}^2 - \frac{5}{2}\mathbf{E} + 1}u_r = \dfrac{1}{(\Delta+1)^2 - \frac{5}{2}(\Delta+1) + 1}u_r$

$$= \frac{1}{\Delta^2 - \frac{1}{2}\Delta - \frac{1}{2}}u_r = \frac{-2}{1 + \Delta - 2\Delta^2}u_r$$

$$= -2(1 - \Delta + 3\Delta^2 + \ldots)u_r + \frac{1}{\mathbf{E}^2 - \frac{5}{2}\mathbf{E} + 1}0$$

$$= -2u_r + 2\Delta u_r - 6\Delta^2 u_r + \ldots + C_1 2^r + C_2 2^{-r},$$

since the roots of the characteristic equation are 2 and $\frac{1}{2}$. As a particular case, if $u_r = r^2$ then $\Delta u_r = 2r+1$ and $\Delta^2 u_r = 2$. Higher order differences are zero, so that

$$x_r = -2r^2 + 4r - 10 + C_1 2^r + C_2 2^{-r}.$$

More complicated equations can be solved, if necessary, by methods analogous to those of the examples worked in **2.3**.

We conclude this section by remarking that general rational fraction operators $F(\mathbf{E})$ can be manipulated algebraically in exactly the same way as similar functions of the operator $\mathbf{D}$. This statement can be justified by a series of theorems analogous to those given in Appendix 6.

EXERCISES   Obtain the general solutions of the difference equations:

1. $6x_{r+2} - 5x_{r+1} + x_r = 2r$,
2. $x_{r+3} - x_r = 2^r$.

13.4 Stability conditions

If u_r and x_r are the input and output sequences of a linear system whose operator is $F(\mathbf{E})$, so that

$$x_r = F(\mathbf{E})u_r, \tag{1}$$

then the system is stable if and only if the complementary solution tends to zero as $r \to \infty$ for all possible values of the arbitrary constants. Reference to **13.3** (8) and (9) shows that necessary and sufficient conditions for this are

$$|\kappa_1|, |\kappa_2|, \ldots |\kappa_n| < 1. \tag{2}$$

In other words the zeros of $Q(\kappa)$ all lie inside the unit circle, that is, the circle in the κ-plane with centre at the origin and unit radius.

In order to determine stability without actually solving the characteristic equation we must determine conditions that the general polynomial

$$f_n(z) = a_0 z^n + a_1 z^{n-1} + \ldots + a_n \tag{3}$$

shall have all n zeros inside the unit circle C in the z-plane. We shall assume that the coefficients $a_0, \ldots a_n$ are real. One way of obtaining these conditions is to make the substitution $z = (z'+1)/(z'-1)$, where $z' = x' + jy'$. Then if $|z| < 1$ we have

$$|x' + jy' + 1| < |x' + jy' - 1|$$

or
$$(x'+1)^2 + y'^2 < (x'-1)^2 + y'^2,$$

that is, $x' < 0$. Thus if the zeros of $f_n(z)$ all lie in C the zeros of the polynomial of degree n,

$$(z'-1)^n f_n\left(\frac{z'+1}{z'-1}\right),$$

all lie in the left half of the z'-plane. We can now use the criteria of Routh or Hurwitz, as stated in **9.4**.

For example, if $n = 2$ the transformed polynomial becomes

$$a_0(z'+1)^2 + a_1(z'+1)(z'-1) + a_2(z'-1)^2.$$

From this we deduce the conditions that $a_0 + a_1 + a_2$, $a_0 - a_2$ and $a_0 - a_1 + a_2$ shall all have the same sign. A little simplification leads to the following necessary and sufficient conditions:

$$a_0{}^2 > a_2{}^2, \qquad (a_0 + a_2)^2 > a_1{}^2. \tag{4}$$

This procedure, although straightforward, leads to involved expressions when $n > 2$. A better approach, particularly when numerical values of the coefficients are given, is as follows.

It is apparent from (2) of this section and (8) of Appendix 2 that, if the system is stable, $|a_n/a_0| < 1$; or

$$\delta_1 = a_0{}^2 - a_n{}^2 > 0. \tag{5}$$

We proceed to deduce $n-1$ similar conditions for a sequence of polynomials $f_{n-1}(x), \ldots f_0(x)$ of degrees $n-1, \ldots 0$, the zeros of which all lie inside C. These are defined as follows.

Let $f_n^*(z)$ be the polynomial formed from $f_n(z)$ by reversing the coefficients. Thus

$$f_n^*(z) = a_n z^n + a_{n-1} z^{n-1} + \ldots + a_0 = z^n f_n(1/z). \tag{6}$$

Let
$$f_{n-1}^*(z) = a_0 f_n^*(z) - a_n f_n(z) \tag{7}$$

$$= (a_0 a_{n-1} - a_n a_1) z^{n-1} + (a_0 a_{n-2} - a_n a_2) z^{n-2} + \ldots + \delta_1, \tag{8}$$

and let $f_{n-1}(z) = z^{n-1} f_{n-1}^*(1/z) = \delta_1 z^{n-1} + \ldots + (a_0 a_{n-1} - a_n a_1)$. \tag{9}

The same process is used to define $f_{n-2}^*(z)$ and $f_{n-2}(z)$ from $f_{n-1}(z)$, and so on. Let the constant terms in $f_{n-2}^*(z), f_{n-3}^*(z), \ldots$ be $\delta_2, \delta_3, \ldots$. Then the remaining conditions required are

$$\delta_2, \delta_3, \ldots \delta_n > 0. \tag{10}$$

In order to prove these we show first that if $f_n(z)$ has all n zeros inside C then $f_{n-1}(z)$ has all $n-1$ zeros inside C. Let

$$\phi(z) = \frac{f_{n-1}^*(z)}{a_0 f_n^*(z)} = 1 - \frac{a_n f_n(z)}{a_0 f_n^*(z)}.$$

Now on C, $|z|^2 = z\bar{z} = 1$, so that $1/z = \bar{z}$. It follows from (6) that on C,

$$|f_n^*(z)| = |z|^n |f_n(1/z)| = |f_n(\bar{z})| = |f_n(z)|.$$

Since $|a_n/a_0| < 1$ we deduce

$$\left| \frac{a_n f_n(z)}{a_0 f_n^*(z)} \right| < 1,$$

so that $\mathscr{R}\phi(z) > 0$ on C. Thus as z describes C the map of $\phi(z)$ lies entirely in the right half of the ϕ-plane and cannot therefore encircle the origin. If Z and P are the numbers of zeros and poles of $\phi(z)$ in C, a generalisation of **9.2** (3) shows that $Z - P = 0$. Now the zeros of $f_n^*(z)$ are the reciprocals of the zeros of $f_n(z)$, and since $f_n(z)$ has no zeros outside C, $f_n^*(z)$ has none inside C, so that $P = 0$. We deduce that Z is also zero, that is, $f_{n-1}^*(z)$ has no zeros inside C (this result is a special case of a general theorem on functions of a complex variable, called *Rouché's theorem*). Thus $f_{n-1}(z)$ has all $n-1$ zeros inside C, so that $\delta_2 > 0$.

The remaining conditions in (10) are deduced by applying the above argument to $f_{n-1}(z), f_{n-2}(z), \ldots$ successively. We then have as necessary conditions for stability,

$$\delta_1, \delta_2, \ldots \delta_n > 0. \tag{11}$$

A slight modification of the above reasoning shows that these conditions are also sufficient.

These rules and their derivation are to be found in a book by Marden.† When $n = 2$ they lead, after some reduction, to the inequalities (4), while if $n = 3$ they reduce to the criteria

$$a_0^2 > a_3^2, \quad (a_0^2 - a_3^2)^2 > (a_0 a_2 - a_1 a_3)^2, \quad (a_0 + a_2)^2 > (a_1 + a_3)^2. \tag{12}$$

For higher values of n the inequalities become very complicated, and it is preferable, if numerical values of the coefficients $a_0, \ldots a_n$ are given, to determine the coefficients of the functions $f_{n-1}^*(z), \ldots$ directly. We show below the working for the example

$$f_4(z) = 6z^4 + 2z^3 + z^2 - z - 2.$$

f_4^*	-2	-1	1	2	6	$\times 6$
f_4	6	2	1	-1	-2	$\times(-2)$
		$(-2$	8	10	$32)$	
f_3^*		-1	4	5	16	$\times 16$
f_3		16	5	4	-1	$\times(-1)$
f_2^*			69	84	$\mathbf{255}$	

† Marden, M., *The Geometry of the Zeros of a Polynomial in a Complex Variable*. American Mathematical Society (New York, 1949).

Here the third row has been formed by subtracting -2 times the second row from 6 times the first row. Notice that a common factor such as the number 2 appearing in this row can be removed before proceeding to the next stage. Notice also that it is not necessary to carry the working beyond f_2^*, since at this stage we can use (4). Since with the present example $255 > 69$ and $255 + 69 > 84$ and since the constants 32 and 255 (in bold type) are positive, we deduce that the given polynomial represents a stable system.

There is a marked similarity between the above process and that associated with Routh's first rule (see **9.4**). It is shown in Appendix 10 how the Hurwitz criteria can be derived from those of Routh. It is possible in the same way to derive rules in determinantal form corresponding to (11) above. These rules, called the *Schur-Cohn criteria*, are stated and proved in Marden's book.

13.5   The z-transform

We saw in earlier chapters how, from a given function $u(t)$ of the continuous variable t, we could form its Laplace transform by multiplying by e^{-pt} and then integrating from $-\infty$ to ∞. In the same way we can form a transform of a sequence u_r by multiplying it by a function z^{-r} and summing from $r = -\infty$ to $r = \infty$. The resulting function of the variable z is called the z-transform of the sequence. It will be denoted by $u^\circ(z)$ or $\mathbf{3}u_r$. Thus

$$\mathbf{3}u_r = u^\circ(z) = \sum_{-\infty}^{\infty} u_r z^{-r}. \tag{1}$$

This transform has the same kinds of applications as the Laplace transform and a whole range of analogous properties. We give in this section a short account of some of the more useful of these properties and applications.

Consider first the effect on the transforms of various operations on the sequence. Since $\mathrm{E}u_r = u_{r+1}$ we have

$$\mathbf{3}\mathrm{E}u_r = \sum_{-\infty}^{\infty} u_{r+1} z^{-r} = \sum_{-\infty}^{\infty} u_r z^{-r+1} = z\sum u_r z^{-r}.$$

Thus
$$\mathbf{3}\mathrm{E}u_r = zu^\circ(z). \tag{2}$$

More generally, if $Q(\mathrm{E})$ is a polynomial,

$$\mathbf{3}\mathrm{E}^n u_r = z^n u^\circ(z) \tag{3}$$

and
$$\mathbf{3}Q(\mathrm{E})u_r = Q(z)u^\circ(z). \tag{4}$$

In particular,
$$\mathbf{3}\Delta u_r = (z-1)u^\circ(z), \tag{5}$$

$$\mathbf{3}\nabla u_r = (1 - z^{-1})u^\circ(z). \tag{6}$$

These rules can be extended to cover inverse operators, for if

$$F(\mathbf{E}) = P(\mathbf{E})/Q(\mathbf{E})$$
$$\mathfrak{Z}F(\mathbf{E})u_r = F(z)u^\circ(z). \tag{7}$$

The resulting function will be the transform of a *particular* solution of the difference equation $Q(\mathbf{E})x_r = P(\mathbf{E})u_r$. It will be in fact the one solution for which the infinite series $\sum_{-\infty}^{\infty} x_r z^{-r}$ converges at both limits for common values of z. This property of the z-transform is analogous to a property of the Laplace transform (see property (VI) of **5.4**).

Just as the Laplace transform is particularly useful when dealing with one-sided functions, so the z-transform is appropriate when we are discussing *one-sided sequences*, that is, sequences u_r which have zero values when $r < 0$. The simplest of these is the *unit step sequence* H_r which has the value unity when $r \geq 0$. Its transform is

$$\mathfrak{Z}H_r = \sum_{r=0}^{\infty} z^{-r} = 1 + z^{-1} + z^{-2} + \ldots = \frac{1}{1-z^{-1}} = \frac{z}{z-1}. \tag{8}$$

Closely associated is the sequence $\nabla H_r = \delta_r$. Then $\delta_r = 0$ if $r \neq 0$ while $\delta_0 = 1$. This sequence is analogous to the unit impulse function $\delta(t)$. Then

$$\mathfrak{Z}\delta_r = 1. \tag{9}$$

From (7) and (9) we have

$$\mathfrak{Z}F(\mathbf{E})\delta_r = F(z). \tag{10}$$

Again, if $u_r = rH_r$ it is easily verified that $\Delta u_r = H_r$. Thus, using (5) and (8),

$$\mathfrak{Z}rH_r = \frac{z}{(z-1)^2}. \tag{11}$$

This result can be verified by expanding the right-hand side directly in powers of z^{-1}. More generally from **13.1** (9) we deduce

$$\Delta^m \binom{r}{m} H_r = \binom{r}{0} H_r = H_r,$$

so that

$$\mathfrak{Z}\binom{r}{m} H_r = \frac{z}{(z-1)^{m+1}}, \tag{12}$$

or

$$\mathfrak{Z}r^{(m)}H_r = \frac{m!\,z}{(z-1)^{m+1}}. \tag{13}$$

If κ is a constant, the transform of the sequence $\kappa^r H_r$ is

$$3\kappa^r H_r = \sum_0^\infty (\kappa/z)^r = \frac{z}{z-\kappa}. \tag{14}$$

More generally,

$$3\kappa^r u_r = \sum_{-\infty}^\infty u_r(z/\kappa)^{-r} = u^\circ(z/\kappa). \tag{15}$$

Combining (12) and (15) we have

$$3\binom{r}{m}\kappa^r H_r = \frac{z\kappa^m}{(z-\kappa)^{m+1}}. \tag{16}$$

By putting $\kappa = \rho e^{j\gamma}$ in (14) and taking real and imaginary parts,

$$3\rho^r H_r \cos r\gamma = \frac{z(z-\rho\cos\gamma)}{z^2-2\rho z\cos\gamma+\rho^2}, \tag{17}$$

$$3\rho^r H_r \sin r\gamma = \frac{\rho z\sin\gamma}{z^2-2\rho z\cos\gamma+\rho^2}. \tag{18}$$

One application of z-transforms is to the solution of difference equations, using methods analogous to those of Chapter 3. To demonstrate this, let us consider example 1 of **13.3**, slightly modified. We will in fact find the solution of the difference equation

$$x_{r+2}-2x_{r+1}+2x_r = 2^r H_r,$$

which vanishes when $r < 0$. Then, using (4) and (14),

$$(z^2-2z+2)x^\circ(z) = \frac{z}{z-2},$$

or $\qquad x^\circ(z) = \dfrac{z}{(z-2)(z^2-2z+2)} = \dfrac{z}{2(z-2)} - \dfrac{z^2}{2(z^2-2z+2)},$

expressing $x^\circ(z)/z$ in partial fractions. Using (14), (17) and (18) with $\rho = \sqrt{2}$ and $\gamma = \frac{1}{4}\pi$ we deduce

$$x_r = \tfrac{1}{2}\{2^r - 2^{\frac{1}{2}r}(\cos\tfrac{1}{4}r\pi + \sin\tfrac{1}{4}r\pi)\}H_r$$
$$= \{2^{r-1} - 2^{\frac{1}{2}(r-1)}\sin\tfrac{1}{4}(r+1)\pi\}H_r.$$

Numerical values for this sequence can be obtained by substituting $r = 0, 1, 2, \ldots$ in this formula. Alternatively we can expand $x^\circ(z)$ and use (1). This gives

$$x^\circ(z) = z^{-2}(1 - 4z^{-1} + 6z^{-2} - 4z^{-3})^{-1}$$
$$= z^{-2} + 4z^{-3} + 10z^{-4} + \ldots.$$

Thus, starting with x_0, we see that the required sequence is

$$0, 0, 1, 4, 10, \ldots .$$

The simplest way of obtaining these values is, however, to substitute $r = -2, -1, 0, 1, \ldots$ in the original difference equation and to solve successively for $x_0, x_1, x_2, \ldots .$

If we put $z = \rho e^{j\theta}$ in (1) we have

$$u^\circ(\rho e^{j\theta}) = \sum_{-\infty}^{\infty} u_r \rho^{-r} e^{-jr\theta}. \tag{19}$$

Comparison with **4.3** (1) shows that this is a complex Fourier series. In order to ensure convergence at the upper limit, ρ must in general be greater than some value ρ_1. Likewise for convergence at the lower limit we must have $\rho < \rho_2$. It follows that in general the series (1) converges if, and only if, z lies in the shaded annular region of the z-plane shown in fig. 13.5(a). This is the analogue of the strip of convergence of a La-

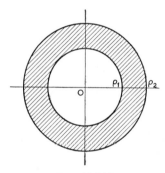

FIG. 13.5(a)

place transform integral (see **5.3**). It can happen that $\rho_1 = 0$ or that $\rho_2 = \infty$ or both. In particular, for a one-sided sequence which vanishes when $r < 0$ we always have $\rho_2 = \infty$. It can be proved that the circle $|z| = \rho_1$ then encloses all the poles of the function $u^\circ(z)$.

Equation (19) provides a formal expression for the inverse z-transform; using **4.3** (2), we have

$$\rho^{-r} u_r = \frac{1}{2\pi} \int_{-\pi}^{\pi} u^\circ(\rho e^{j\theta}) e^{jr\theta} \, d\theta. \tag{20}$$

If ρ is constant, $dz = j\rho e^{j\theta} \, d\theta = jz \, d\theta$. Thus (20) can be written

$$u_r = \mathbf{3}^{-1} u^\circ(z) = \frac{1}{2\pi j} \int_C u^\circ(z) z^{r-1} \, dz, \tag{21}$$

where C is a circle in the annulus of convergence and with centre at the origin. This expression allows the theory of contour integrals and the calculus of residues to be used in problems involving difference equations. In this book, however, more elementary methods will be found to be adequate for all purposes.

If we put $\rho = 1$ (provided of course that convergence conditions allow us to do this) we have the special case of the z-transform which is the analogue of the Fourier transform. The corresponding transform pair are related by the equations:

$$u^{\circ}(e^{j\theta}) = \sum_{-\infty}^{\infty} u_r e^{-jr\theta}, \tag{22}$$

$$u_r = \frac{1}{2\pi} \int_{-\pi}^{\pi} u^{\circ}(e^{j\theta}) e^{jr\theta} \, d\theta. \tag{23}$$

Another useful result concerning z-transforms is as follows. Let u_r, v_r and w_r be three sequences whose transforms satisfy the relation $w^{\circ}(z) = u^{\circ}(z)v^{\circ}(z)$. Then

$$w^{\circ}(z) = \left\{ \sum_{r_1 = -\infty}^{\infty} u_{r_1} z^{-r_1} \right\} \left\{ \sum_{r_2 = -\infty}^{\infty} v_{r_2} z^{-r_2} \right\}.$$

By picking out the coefficient of z^{-r} from this product we deduce

$$w_r = \sum_{r_1 = -\infty}^{\infty} u_{r_1} v_{r-r_1}. \tag{24}$$

This result is analogous to the convolution theorem.

Comprehensive tables of z-transforms are to be found in a number of papers and books on sampled-data systems.†

13.6 Difference operations on functions

If $u(t)$ is a function of the continuous variable t and if T is a given constant we define the shift operator $\mathbf{E}$ by the formula

$$\mathbf{E}u(t) = u(t+T), \tag{1}$$

or, more generally,

$$\mathbf{E}^n u(t) = u(t+nT). \tag{2}$$

† Among these may be mentioned the following:
Barker, R. H., The Pulse Transfer Function and its Application to Sampling Servo Systems, *Proc. Inst. Elect. Engrs*, (London) **99** (Part IV) (1952), pp. 302–317.
Ragazzini, J. R. and Franklin, G. F., *Sampled-Data Control Systems*. McGraw-Hill (New York, 1958).
Jury, E. I., *Sampled-Data Control Systems*. Wiley (New York, 1958).

Then, by Taylor's theorem,

$$u(t+T) = u(t) + Tu'(t) + \frac{T^2}{2!}u''(t) + \ldots$$

$$= \left(1 + T\mathbf{D} + \frac{T^2\mathbf{D}^2}{2!} + \ldots\right)u(t).$$

We can therefore write formally

$$\mathbf{E} = 1 + T\mathbf{D} + \frac{T^2\mathbf{D}^2}{2!} + \ldots = e^{T\mathbf{D}}. \tag{3}$$

Inverting this formula,

$$\mathbf{D} = \frac{1}{T}\log \mathbf{E} = \frac{1}{T}\log(1+\mathbf{\Delta}). \tag{4}$$

Expansion of the logarithmic operator (see equation (9) of Appendix 4) gives

$$\mathbf{D} = \frac{1}{T}(\mathbf{\Delta} - \tfrac{1}{2}\mathbf{\Delta}^2 + \tfrac{1}{3}\mathbf{\Delta}^3 - \ldots). \tag{5}$$

This important formula allows derivatives of any order to be calculated for tabulated functions to whatever accuracy the truncation of tabular values permits.

It should be stressed that the notation of the exponential and logarithmic functions of operators used above has no more significance than that of a shorthand representation of the corresponding series. It is possible, although tedious, to deduce (5) from (3) by pure algebraic methods. Furthermore, the validity of these expansions depends on the convergence of the series obtained when the operators are applied to particular functions $u(t)$. This will vary in general for different functions and also with the value of T.

13.7   Difference-differential equations

It is possible to apply to a function $u(t)$ operations that involve both differentiation and differencing or shifting. The notation and methods of operators can be extended to problems in which this occurs. Such problems will usually be associated in practice with systems in which finite time delays occur.

As an example of the notation, the expression

$$au''(t) + bu'(t+T) + u(t-2T)$$

can be denoted by $(a\mathbf{D}^2 + b\mathbf{E}\mathbf{D} + c\mathbf{E}^{-2})u(t)$. We will denote a general operator which is a polynomial in $\mathbf{D}$ and $\mathbf{E}$ with constant coefficients by $Q(\mathbf{D}, \mathbf{E})$. Using **13.6** (3), this can be written $Q(\mathbf{D}, e^{T\mathbf{D}})$, involving $\mathbf{D}$ only.

An equation of the type

$$Q(\mathbf{D}, \mathbf{E})x(t) = f(t) \tag{1}$$

is called a *linear difference-differential equation* with constant coefficients. If it is written in the form

$$Q(\mathbf{D}, e^{T\mathbf{D}})x(t) = f(t) \tag{2}$$

and if $e^{T\mathbf{D}}$ is expanded in powers of $\mathbf{D}$ it is seen that (2) can be regarded as a differential equation of infinite order. The general solution will be the sum of a particular integral, which can be obtained by standard methods, and a complementary function. The latter will take the form $\sum_r C_r e^{\lambda_r t}$, where $\lambda_1, \lambda_2, \ldots$ are the roots of the characteristic equation

$$Q(\lambda, e^{\lambda T}) = 0. \tag{3}$$

This equation, being transcendental, will have an infinite number of roots, so that the complementary function will have an infinite number of terms.

The theory of difference-differential equations has been investigated extensively (see, for example, Pinney†). In linear systems the most important consideration is that of stability, the condition for which is that none of the roots $\lambda_1, \lambda_2, \ldots$ has a positive real part. A general discussion of this problem is beyond the scope of this book. We shall, however, indicate some of its features by means of a simple example.

Consider the equation

$$T_1 x'(t) + x(t - T) = f(t). \tag{4}$$

This can be regarded as a generalisation of **2.4** (1) with T_1 as time constant, and where the second term is subject to a delay T. Writing this as $(T_1\mathbf{D} + \mathbf{E}^{-1})x(t) = f(t)$, the characteristic equation is seen to be

$$Q = T_1\lambda + e^{-\lambda T} = 0. \tag{5}$$

Stability can then be determined using a generalisation of **9.2** (3). This states that if C is the large semicircle shown in the right half of the λ-plane in fig. 13.7(a), the system is stable if and only if its map C' in the Q-plane does not enclose the origin.

Now if $\lambda = \mu + jv$ and $Q = X + jY$,

$$\left|e^{-\lambda T}\right| = \left|e^{-\mu T}\right|\left|e^{-jvT}\right| = \left|e^{-\mu T}\right| < 1$$

if $\mu > 0$. It follows that on the semicircular arc AB, $Q = T_1\lambda$ approximately. The corresponding arc of C' is therefore approximately semi-

† Pinney, E., *Ordinary Difference-differential Equations*. University of California Press (Berkeley and Los Angeles, 1958).

circular. On the diameter AB, $\lambda = jv$ so that $Q = T_1 jv + e^{-jvT}$. Put $vT = \theta$ and $T_1/T = k$. Then $Q = jk\theta + e^{-j\theta}$. The required map $A'B'$ is therefore the locus of a point fixed to a circle at unit distance from the centre when the circle, whose radius is k, rolls along the line $X = k$. If

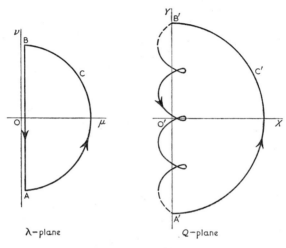

λ–plane   Q–plane

FIG. 13.7(a)

$k = 1$ this locus is a cycloid; otherwise it is a trochoid. If $k > 1$ it is roughly sinusoidal in shape, while if $k < 1$ it has loops. It is evident that the map C' does not enclose the origin unless it has a loop with a node on the negative real axis. At such a node

$$Y = k\theta - \sin\theta = 0, \qquad X = \cos\theta < 0.$$

Thus $\theta > \tfrac{1}{2}\pi$ and $k\theta < 1$, so that $k < 2/\pi$. The necessary and sufficient condition for stability is therefore

$$T < \tfrac{1}{2}\pi T_1. \tag{6}$$

The reason why there is an infinite number of roots of transcendental equations such as (3) or (5) is associated with the fact that exponential functions are periodic. More precisely, there is an infinite number of values of the complex variable z for which e^z takes a given value. If z_0 is any one of these values the others can be expressed as $z_0 + 2m\pi j$, where m ranges over all the positive and negative integers. We now develop this property in order to investigate the distribution of the roots of (5).

Putting $z = -\lambda T$, (5) can be written $e^z = kz$. Let $z_m = 2m\pi j + w_m$ be the root nearest to $2m\pi j$. Substituting,

$$e^{w_m} = 2mk\pi j\left(1 + \frac{w_m}{2m\pi j}\right),$$

since $e^{2m\pi j} = 1$. Taking logarithms,

$$w_m = \log 2mk\pi j + \log\left(1 + \frac{w_m}{2m\pi j}\right). \tag{7}$$

This can be used as an iterative formula for the evaluation of w_m, starting from the value zero. If m is sufficiently large the last term can be neglected, to give the approximate formula

$$w_m = \log 2mk\pi j.$$

If $m > 0$ this gives as an approximate root of (5)

$$\lambda_m = -\frac{1}{T}(\log 2\pi k + \log m) - \frac{j\pi}{T}(2m + \tfrac{1}{2}), \tag{8}$$

since $\log j = \log e^{\frac{1}{2}j\pi} = \frac{1}{2}j\pi$. The points representing these zeros, together with their conjugates, in the λ-plane lie on two exponential curves, as shown in fig 13.7(b).

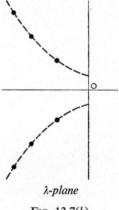

λ-plane

Fig. 13.7(b)

An important special case of (1) is

$$Q(\mathbf{E})x(t) = f(t), \tag{9}$$

in which the operator does not contain **D**. This is a pure difference equation. Unlike those discussed in **13.3**, which expressed a relation between sequences, this equation expresses a relation between functions of the continuous variable t.

The characteristic equation is

$$Q(\kappa) = 0, \tag{10}$$

where $\kappa = e^{\lambda T}$. If its degree is n there will be n roots $\kappa_1, \kappa_2, \ldots \kappa_n$. Each of these will give rise to an infinite number of values of λ. If λ_1 is one of the values corresponding to the root κ_1 the others can be written $\lambda_1 + 2m\pi j/T$. The corresponding terms of the complementary function will take the form

$$\sum_{m=-\infty}^{\infty} C_{1m} e^{(\lambda_1 + 2m\pi j/T)t} = e^{\lambda_1 t} \sum_m C_{1m} e^{2m\pi jt/T}.$$

But $e^{\lambda_1 t} = \kappa_1^{t/T}$ and the sum by which this is multiplied, being a Fourier series with arbitrary coefficients, is an arbitrary function $C_1(t)$ with period T. The general solution of (9) can therefore be written

$$x(t) = g(t) + C_1(t)\kappa_1^{t/T} + C_2(t)\kappa_2^{t/T} + \ldots + C_n(t)\kappa_n^{t/T}, \tag{11}$$

where $g(t)$ is a particular integral. This expression should be compared with **13.3** (8).

CHAPTER 14

THE GENERAL LINEAR OPERATOR

14.1 General formulae

The linear operator was defined in **7.1** by the formula

$$x = \Phi u,$$

subject to the superposition rule

$$\Phi(u + v) = \Phi u + \Phi v,$$

for any two admissible inputs u and v. The input u and output x may be functions of t or sequences.

It is convenient at this stage to derive explicit formulae for the relations between the input and output in the different cases that can arise. Apart from revealing the scope of linear operators given by the above definition, the formulae obtained will allow us to classify operators in several ways and also to introduce generalised rules for their manipulation. These will help to clarify the operational processes developed in the next two chapters.

We consider first the case where the input and output are both functions of t. Using a generalisation of the method of **8.4** we first analyse the input into impulse components. Thus

$$u(t) = \int_{-\infty}^{\infty} u(t_1)\delta(t - t_1)\, dt_1. \tag{1}$$

Let the response of the system to an input $\delta(t - t_1)$ be $\phi(t, t_1),$† that is,

$$\phi(t, t_1) = \Phi\delta(t - t_1). \tag{2}$$

Then, by the superposition principle, for a general input $u(t)$ we have

$$x(t) = \int_{-\infty}^{\infty} u(t_1)\phi(t, t_1)\, dt_1. \tag{3}$$

The operation Φ is therefore defined by the function $\phi(t, t_1)$, called the *kernel*, which can be regarded as a measure of the contribution to

† The function $\phi(t, t_1)$ used in the earlier part of this chapter should not be confused with the correlation functions of Chapters 11 and 12.

the output function at time t per unit of input function at time t_1, for any two times t and t_1.

If the input and output are both sequences u_r and x_r respectively, a similar argument shows that they must be related by a formula of the type

$$x_r = \sum_{r_1=-\infty}^{\infty} \phi_{rr_1} u_{r_1}. \tag{4}$$

Here ϕ_{rr_1} is by definition $\Phi \delta_{r-r_1}$, where δ_r is the sequence defined in **13.5** to take the value unity when $r = 0$ and zero otherwise. Equation (4) shows that the operator Φ is equivalent to a matrix with, in general, an infinite number of rows and columns (see Appendix 13).

Finally, when the input is a function of t and the output a sequence and vice versa the corresponding formulae are respectively

$$x_r = \int_{-\infty}^{\infty} \phi(r, t_1) u(t_1)\, dt_1 \tag{5}$$

and

$$x(t) = \sum_{r_1=-\infty}^{\infty} \phi(t, r_1) u_{r_1}. \tag{6}$$

In (5), $\phi(r, t_1)$ which is by definition $\Phi \delta(t-t_1)$, the response sequence when the input is an impulse at time t_1, is a function of the discrete variable r and the continuous variable t. On the other hand, in (6), $\phi(t, r_1)$ is $\Phi \delta_{r-r_1}$, the response to an input sequence which takes the value unity when $r = r_1$ and is zero otherwise.

14.2 Time-invariant systems

A very important property possessed by many linear systems is that of being *time-invariant*. This means that the relation between the input and output is not affected by any change of origin in time. We can express this symbolically by saying that if $\Phi u(t) = x(t)$ then $\Phi u(t+t_0) = x(t+t_0)$ for all t_0 and for all inputs $u(t)$. As a special case, if $u(t) = \delta(t)$ then $x(t) = \phi(t, 0)$, so that $\Phi \delta(t-t_1) = \phi(t-t_1, 0)$. But $\Phi \delta(t-t_1) = \phi(t, t_1)$. This gives

$$\phi(t, t_1) = \phi(t-t_1, 0). \tag{1}$$

Thus for any pair of values of t and t_1, $\phi(t, t_1)$ depends only on the difference between these times. In this case it is convenient to denote the kernel $\phi(t, t_1)$ by $W(t-t_1)$, so that

$$x(t) = \int_{-\infty}^{\infty} W(t-t_1) u(t_1)\, dt_1 \tag{2}$$

or

$$x(t) = \int_{-\infty}^{\infty} W(\tau) u(t-\tau)\, d\tau, \tag{3}$$

changing the variable of integration t_1 to $t-\tau$. It is seen that $W(\tau)$ is the *weighting function* of the system, defined in **8.4** (5).

A particularly important property of time-invariant systems becomes evident when we find the response to an exponential input function. Thus if $u(t) = e^{\alpha t}$ then

$$x(t) = \int_{-\infty}^{\infty} W(\tau)\, e^{\alpha(t-\tau)}\, d\tau = e^{\alpha t} \int_{-\infty}^{\infty} W(\tau)\, e^{-\alpha\tau}\, d\tau.$$

The integral in this last form is independent of t and depends only on α. Thus for a given value of α the output is a constant multiple of the input. If Φ is the system operator we can write this result

$$\Phi e^{\alpha t} = F(\alpha)\, e^{\alpha t}, \tag{4}$$

where

$$F(\alpha) = \int_{-\infty}^{\infty} W(\tau)\, e^{-\alpha\tau}\, d\tau. \tag{5}$$

The function $F(\alpha)$ is in fact the bilateral Laplace transform of the weighting function $W(\tau)$.

A comparison of (4) with property (Ic) of **2.6** suggests that the operator Φ might be denoted by $F(\mathbf{D})$. We have in fact obtained in this section a definition of an operator which is a general function of the differential operator $\mathbf{D}$ and which includes as a special case the rational fraction operator considered in **2.6**.

The constant α in (4) can be complex, so that the function $F(\alpha)$ must be considered as a function of a complex variable. As was explained in **5.3**, the integral (5) defining it will converge in general in a strip of the α-plane bounded by lines parallel to the imaginary axis, in other words, if the real part of α lies within specified limits, depending on the weighting function $W(\tau)$. The definition of $F(\alpha)$ can usually be extended to other values of α by a process known as analytical continuation.† The function obtained will be regular at every point of the plane with the exception of certain singularities.

In certain cases, such as polynomials in α or exponential functions of α, $F(\alpha)$ has no finite singularities. When this happens the operator $F(\mathbf{D})$ is simple, in the sense defined in **7.2**. In other cases, such as rational fractions, $F(\alpha)$ will have a number of poles. Provided it has no other

---

† The theory of linear operators developed so far in this book has made use of no concept or technique more advanced than those of linear differential and difference equations. At this stage, however, a knowledge of the theory of functions of a complex variable becomes necessary. Accounts of this are to be found in standard textbooks; for example,

Copson, E. T., *Theory of Functions of a Complex Variable*. Oxford University Press (1935).

finite singularities we can write $F(\alpha) = P(\alpha)/Q(\alpha)$, a fraction in its lowest terms, where $P(\alpha)$ and $Q(\alpha)$ are both regular everywhere. The poles of $F(\alpha)$ will be the zeros of $Q(\alpha)$. To be consistent with the convention introduced in **2.2** we must regard the operator $F(\mathbf{D}) = P(\mathbf{D})/Q(\mathbf{D})$ as introducing a complementary function $\{1/Q(\mathbf{D})\}0$. This will take the form $\sum C_r e^{\alpha_r t}$ where $\alpha_1, \alpha_2, \ldots$ are the poles of $F(\alpha)$ (that is to say, the roots of the characteristic equation $Q(\lambda) = 0$). In other words the operator $F(\mathbf{D})$ is multiple. The general relation between the input u and the output x is given by

$$Q(\mathbf{D})x = P(\mathbf{D})u. \tag{6}$$

Since $P(\alpha)$ and $Q(\alpha)$ are regular at all finite points they can be expanded in power series convergent for all α. Equation (6) is thus a differential equation of infinite order in general. Finally, it should be noted that a *particular* weighting function will correspond to a particular solution of (6).

We have shown that, for the general operator $F(\mathbf{D})$ defined above,

$$F(\mathbf{D}) e^{\alpha t} = F(\alpha) e^{\alpha t} + F(\mathbf{D})0. \tag{7}$$

We have thus generalised property (Ic) of **2.6**. It is easily proved that property (IIc) also holds, that is,

$$F(\mathbf{D})(e^{\alpha t} u) = e^{\alpha t} F(\mathbf{D} + \alpha)u. \tag{8}$$

It is also possible to expand the operator $F(\mathbf{D})$ algebraically provided the resulting expressions converge (or give useful asymptotic expansions) and provided care is taken to avoid the introduction of spurious complementary function terms. It usually happens that the weighting function $W(\tau) = W(t - t_1)$ vanishes for negative values of the argument. This means that for any given time t the value of $x(t)$ depends only on past and not on future values of t_1. In other words the system is *non-anticipatory*. In this case (3) can be written

$$x(t) = \int_0^\infty W(\tau)u(t - \tau)\,d\tau. \tag{9}$$

We conclude this section with a number of examples of time-invariant operators together with their weighting functions. First of all we have the identity operator, which converts $u(t)$ into itself, or, in other words, multiplies it by unity. Since, from **6.3** (3),

$$u(t) = \int_{-\infty}^\infty \delta(t - t_1)u(t_1)\,dt_1, \tag{10}$$

the weighting function in this case is the unit impulse function

$$\delta(t - t_1) = \delta(\tau).$$

Differentiating (10) with respect to t it follows immediately that the operators $\mathbf{D}$, and more generally $\mathbf{D}^n$, have weighting functions $\delta'(\tau)$ and $\delta^{(n)}(\tau)$, the corresponding derivatives of the unit impulse function defined in **6.5**.

Again, since

$$u(t+T) = \int_{-\infty}^{\infty} \delta(t+T-t_1)u(t_1) \, dt_1$$

the weighting function for the operator $\mathbf{E}$ is $\delta(\tau+T)$. The forward difference operator $\mathbf{\Delta} = \mathbf{E}-1$ then has weighting function

$$\delta(\tau+T)-\delta(\tau).$$

Consider now two inverse operators. Firstly if $\mathbf{\Phi} = 1/(\mathbf{D}-\alpha)$, $W(t)$ is the general solution of the differential equation $(\mathbf{D}-\alpha)x = \delta(t)$. This is easily shown to give

$$W(\tau) = (H(\tau)+A)\,e^{\alpha\tau}.$$

This is non-anticipatory only if $A = 0$.

The inverse difference operator $\mathbf{\Phi} = 1/(\mathbf{E}-k)$ likewise has for weighting function the general solution of the difference equation $(\mathbf{E}-k)x = \delta(t)$. By expanding the inverse operator in powers of $\mathbf{E}^{-1}$ and using **13.7** (11) this is found to be

$$W(\tau) = \delta(\tau-T)+k\delta(\tau-2T)+k^2\delta(\tau-3T)+ \ldots +A(\tau)k^{\tau/T},$$

where $A(\tau)$ is an arbitrary function with period T, which again must vanish if the operator is non-anticipatory.

14.3   Combination of operators

The expression **14.1** (3) for the linear operation enables us both to classify operators and also to obtain certain general properties. The first of these that we shall derive is the relation between the kernels when two operators are multiplied together in the sense of **7.1** (2). If

$$x = \mathbf{\Phi}u = \mathbf{\Phi}_2 \,.\, \mathbf{\Phi}_1 u = \mathbf{\Phi}_2(\mathbf{\Phi}_1 u), \tag{1}$$

let ϕ, ϕ_1 and ϕ_2 be the kernels of the operators $\mathbf{\Phi}$, $\mathbf{\Phi}_1$ and $\mathbf{\Phi}_2$. Then by repeated application of **14.1** (3)

$$x(t) = \int_{t_1=-\infty}^{\infty} \phi_2(t, t_1)\int_{t_2=-\infty}^{\infty} \phi_1(t_1, t_2)u(t_2) \, dt_2 \, dt_1$$

$$= \int_{-\infty}^{\infty} \int_{-\infty}^{\infty} \phi_2(t, t_1)\phi_1(t_1, t_2)u(t_2) \, dt_1 \, dt_2.$$

Inverting the order of integration,

$$x(t) = \int_{-\infty}^{\infty} \phi(t, t_2) u(t_2) \, dt_2$$

where

$$\phi(t, t_2) = \int_{-\infty}^{\infty} \phi_2(t, t_1) \phi_1(t_1, t_2) \, dt_1.$$

Interchanging t_1 and t_2 we have the required relation

$$\phi(t, t_1) = \int_{-\infty}^{\infty} \phi_2(t, t_2) \phi_1(t_2, t_1) \, dt_2. \tag{2}$$

This can be recognised as a generalisation of the standard rule for matrix multiplication (see Appendix 13). Like a matrix product this type of operational product is not necessarily commutative. Thus in general $\mathbf{\Phi}_2 . \mathbf{\Phi}_1 u \neq \mathbf{\Phi}_1 . \mathbf{\Phi}_2 u$. There are, however, important special cases when the order in which the operations are performed can be interchanged.

We now consider the process of operational multiplication with time-invariant operators. Expressing (2) in terms of weighting functions,

$$W(t - t_1) = \int_{-\infty}^{\infty} W_2(t - t_2) W_1(t_2 - t_1) \, dt_2.$$

Putting $t - t_1 = \tau$ and $t_2 - t_1 = \tau_1$,

$$W(\tau) = \int_{-\infty}^{\infty} W_2(\tau - \tau_1) W_1(\tau_1) \, d\tau_1, \tag{3}$$

which is the ordinary convolution integral. By changing the variable from τ_1 to $\tau_2 = \tau - \tau_1$ we obtain the alternative form

$$W(\tau) = \int_{-\infty}^{\infty} W_1(\tau - \tau_2) W_2(\tau_2) \, d\tau_2. \tag{4}$$

This shows that two simple time-invariant operators are always commutative. In the special case when the operators are non-anticipatory (3) reduces to

$$W(\tau) = \int_0^{\tau} W_2(\tau - \tau_1) W_1(\tau_1) \, d\tau_1. \tag{5}$$

Expressing the operators in terms of $\mathbf{D}$ and denoting operational multiplication by a dot as above, let $\mathbf{\Phi}_1 = F_1(\mathbf{D})$ and $\mathbf{\Phi}_2 = F_2(\mathbf{D})$. Then

$$\mathbf{\Phi}_2 . \mathbf{\Phi}_1 e^{\alpha t} = \mathbf{\Phi}_2 F_1(\alpha) e^{\alpha t} = F_2(\alpha) F_1(\alpha) e^{\alpha t},$$

so that

$$F_2(\mathbf{D}) . F_1(\mathbf{D}) = F_2(\mathbf{D}) F_1(\mathbf{D}). \tag{6}$$

Thus functions of $\mathbf{D}$ can be combined operationally by algebraic multiplication. It is again immediately evident that operators of this type are commutative.

14.4 Time-variant systems

The idea of a weighting function, as developed in **14.2** for time-invariant systems, can be extended to apply to any system. For, if we put $t - t_1 = \tau$ in the general kernel ϕ, we obtain

$$\phi(t, t_1) = \phi(t, t-\tau) = W(t, \tau), \tag{1}$$

by definition. The weighting function now depends not only on the difference between t_1 and t, the times at which the input and output are related, but also on t itself. We thus have the concept of a variable weighting function. In terms of this, the relation between input and output now becomes

$$x(t) = \int_{-\infty}^{\infty} W(t, \tau)u(t-\tau)\,d\tau. \tag{2}$$

The simplest example of such an operation is when the input function $u(t)$ is multiplied by a specified function $f(t)$. It is found in this case that $W(t, \tau) = f(t)\,\delta(\tau)$. Another example of this type of operator is a polynomial in $\mathbf{D}$ with coefficients which are functions of t; also its inverse, the response from which is the solution of a linear differential equation with non-constant coefficients. The latter case could arise for example in a linear system of conventional type with time-varying parameters.

Certain of the special properties already derived for time-invariant systems can, if suitably modified, be applied to the more general systems of the present section. For example, if the input is an exponential function the output is given by

$$x(t) = \int_{-\infty}^{\infty} W(t, \tau)\,e^{\alpha(t-\tau)}\,d\tau,$$

so that $$\mathbf{\Phi}\,e^{\alpha t} = F(t, \alpha)\,e^{\alpha t} \tag{3}$$

where $$F(t, \alpha) = \int_{-\infty}^{\infty} W(t, \tau)\,e^{-\alpha\tau}\,d\tau. \tag{4}$$

Replacing α by p, the function $F(t, p)$ is seen to be the bilateral Laplace transform of $W(t, \tau)$ evaluated with respect to τ, t being regarded as a constant. Following the convention adopted earlier we can denote $\mathbf{\Phi}$ in this case by $F(t, \mathbf{D})$ so that (3) becomes

$$F(t, \mathbf{D})\,e^{\alpha t} = F(t, \alpha)\,e^{\alpha t}. \tag{5}$$

We consider now the effect of two operators applied successively. This is the process we have called operational multiplication. We saw in **14.3** (6) that with time-invariant operators this is effected by multiplying the operators algebraically. This is not the case in general. Before deriving the appropriate relation it is desirable to reiterate the conventions as to the notation we are using. If $F_1(t, \mathbf{D})$ and $F_2(t, \mathbf{D})$ are two time-variant operators $F_2(t, \mathbf{D})F_1(t, \mathbf{D})$ denotes the operator obtained by multiplying the operators, treating both t and $\mathbf{D}$ as algebraic symbols. On the other hand, $F(t, \mathbf{D}) = F_2(t, \mathbf{D}).F_1(t, \mathbf{D})$ is the operator converting u into x in the system shown in fig. 14.4(a).

FIG. 14.4(a)

In order to find this operator let $u(t) = e^{\alpha t}$. Then

$$x(t) = F_2(t, \mathbf{D}).F_1(t, \mathbf{D})\, e^{\alpha t}$$
$$= F_2(t, \mathbf{D})\{e^{\alpha t} F_1(t, \alpha)\}$$
$$= e^{\alpha t}F_2(t, \mathbf{D}+\alpha)F_1(t, \alpha),$$

using **14.2** (7) and (8). Thus

$$F(t, \alpha) = F_2(t, \mathbf{D}+\alpha)F_1(t, \alpha). \tag{6}$$

In order to express this relation operationally by replacing α by $\mathbf{D}$ we must replace the $\mathbf{D}$ already there by another symbol such as $\partial/\partial t$ to indicate that it operates only on the variable t in F_1. This gives

$$F(t, \mathbf{D}) = F_2(t, \mathbf{D}).F_1(t, \mathbf{D}) = F_2(t, \mathbf{D}+\partial/\partial t)F_1(t, \mathbf{D}). \tag{7}$$

By expanding the operator F_2 formally in powers of $\partial/\partial t$ by Taylor's theorem this important result can be written

$$F_2(t, \mathbf{D}).F_1(t, \mathbf{D}) = F_2F_1 + \frac{\partial F_2}{\partial \mathbf{D}}\frac{\partial F_1}{\partial t} + \frac{1}{2!}\frac{\partial^2 F_2}{\partial \mathbf{D}^2}\frac{\partial^2 F_1}{\partial t^2} + \dots. \tag{8}$$

In this form it is called Bourlet's operational product. It is immediately evident that operational multiplication and algebraic multiplication will be identical only if F_2 is independent of $\mathbf{D}$ or F_1 is independent of t.

An interesting special case occurs when the inner operator does not contain $\mathbf{D}$. If in (7) we replace $F_2(t, \mathbf{D})$ by $F(t, \mathbf{D})$, $F_1(t, \mathbf{D})$ by $u_1(t)$, and denote the function operated on by $u_2(t)$ we obtain

$$F(t, \mathbf{D})\{u_1(t)u_2(t)\} = F(t, \mathbf{D}_1+\mathbf{D}_2)\{u_1(t)u_2(t)\}, \tag{9}$$

where $\mathbf{D}_1$ operates on u_1 only and $\mathbf{D}_2$ on u_2 only. This relation is in fact a generalised form of the familiar formula of Leibnitz for the nth derivative of a product. The equivalent formula for a difference operator is

$$F(\mathbf{E})\{u_1u_2\} = F(\mathbf{E}_1\mathbf{E}_2)\{u_1u_2\}, \tag{10}$$

where $\mathbf{E}_1$ and $\mathbf{E}_2$ operate separately on the respective functions or sequences u_1 and u_2.

Just as we must distinguish between operational and algebraic multiplication of general linear operators, so also must we observe the differences between, and introduce special notations for, the inverses and the reciprocals of such operators. If $F(t, \mathbf{D})$ is a linear operator we shall denote its inverse by $\{F(t, \mathbf{D})\}^{-1}$ or $F^{-1}(t, \mathbf{D})$ and its reciprocal by $1/F(t, \mathbf{D})$. Then the inverse operator is defined by the relation

$$F(t, \mathbf{D}) . F^{-1}(t, \mathbf{D})u = u, \tag{11}$$

or $$F(t, \mathbf{D}) . F^{-1}(t, \mathbf{D}) = 1. \tag{12}$$

If F is given, the equation determining F^{-1} is

$$1 = FF^{-1} + \frac{\partial F}{\partial \mathbf{D}}\frac{\partial F^{-1}}{\partial t} + \frac{1}{2!}\frac{\partial^2 F}{\partial \mathbf{D}^2}\frac{\partial^2 F^{-1}}{\partial t^2} + \dots, \tag{13}$$

using (8). This is in general a differential equation of order equal to the degree of F in $\mathbf{D}$. This order may well be infinite.

An alternative and on the whole more satisfactory way of finding the inverse operator is to obtain its kernel $\phi(t, t_1)$ by solving the differential equation $F(t, \mathbf{D})\phi = \delta(t-t_1)$, using the property **14.1** (2) that the kernel is the response to a unit impulse at time t_1. For example, if $F(t, \mathbf{D}) = 1 + t\mathbf{D}$ the corresponding differential equation becomes

$$t\frac{d\phi}{dt} + \phi = \delta(t-t_1).$$

The general solution of this is easily found to be

$$\phi(t, t_1) = \{H(t-t_1) + A\}/t.$$

The weighting function $W(t, \tau)$ is then $\{H(\tau) + A\}/t$. Substitution in (4) and (5) shows that $F^{-1}(t, \mathbf{D}) = 1/(t\mathbf{D})$. It is easily verified that this expression satisfies (13). This result can be expressed differently by saying that $(1 + t\mathbf{D})^{-1}$ is equivalent to $1/(t\mathbf{D})$ and not to $1/(1 + t\mathbf{D})$. The latter operator has weighting function

$$W(t, \tau) = \frac{1}{t}\{H(\tau) + A\}e^{-\tau/t}.$$

14.5 Transform methods

The fact that a time-invariant operator can always be expressed as $F(\mathbf{D})$, with the property $F(\mathbf{D})e^{\alpha t} = F(\alpha)e^{\alpha t}$, allows all the methods described in **8.2** and **8.3**, based on harmonic response or using Fourier or Laplace transforms, to be applied to any system with an operator of this type. With this general operator the relation between the Laplace transforms of the input and output is

$$x^*(p) = F(p)u^*(p). \tag{1}$$

These techniques can be applied to a certain extent to time-variant systems. Consider a system with operator $F(t, \mathbf{D})$. With a sinusoidal input $e^{j\omega t}$ the output will be $F(t, j\omega)e^{j\omega t}$. Comparing this with **8.2** (3), we can regard $F(t, j\omega)$ as a varying harmonic response multiplier. This approach to the problem is particularly suitable when the variation of $F(t, j\omega)$ with t is slow compared with that of the input.

In order to show how Laplace transforms can be used, let the weighting function be $W(t, \tau)$. Then, by **14.4** (4), $F(t, p)$ is the transform of $W(t, \tau)$ relative to the variable τ. Also

$$x(t) = \int_{-\infty}^{\infty} W(t, \tau)u(t-\tau)\,d\tau.$$

Since this expression is a convolution integral, $x(t)$ is the inverse transform of $x^*(t, p)$ where

$$x^*(t, p) = F(t, p)u^*(p). \tag{2}$$

In fact,
$$x(t) = \frac{1}{2\pi j}\int_L x^*(t, p)\,e^{pt}\,dp, \tag{3}$$

using the symbol L to indicate the line in the p-plane along which the integral is taken. This symbol is equivalent to the limits $\gamma \pm j\infty$ used in similar integrals in Chapter 5.

This argument can be justified if we write $W(t_1, \tau)$ for $W(t, \tau)$ and treat t_1 as a fixed parameter. None of the steps is invalidated if t_1 is subsequently replaced by t.

An alternative approach using transforms is as follows. Let the input $u(t) = e^{p_1 t}$. Then $x(t) = F(t, p_1)e^{p_1 t}$. If we denote the transform of $F(t, p_1)$ relative to the variable t by $F^*(p, p_1)$ and use property (I) of **5.4**, we have

$$x^*(p) = F^*(p-p_1, p_1). \tag{4}$$

This result can be extended to any input having a transform by analysing it into exponential components, using the inverse transform. Thus

$$u(t) = \frac{1}{2\pi j} \int_L u^*(p_1) e^{p_1 t} dp_1.$$

It follows immediately from (4) that

$$x^*(p) = \frac{1}{2\pi j} \int_L F^*(p - p_1, p_1) u^*(p_1) dp_1. \tag{5}$$

When this integral is evaluated, the real parts of p and p_1 must be chosen so that p_1 and $p - p_1$ lie in the strips of convergence of the various transform integrals (see 5.3).

This formula can be confirmed in the two extreme cases as follows. First, if the system is time-invariant $F(t, \mathbf{D}) = F(\mathbf{D})$. Using 6.3 (13) we deduce that

$$F^*(p, p_1) = 2\pi \, \delta(jp) F(p_1). \tag{6}$$

With this expression for F^*, 6.3 (14) shows that (5) reduces to (1). Again, if $F(t, \mathbf{D}) = F(t)$,

$$F^*(p, p_1) = F^*(p), \tag{7}$$

the transform of $F(t)$. In this case (5) becomes

$$x^*(p) = \frac{1}{2\pi j} \int_L F^*(p - p_1) u^*(p_1) dp_1. \tag{8}$$

As might be expected (see property (VII) of 5.4), multiplication in the time domain is equivalent to convolution in the frequency domain.

If the input to a time-invariant system is sinusoidal, the output must also be sinusoidal with the same frequency, since

$$F(\mathbf{D}) e^{j\omega_1 t} = F(j\omega_1) e^{j\omega_1 t}. \tag{9}$$

On the other hand, if the system is time-variant and $u(t) = e^{j\omega_1 t}$, we deduce from (4)

$$x^*(j\omega) = F^*(j\omega - j\omega_1, j\omega_1)$$

so that instead of (9) we have

$$x(t) = F(t, \mathbf{D}) e^{j\omega_1 t} = \frac{1}{2\pi} \int_{-\infty}^{\infty} F^*(j\omega - j\omega_1, j\omega_1) e^{j\omega t} d\omega. \tag{10}$$

This shows that the response to a single sinusoidal input of frequency ω_1 includes sinusoidal components of other frequencies ω in addition to ω_1.

The condition that a sinusoidal input shall always produce a sinu-soidal output of the same frequency is sometimes taken as the basis of a definition of *linearity* of a system. Since, as we have shown, such a definition definitely excludes time-variant systems it is clearly un-necessarily restrictive.

14.6   Systems with multiple inputs and outputs

The theory of this chapter can be extended to systems having h

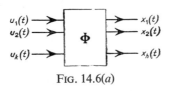

FIG. 14.6(a)

outputs $x_1(t), \ldots x_h(t)$, each of which depends linearly on k inputs $u_1(t), \ldots u_k(t)$, that is,

$$x_i(t) = \sum_{j=1}^{k} \Phi_{ij} u_j(t), \qquad i = 1, 2, \ldots h. \tag{1}$$

These relations can be expressed in matrix form (see Appendix 13) thus,

$$\begin{pmatrix} x_1(t) \\ x_2(t) \\ \cdot \\ \cdot \\ x_h(t) \end{pmatrix} = \begin{pmatrix} \Phi_{11} & \Phi_{12} & \cdots & \Phi_{1k} \\ \Phi_{21} & \Phi_{22} & \cdots & \Phi_{2k} \\ \cdot & \cdot & & \cdot \\ \cdot & \cdot & & \cdot \\ \Phi_{h1} & \Phi_{h2} & \cdots & \Phi_{hk} \end{pmatrix} \begin{pmatrix} u_1(t) \\ u_2(t) \\ \cdot \\ \cdot \\ u_k(t) \end{pmatrix}, \tag{2}$$

or $$\{x_i(t)\} = \{\Phi_{ij}\}\{u_j(t)\}, \tag{3}$$

or $$X = \Phi U, \tag{4}$$

where U and X are column matrices representing the inputs and outputs respectively and Φ is the operational matrix. Any or all of the inputs and outputs can of course be sequences instead of functions.

If the system is time-invariant, (3) becomes

$$\{x_i(t)\} = \{F_{ij}(\mathbf{D})\}\{u_j(t)\}. \tag{5}$$

If, further, the operators $F_{ij}(\mathbf{D})$ are rational and if the inputs are given, the outputs are usually given by a set of h simultaneous linear differential equations with constant coefficients

$$\{Q_{ij}(\mathbf{D})\}\{x_j(t)\} = \{P_{il}(\mathbf{D})\}\{u_l(t)\} = \{f_i(t)\},$$

or $$\sum_{j=1}^{h} Q_{ij}(\mathbf{D})x_j(t) = f_i(t), \qquad i = 1, 2, \ldots h. \tag{6}$$

To show how such a set of equations can be solved, consider as an example the equations

$$(\mathbf{D}+6)x_1 + \mathbf{D}x_2 = 3\,e^{-t}, \qquad (7)$$

$$(\mathbf{D}+8)x_1 + (2\mathbf{D}+1)x_2 = 5\,e^{-t}. \qquad (8)$$

The function x_2 can be eliminated by applying the operators $2\mathbf{D}+1$ and $\mathbf{D}$ respectively and subtracting. After simplification it is found that

$$(\mathbf{D}+2)(\mathbf{D}+3)x_1 = 2\,e^{-t}.$$

Solution by standard methods then gives

$$x_1 = e^{-t} + A\,e^{-2t} + B\,e^{-3t}.$$

A similar method can be used to show that

$$x_2 = 2\,e^{-t} + A'\,e^{-2t} + B'\,e^{-3t}.$$

The four arbitrary constants are not however independent, for it can be verified by substitution in (7) and (8) that we must have

$$A' = 2A, \qquad B' = B.$$

The general solution of these equations is, therefore,

$$x_1 = e^{-t} + A\,e^{-2t} + B\,e^{-3t}, \qquad (9)$$

$$x_2 = 2\,e^{-t} + 2A\,e^{-2t} + B\,e^{-3t}. \qquad (10)$$

Systematic methods are available for finding the solution of a general set of equations of the type (6). It is found, as in the above example, that the solution for each function $x_j(t)$ is the sum of a complementary function and a particular integral, that is,

$$x_j(t) = A_{j1}\,e^{\lambda_1 t} + \ldots + A_{jn}\,e^{\lambda_n t} + g_j(t). \qquad (11)$$

The particular integrals $g_j(t)$ can be found without undue difficulty using the operational methods described in Chapter 2. In order to find the complementary function, let $x_j(t) = A_j\,e^{\lambda t}(j = 1, \ldots h)$ be a set of solutions of the corresponding homogeneous equations

$$\sum_{j=1}^{h} Q_{ij}(\mathbf{D})x_j(t) = 0, \qquad i = 1, \ldots h.$$

Substituting and dividing by $e^{\lambda t}$, we have

$$\sum_{j=1}^{h} Q_{ij}(\lambda)A_j = 0. \qquad (12)$$

This gives a set of h simultaneous equations in the h unknowns A_j. In order that non-zero solutions may exist, λ must satisfy the *characteristic* or *determinantal equation*

$$|Q_{ij}(\lambda)| = 0, \tag{13}$$

where the left-hand side of this equation denotes the determinant a typical element of which is $Q_{ij}(\lambda)$. Then $\lambda_1, \ldots \lambda_n$ are the roots of this equation. If we now substitute a typical root λ_k in (12) we obtain the equations

$$\sum_{j=1}^{h} Q_{ij}(\lambda_k)A_{jk} = 0. \tag{14}$$

Although there are h of these equations and h unknowns, since the equations are homogeneous they are not sufficient in number to determine the constants A_{jk} uniquely. It is possible, however, to determine their ratios uniquely, so that if one of the constants is chosen arbitrarily the others will be determined. Alternatively, $h-1$ of these constants can be expressed as numerical multiples of the remaining one.

A different set of ratios will be obtained for each root λ_k. When these have been found the general solution (11) can be written down by superposition. It is seen that only n of the nh constants in (11) can be chosen arbitrarily.

If a sufficient number of initial conditions is given, a set of equations of the type (6) can be solved directly by using Laplace transforms; for if we take transforms of these equations we have

$$\sum_{j=1}^{h} Q_{ij}(p)x_j^*(p) = f_i^*(p)+q_i(p), \qquad i = 1, \ldots h, \tag{15}$$

where, as in **3.4** (2), the functions $q_i(p)$ depend on the initial values of the functions $x_j(t)$ and of their derivatives. The equations (15) are simultaneous linear algebraic equations in the functions $x_j^*(p)$ and can be solved by standard methods. It remains to express the functions $x_j^*(p)$ in partial fractions and to deduce their inverse transforms, using results obtained in **3.2**.

EXERCISES   1. Solve the equations (7) and (8) if $x_1 = x_2 = 0$ when $t = 0$.

2. Solve the equations

$$(D^2+1)x_1+2Dx_2 = 0$$
$$(2D+1)x_1+(D+2)x_2 = 12\,e^{-2t},$$

if $x_1 = x_2 = Dx_1 = 0$ when $t = 0$.

CHAPTER 15

SAMPLING SYSTEMS

15.1 Sampling operators

We turn now to a discussion of systems containing two types of elements, those that operate continuously and those that operate intermittently. The former will be electrical networks or mechanical devices having time-invariant operators that can be expressed as functions of $\mathbf{D}$, rational or otherwise. The inputs and outputs of these elements will be functions of continuous time. Elements of the other type will handle sequences, the individual values of which are associated with equally spaced values of t. The sequences may well be transmitted in the system in digital form and processed by digital devices. The latter will usually have operators which are functions of $\mathbf{E}$, provided of course that the devices are linear.

Such systems can occur in automatic control when the input is a sequence or when it is not possible to measure the error continuously. Another example is provided by communication systems which make use of pulse trains at some stage. Again, digital elements may be introduced into a system to carry out operations for which they are more effective than analogue elements. The input and output of such devices must necessarily be sequences.

In order to represent analytically the behaviour of the system as a whole we must introduce operators for converting functions of continuous time into sequences and vice versa. We shall see that by combining with operators already defined, one new operator of each type will suffice for this purpose.

Given a function $u(t)$ of continuous time and a constant time interval T we can form a sequence u_r, where u_r is by definition $u(rT)$. This operation is known as *sampling*, and will be denoted by $\mathbf{S}$, so that we write

$$u_r = \mathbf{S}u(t) = u(rT). \tag{1}$$

The operation $\mathbf{S}$ is represented graphically by drawing a series of equally spaced ordinates of the graph of $u(t)$, as shown in fig. 15.1(a). We call T the *sampling period*.

In a particular system the operation of sampling may be performed physically as an essential process of the system. Alternatively it may be considered as a mathematical operation on a particular signal carried out to determine some characteristic of the system.

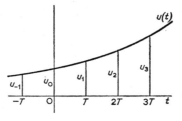

Fig. 15.1(*a*)

The simplest operation whereby a sequence u_r may be converted into a function of continuous time is that of *pulsing*, denoted by **P**. A pulsed sequence is by definition a pulse train such that for each value of r an impulse of amplitude u_r occurs at time rT. The corresponding function, shown in fig. 15.1(*b*), can be written

$$\mathbf{P}u_r = \sum_{r=-\infty}^{\infty} u_r \delta(t-rT). \tag{2}$$

Notice that between sampling instants this function has value zero.

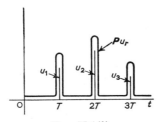

Fig. 15.1(*b*)

Since the operations represented by **S** and **P** clearly satisfy **7.1** (3), they are both linear. They are in fact special cases of **14.1** (5) and (6) with $\phi(r, t_1) = \delta(rT - t_1)$ and $\phi(t, r_1) = \delta(t - r_1 T)$ respectively.

The process of pulsing is a mathematical operation which, at best, can only be carried out approximately, physically. In many cases the characteristics of the pulses actually obtained will differ to a negligible extent from those of the ideal impulses. Account can, however, be taken of the actual pulse shape or duration by following the operation **P** by a suitable function of **D**, the latter being chosen to have a weighting function corresponding to the pulse shape.

For example, if the pulses rise instantaneously to their peak values but die away exponentially, as shown in fig. 15.1(c), a suitable combined operator might be $(1+T_1\mathbf{D})^{-1}\mathbf{P}$, where the time constant T_1 is very small.

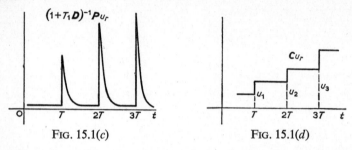

FIG. 15.1(c)   FIG. 15.1(d)

A frequently used method of introducing a sequence u_r to a continuously operating element of a system is that of *clamping*. The resulting function is defined to take the value u_r when $rT < t < (r+1)T$, for all values of r. Its graph is shown in fig. 15.1(d). The operation of clamping, which is clearly linear, is denoted by $\mathbf{C}$. The relation between u_r and $\mathbf{C}u_r$ can be expressed by means of step functions as follows.

$$\mathbf{C}u_r = \sum_r u_r\{H(t-rT)-H(t-T-rT)\}$$

$$= \sum_r u_r\nabla H(t-rT) = \nabla\frac{1}{\mathbf{D}}\sum_r u_r\delta(t-rT)$$

$$= \nabla\frac{1}{\mathbf{D}}\mathbf{P}u_r.$$

Thus $\mathbf{C} = \nabla\mathbf{D}^{-1}\mathbf{P}.$ (3)

To demonstrate the use of these operators, consider the digital to analogue converter operating as an error-controlled servo, which is shown in fig. 15.1(e).† It is assumed that the analogue output $x(t)$ is

FIG. 15.1(e)

sampled and converted into digital form and subtracted from the digital input u_r to form the error sequence c_r. The latter is subjected to a

† In order to distinguish between functions of t and sequences in flow diagrams of this type, continuous lines will be used for the former and broken lines for the latter.

difference operation $K(\mathbf{E})$ chosen by the designer to give certain desired characteristics to the system response. The next stage is to clamp. The resulting function is then fed through an amplifier to the output driving member, the combined operation being represented by $G(\mathbf{D})$. The operating equation of the system is

$$x(t) = G(\mathbf{D})\mathbf{V}\mathbf{D}^{-1}\mathbf{P}K(\mathbf{E})\{u_r - \mathbf{S}x(t)\}. \tag{4}$$

The ultimate requirement is to express $x(t)$ in terms of u_r. This cannot be done directly from (4). If, however, this equation is sampled we have

$$x_r = \mathbf{S}G(\mathbf{D})\mathbf{V}\mathbf{D}^{-1}\mathbf{P}K(\mathbf{E})(u_r - x_r). \tag{5}$$

By means of rules to be developed in the next section the operator $\mathbf{S}G(\mathbf{D})\mathbf{V}\mathbf{D}^{-1}\mathbf{P}K(\mathbf{E})$ can be reduced to a difference operator $A(\mathbf{E})$, so that (5) becomes

$$x_r = A(\mathbf{E})(u_r - x_r)$$

or

$$x_r = \frac{A(\mathbf{E})}{1 + A(\mathbf{E})} u_r. \tag{6}$$

This equation gives the values x_r of the analogue output at the sampling times as the solution of a linear difference equation. Substitution of this expression of x_r for $\mathbf{S}x(t)$ in (4) gives $x(t)$ directly in terms of u_r. It is shown in **15.3** (8) that $x(t)$ also satisfies a difference equation, from which the stability of the system may be determined. Explicit expressions for the steady state and transient can also be obtained.

15.2   Operational rules

It is our purpose in this section to show how to reduce to manageable form operators like those appearing in **15.1** (4) and (5). In addition to the elements $\mathbf{P}$ and $\mathbf{S}$ such operators will contain rational functions of $\mathbf{E}$ and rational and non-rational functions of $\mathbf{D}$. We will determine first the extent to which these operators are commutative.

Consider first the operator $\mathbf{E}$. Starting from **15.1** (1) and the formula $\mathbf{E}u(t) = u(t+T)$ we can write

$$\mathbf{S}u(t+T) = u(rT+T) = u_{r+1},$$

or

$$\mathbf{S}\mathbf{E}u(t) = \mathbf{E}\mathbf{S}u(t). \tag{1}$$

Again, from **15.1** (2) we have

$$\mathbf{P}\mathbf{E}u_r = \sum_{r=-\infty}^{\infty} \delta(t - rT)u_{r+1} = \sum_{r=-\infty}^{\infty} \delta(t + T - rT)u_r,$$

replacing r by $r-1$. Thus

$$\mathbf{P}\mathbf{E}u_r = \mathbf{E}\mathbf{P}u_r. \tag{2}$$

By extended application of (1) and (2) we can deduce that if $F(\mathbf{E})$ is a *rational* fraction in $\mathbf{E}$,

$$SF(\mathbf{E})u(t) = F(\mathbf{E})Su(t), \tag{3}$$

$$\mathbf{P}F(\mathbf{E})u_r = F(\mathbf{E})\mathbf{P}u_r, \tag{4}$$

subject only to the restriction that any complementary function term on the right-hand side of (4) must vanish between sampling times.

In addition, since $F(\mathbf{E}) = F(e^{T\mathbf{D}})$ it is time-invariant, and is therefore commutative with other time-invariant functions of $\mathbf{D}$. This is proved in **14.3**. *Rational difference operators are therefore freely commutative with* $\mathbf{S}$, $\mathbf{P}$ *and functions of* $\mathbf{D}$. This rule is subject only to certain reservations as to complementary functions. These reservations are of the same type as that given in theorem 5 of Appendix 6 and do not usually cause any inconvenience. Use of this rule enables all difference operators to be transferred to the right or to the left of any multiple operator in which they appear.

When this has been done the rest of the operator will often take the form $SF(\mathbf{D})\mathbf{P}$, or be made up of elements of this form. Now this is an operation the input and output of which are both sequences. We can therefore expect it to be equivalent to a difference operator $F_p(\mathbf{E})$. This will now be verified and rules for obtaining $F_p(\mathbf{E})$ from $F(\mathbf{D})$ will be derived.

The operation $SF(\mathbf{D})\mathbf{P}$ applied to a sequence u_r implies the following processes. First, the sequence is converted into a pulse train

$$\sum_r u_r \delta(t - rT).$$

This pulse train is passed through a network or similar continuously acting system to produce a function $x(t)$ of continuous time. Finally, this function is sampled to produce the output sequence x_r. These operations are shown in fig. 15.2(*a*).

FIG. 15.2(*a*)

Assume that $F(\mathbf{D})$ is a proper rational fraction, that is, one the degree of whose numerator is less than that of the denominator. Express $F(\mathbf{D})$ in partial fractions and apply the following process term by term. Our problem is then effectively reduced to that of expressing

$$S\{1/(\mathbf{D}+\lambda)\}\mathbf{P}$$

in terms of $\mathbf{E}$.

Since the function $x(t)$ may contain steps at the sampling times it is necessary to specify which value we shall take when sampling in this case. If t_r is any sampling time we denote by $x(t_r \pm 0)$ the limit of $x(t)$ as $t - t_r \to 0$ through positive and negative values respectively. Strictly the sampled value of $x(t)$ should be $\frac{1}{2}\{x(t_r+0)+x(t_r-0)\}$. It is, however, more convenient to take either of the two limits. Following the practice of other authors on this subject we shall take $x(t_r+0)$. This is equivalent to sampling just *after* the step occurs.

Then if
$$F(\mathbf{D}) = 1/(\mathbf{D}+\lambda),$$

$$(\mathbf{D}+\lambda)x(t) = \sum_n u_n \delta(t-nT). \tag{5}$$

Multiplying by the integrating factor $e^{\lambda t}$ (see **1.4**),

$$\mathbf{D}\{e^{\lambda t}x(t)\} = e^{\lambda t}\sum_n u_n \delta(t-nT) = \sum_n e^{\lambda nT}u_n \delta(t-nT),$$

using **6.3** (2). We now integrate both sides of this equation from $(r-1)T+0$ to $rT+0$. Using **6.3** (3) and observing that the only pulse occurring during the range of integration is the one when $t = rT$, we have

$$e^{r\lambda T}x_r - e^{(r-1)\lambda T}x_{r-1} = e^{r\lambda T}u_r. \tag{6}$$

Dividing by $e^{r\lambda T}$,

$$(1-e^{-\lambda T}\mathbf{E}^{-1})x_r = u_r,$$

so that
$$x_r = \frac{1}{1-e^{-\lambda T}\mathbf{E}^{-1}}u_r. \tag{7}$$

Notice that if $\lambda = 0$, $x_r = (1/\mathbf{V})u_r$, where $\mathbf{V}$ is the backward difference operator $1-\mathbf{E}^{-1}$. We shall find it convenient to write $e^{\lambda T}\mathbf{E} = \mathbf{E}_\lambda$ and

$$1-\mathbf{E}_\lambda^{-1} = \mathbf{V}_\lambda. \tag{8}$$

We call $\mathbf{V}_\lambda$ an *attenuating difference*. The following key results are therefore obtained:

$$\mathbf{S}\frac{1}{\mathbf{D}}\mathbf{P} = \frac{1}{\mathbf{V}}, \tag{9}$$

$$\mathbf{S}\frac{1}{\mathbf{D}+\lambda}\mathbf{P} = \frac{1}{\mathbf{V}_\lambda}. \tag{10}$$

For a partial fraction of $F(\mathbf{D})$ with a quadratic denominator we use the formula

$$\mathbf{S}\frac{\alpha\mathbf{D}+\beta}{(\mathbf{D}+\mu)^2+v^2}\mathbf{P} = \frac{\alpha v - \mathbf{E}_\mu^{-1}\{\alpha v \cos vT + (\alpha\mu-\beta)\sin vT\}}{v(1-2\mathbf{E}_\mu^{-1}\cos vT + \mathbf{E}_\mu^{-2})}. \tag{11}$$

This follows after some reduction if (10) is applied after the operator on the left-hand side of (11) has been split into partial fractions with complex linear denominators.

Repeated linear factors in the denominator are dealt with by differentiating both sides of (10) partially one or more times with respect to λ, using the formula

$$\frac{\partial \mathbf{V}_\lambda}{\partial \lambda} = T e^{-\lambda T} \mathbf{E}^{-1} = T(1 - \mathbf{V}_\lambda). \tag{12}$$

It follows that

$$\mathbf{S}\frac{1}{(\mathbf{D}+\lambda)^n}\mathbf{P} = K_n(\mathbf{V}_\lambda) \tag{13}$$

where

$$nK_{n+1}(\mathbf{V}_\lambda) = -T(1-\mathbf{V}_\lambda)K_n'(\mathbf{V}_\lambda). \tag{14}$$

We deduce successively that

$$K_2(\mathbf{V}_\lambda) = T(\mathbf{V}_\lambda^{-2} - \mathbf{V}_\lambda^{-1}), \tag{15}$$

$$K_3(\mathbf{V}_\lambda) = \tfrac{1}{2}T^2(2\mathbf{V}_\lambda^{-3} - 3\mathbf{V}_\lambda^{-2} + \mathbf{V}_\lambda^{-1}), \tag{16}$$

$$K_4(\mathbf{V}_\lambda) = \tfrac{1}{6}T^3(6\mathbf{V}_\lambda^{-4} - 12\mathbf{V}_\lambda^{-3} + 7\mathbf{V}_\lambda^{-2} - \mathbf{V}_\lambda^{-1}). \tag{17}$$

An important special case of (13) is

$$\mathbf{S}\frac{1}{\mathbf{D}^n}\mathbf{P} = K_n(\mathbf{V}). \tag{18}$$

Finally in this section we consider the effect of elements in cascade. If two networks with operators $F(\mathbf{D})$ and $G(\mathbf{D})$ are separated by a

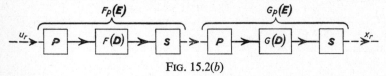

Fig. 15.2(b)

sampling and a pulsing unit as in fig. 15.2(b), the corresponding difference operators can be combined by multiplication to give

$$x_r = G_p(\mathbf{E})F_p(\mathbf{E})u_r.$$

If, however, the networks are connected directly as in fig. 15.2(c), the

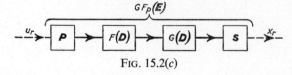

Fig. 15.2(c)

overall operator is not $G_p(\mathbf{E})F_p(\mathbf{E})$. It is in fact obtained by expressing $G(\mathbf{D})F(\mathbf{D})$ in partial fractions and applying (10) or derived formulae.

The overall operator can be denoted by $GF_p(\mathbf{E})$. These two results can be expressed symbolically as follows:

$$SG(\mathbf{D})\mathbf{P}SF(\mathbf{D})\mathbf{P} = G_p(\mathbf{E})F_p(\mathbf{E}), \tag{19}$$

$$SG(\mathbf{D})F(\mathbf{D})\mathbf{P} = GF_p(\mathbf{E}). \tag{20}$$

15.3 Delayed sampling

We consider in this section the system shown in fig. 15.2(a) in which the final sampling operation is delayed by a time sT, where $0 \leq s < 1$. This not only enables us to study systems in which the various sampling and pulsing operations are not synchronised; by allowing s to vary we can also determine the response of systems between sampling instants. If $x(rT+sT)$ is denoted by x_{r+s} we can write formally

$$x_{r+s} = SE^s F(\mathbf{D})\mathbf{P}u_r = F_p(\mathbf{E}, s)u_r. \tag{1}$$

In the special case where $F(\mathbf{D}) = 1/(\mathbf{D}+\lambda)$, $x(t)$ is still given by the differential equation **15.2** (5), but instead of the solution **15.2** (6) we now use

$$e^{(r+s)\lambda T}x_{r+s} - e^{(r+s-1)\lambda T}x_{r+s-1} = e^{\lambda rT}u_r,$$

whence

$$x_{r+s} = \frac{e^{-\lambda sT}}{\nabla_\lambda}u_r. \tag{2}$$

Otherwise stated,

$$SE^s\frac{1}{\mathbf{D}+\lambda}\mathbf{P} = \frac{e^{-\lambda sT}}{\nabla_\lambda}. \tag{3}$$

For a lag outside the range 0 to T, say $(m+s)T$, where m is a positive or negative integer and $0 \leq s < 1$, the corresponding operator is

$$e^{-\lambda sT}\mathbf{E}^m/\nabla_\lambda.$$

If the factor $\mathbf{D}+\lambda$ is repeated, the corresponding difference operator can again be found by differentiation with respect to λ. In general, using property (IIa) of **2.2**, we have

$$\begin{aligned}
SE^s\frac{1}{(\mathbf{D}+\lambda)^n}\mathbf{P} &= \frac{(-)^{n-1}}{(n-1)!}\left(\frac{\partial}{\partial\lambda}\right)^{n-1}\left(e^{-\lambda sT}\frac{1}{\nabla_\lambda}\right) \\
&= \frac{(-)^{n-1}e^{-\lambda sT}}{(n-1)!}\left(\frac{\partial}{\partial\lambda}-sT\right)^{n-1}\frac{1}{\nabla_\lambda} \\
&= e^{-\lambda sT}\sum_{k=0}^{n-1}\frac{(sT)^k}{k!}K_{n-k}(\nabla_\lambda), \tag{4}
\end{aligned}$$

expanding the binomial operator, substituting **15.2** (10) and (13) and simplifying. For $n = 2$ and $n = 3$ this gives

$$\mathbf{SE}^s \frac{1}{(\mathbf{D}+\lambda)^2}\mathbf{P} = T\,e^{-\lambda sT}\{\nabla_\lambda^{-2}-(1-s)\nabla_\lambda^{-1}\}, \tag{5}$$

$$\mathbf{SE}^s \frac{1}{(\mathbf{D}+\lambda)^3}\mathbf{P} = \tfrac{1}{2}T^2\,e^{-\lambda sT}\{2\nabla_\lambda^{-3}-(3-2s)\nabla_\lambda^{-2}+(1-s)^2\nabla_\lambda^{-1}\}. \tag{6}$$

It is apparent from (3) and (4) that, in the general case, $F_p(\mathbf{E}, s)$ is a rational fraction in $\mathbf{E}$ whose denominator is independent of s. We can therefore write

$$x_{r+s} = F_p(\mathbf{E}, s)u_r = \frac{P(\mathbf{E}, s)}{Q(\mathbf{E})}u_r. \tag{7}$$

This shows that the unsampled output $x(t)$ of the system shown in

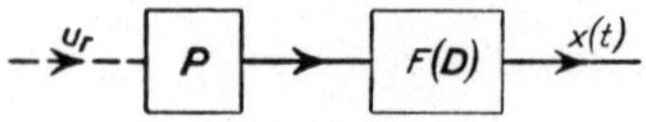

FIG. 15.3(a)

fig. 15.3(a) satisfies the difference equation

$$Q(\mathbf{E})x(t) = P(\mathbf{E}, s)u_r. \tag{8}$$

As was shown in Chapter 13 the condition for stability is that the zeros of the polynomial $Q(\kappa)$ shall all lie inside the unit circle.

In order to determine the transient and steady state response of a stable system we must first solve the difference equation giving x_r. Putting $s = 0$ in (7), this becomes

$$Q(\mathbf{E})x_r = P(\mathbf{E})u_r. \tag{9}$$

where $P(\mathbf{E}, 0)$ is denoted by $P(\mathbf{E})$. The solution is

$$x_r = X_r + \sum_q A_q \kappa_q^{\,r}, \tag{10}$$

where the sequence X_r is a particular solution, κ_q is a zero of $Q(\kappa)$ and A_q is an arbitrary constant to be determined by initial conditions. The summation extends over all the zeros of $Q(\kappa)$.

The general solution is derived from (10) using the formula

$$x_{r+s} = \frac{P(\mathbf{E}, s)}{P(\mathbf{E})}x_r, \tag{11}$$

which follows from (7) and (9). Notice that, in order that x_{r+s} shall equal x_r when $s = 0$, no complementary function terms should be included in (11), either from the operator $P(\mathbf{E})$ or from $Q(\mathbf{E})$. Substituting for x_r from (10) in (11) and using **13.3** (15), we have

$$x_{r+s} = \frac{P(\mathbf{E}, s)}{P(\mathbf{E})} X_r + \sum_q A_q \frac{P(\kappa_q, s)}{P(\kappa_q)} \kappa_q{}^r. \tag{12}$$

15.4 Sampling servos

Fig. 15.4(a) shows a servo with an intermittent input and a continuous output, in which the error sequence is pulsed, before being fed to a

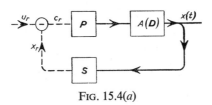

Fig. 15.4(a)

smoothing amplifier and thence to the motor. Let the combined operator of the latter be $A(\mathbf{D})$. We shall show how the main characteristics of the response of the system can be determined.

The governing equation is

$$x(t) = A(\mathbf{D})P(u_r - x_r) = A(\mathbf{D})Pc_r, \tag{1}$$

where c_r is the error sequence. Let

$$\mathbf{S}A(\mathbf{D})P = A_p(\mathbf{E}) = \frac{P(\mathbf{E})}{R(\mathbf{E})}. \tag{2}$$

Then by sampling (1) we have

$$x_r = A_p(\mathbf{E})(u_r - x_r) = A_p(\mathbf{E})c_r,$$

or

$$x_r = \frac{A_p(\mathbf{E})}{1 + A_p(\mathbf{E})} u_r = \frac{P(\mathbf{E})}{Q(\mathbf{E})} u_r, \tag{3}$$

where

$$Q(\mathbf{E}) = P(\mathbf{E}) + R(\mathbf{E}). \tag{4}$$

By solving the characteristic equation $Q(\kappa) = 0$ the stability and the nature of the transient response can be determined. The steady state response can be obtained from (3) using operational methods, as in **13.3**. A particularly useful procedure is to express the operator in (3) in terms of $\mathbf{V}$ and then expand in powers of $\mathbf{V}$. This process is analogous to that described in **8.1** and **10.2** and yields relatively easily the nature of the steady state error at the sampling instants for different general types of the input sequence u_r.

In many applications this is all that is required. If, however, information about the response between sampling instants is desired, it can be determined by applying the operation of delayed sampling to (1) and using the method of the last section. This gives

$$x_{r+s} = \frac{P(\mathbf{E}, s)}{R(\mathbf{E})} c_r = \frac{P(\mathbf{E}, s)}{P(\mathbf{E})} x_r, \tag{5}$$

where
$$\mathbf{SE}^s A(\mathbf{D})\mathbf{P} = A_p(\mathbf{E}, s) = \frac{P(\mathbf{E}, s)}{R(\mathbf{E})}. \tag{6}$$

Application of **15.3** (12) then gives both steady state and transient responses for all values of t.

As an example consider a system for which

$$A(\mathbf{D}) = \frac{K}{\mathbf{D}(\mathbf{D}+\lambda)} = \frac{K}{\lambda}\left(\frac{1}{\mathbf{D}} - \frac{1}{\mathbf{D}+\lambda}\right). \tag{7}$$

Applying **15.2** (9) and (10) we have

$$A_p(\mathbf{E}) = \frac{K}{\lambda}\left(\frac{1}{\nabla} - \frac{1}{\nabla_\lambda}\right), \tag{8}$$

or, more generally, from **15.3** (3),

$$A_p(\mathbf{E}, s) = \frac{K}{\lambda}\left(\frac{1}{\nabla} - \frac{e^{-\lambda sT}}{\nabla_\lambda}\right). \tag{9}$$

Putting $\nabla = 1-\mathbf{E}^{-1}$ and $\nabla_\lambda = 1-\mathbf{E}^{-1}e^{-\lambda T}$ and simplifying, (8) and (9) give

$$P(\mathbf{E}) = K\mathbf{E}(1-e^{-\lambda T}), \tag{10}$$

$$P(\mathbf{E}, s) = K\mathbf{E}\{\mathbf{E}-e^{-\lambda T}-e^{-\lambda sT}(\mathbf{E}-1)\}, \tag{11}$$

$$R(\mathbf{E}) = \lambda(\mathbf{E}-1)(\mathbf{E}-e^{-\lambda T}). \tag{12}$$

The characteristic equation is therefore

$$Q(\kappa) \equiv K\kappa(1-e^{-\lambda T}) + \lambda(\kappa-1)(\kappa-e^{-\lambda T}) = 0. \tag{13}$$

It is found, using **13.4** (4), that the two zeros of $Q(\kappa)$ lie in the unit circle if

$$K(1-e^{-\lambda T}) < 2\lambda(1+e^{-\lambda T}),$$

or
$$K < 2\lambda \coth \tfrac{1}{2}\lambda T. \tag{14}$$

This limitation on the gain K is the condition for stability.

Now $$x_r = \frac{A_p(\mathbf{E})}{1+A_p(\mathbf{E})}u_r = \frac{K(\mathbf{V}_\lambda-\mathbf{V})}{\lambda\mathbf{V}\mathbf{V}_\lambda+K(\mathbf{V}_\lambda-\mathbf{V})}u_r.$$

By putting $\mathbf{V}_\lambda = 1-e^{-\lambda T}(1-\mathbf{V})$ and expanding in ascending powers of $\mathbf{V}$, we deduce

$$x_r = u_r - \frac{\lambda}{K}\nabla u_r + \dots \tag{15}$$

There is therefore a steady state error even when the first differences of the input are constant.

Between sampling instants we have from **15.3** (11) and from (10) and (11) above

$$x_{r+s} = \frac{P(\mathbf{E},s)}{P(\mathbf{E})}x_r = x_r + \frac{1-e^{-\lambda sT}}{1-e^{-\lambda T}}\Delta x_r, \tag{16}$$

after some rearrangement. By allowing s to vary it is seen that $x(t)$ varies

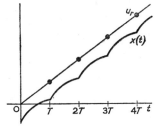

FIG. 15.4(*b*)

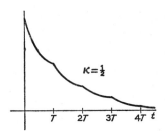

FIG 15.4(*c*)

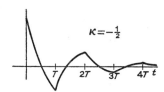

FIG. 15.4(*d*)

exponentially from one value of the sequence x_r to the next. This is true for the steady state and the individual transient terms as well as for the general solution. Figs. 15.4(*b*), (*c*) and (*d*) show this for the steady state response to an input with constant first differences and for transients in which $\kappa = \frac{1}{2}$ and $\kappa = -\frac{1}{2}$ respectively. The periodic component in the response which is characteristic of sampling systems is sometimes called *ripple*.

As a second example consider the servo shown in fig. 15.4(e). Here the error sequence c_r is processed by a difference operator $G(E)$ to form another sequence which is clamped. The resulting signal is assumed to

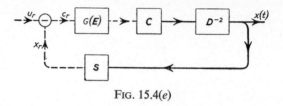

Fɪɢ. 15.4(e)

be proportional to the torque produced by the motor. Our problem is to choose $G(E)$ to give prescribed characteristics both to the steady state and the transient response. The governing equation of the system is then

$$x(t) = \frac{1}{D^2}CG(E)(u_r - x_r) = \frac{V}{D^3}PG(E)(u_r - x_r). \qquad (17)$$

Sampling and using **15.2** (16), the error sequence is given by

$$u_r - c_r = \tfrac{1}{2}T^2\frac{2 - 3V + V^2}{V^2}G(E)c_r.$$

If $G(E) = A(V)/B(V)$, a rational fraction in V, we have

$$c_r = \frac{V^2B(V)}{V^2B(V) + \tfrac{1}{2}T^2A(V)(2 - 3V + V^2)}u_r. \qquad (18)$$

The characteristic equation is obtained by replacing V by $1 - \kappa^{-1}$ in the denominator and equating the resulting expression to zero. The operators $A(V)$ and $B(V)$ must then be chosen to give stability. Assume that these operators take the forms $A(V) = K(1 + aV)$ and $B(V) = 1 + bV$. Expanding the operator in (18) we have

$$c_r = \frac{1}{KT^2}\{V^2u_r + (b - a + \tfrac{3}{2})V^3u_r + \dots\}.$$

There will therefore be a constant steady state error at sampling instants if the second differences of the input sequence are constant, while there will be no error if the first differences are constant.

The features of the transient response, such as the settling time and the extent to which it is oscillatory, are determined by the roots of the characteristic equation. After some simplification this can be written

$$(\kappa - 1)^2(\kappa + b\kappa - b) + \tfrac{1}{2}KT^2(\kappa + a\kappa - a)(\kappa + 1) = 0, \qquad (19)$$

which is a cubic in κ. By giving the three constant K, a and b suitable values, the roots can be chosen arbitrarily, thus giving the system a specified transient performance. For example, if the equation is to have three equal roots α where $0 < \alpha < 1$, it will take the form

$$(\kappa - \alpha)^3 = 0. \tag{20}$$

By expanding (19) and (20) and equating coefficients, three equations are obtained which can be solved for K, a and b. This type of system, first proposed by Holt-Smith, Lawden and Bailey,† introduces a form of smoothing which they called *staleness weighting*.

Since in any sampling interval the output is generated by double integration of a constant, its graph must be made up of parabolic segments. Moreover, since the clamped error signal will always be finite, the gradient of the graph will be continuous at the sampling instants. This is in contrast with the first example in which, as figs. 15.4(b), (c) and (d) show, the derivative of the output has discontinuities.

It is possible to estimate the performance of a sampling servo in general terms by using methods similar to those of Chapter 10; for if the sampled error and output sequences are related by the operator $A(\mathbf{E})$ we have

$$x_r = A(\mathbf{E})c_r, \tag{21}$$

where

$$c_r = u_r - x_r. \tag{22}$$

Now the operator $A(\mathbf{E})$ can be expressed in a form analogous to that of $A(\mathbf{D})$ in **10.1** (4). Thus

$$A(\mathbf{E}) = \frac{KP(\mathbf{V})}{\mathbf{V}^\sigma R(\mathbf{V})}, \tag{23}$$

where $P(0) = R(0) = 1$ and σ is a positive integer called the *order* of the system. Also if $A(\mathbf{E})$ is expressed as a fraction whose numerator and denominator contain only *positive* powers of $\mathbf{E}$, the degree of the former can never exceed the degree of the latter in a non-anticipatory system.

Stability and transient response will be determined by the zeros of the function $F(\kappa) = 1 + A(\kappa)$. The steady state error sequence is given by

$$c_r = \frac{1}{1 + A(\mathbf{E})} u_r = \frac{1}{K} \mathbf{V}^\sigma u_r + \ldots, \tag{24}$$

expanding in ascending powers of $\mathbf{V}$ by a process analogous to that used to obtain **10.2** (3). It is apparent that there will be no steady state error

† Holt-Smith, C., Lawden, D. F. and Bailey, A. E., "Characteristics of Sampling Servo Systems". *Proc. D.S.I.R. Conference on Automatic Control* (edited by A. Tustin). Butterworth (London, 1952).

at sampling instants if the differences of order σ of the input sequence u_r are all zero. This will be the case in particular if $u_r = Su(t)$ where $D^\sigma u(t)$ is zero.

Graphical methods can be used to investigate stability. For if C is the circle $|\kappa| = 1$ in the κ-plane, let Z_C, P_C, Z_C', and P_C' be the numbers of zeros and poles of $F(\kappa)$ inside and outside C respectively. Observe that the factor $\mathbf{V}^\sigma$ in the denominator of $A(\mathbf{E})$ gives a factor $(\kappa - 1)^\sigma$ in the denominator of $F(\kappa)$ and therefore a pole of order σ at the point $\kappa = 1$ on C. Then, since the numerator and denominator of $F(\kappa)$ have the same degree,

$$Z_C + Z_C' = P_C + P_C' + \sigma. \tag{25}$$

Also, using an extension of **9.2** (3),

$$[\text{ang } F(\kappa)]_C = 2\pi(Z_C - P_C - \tfrac{1}{2}\sigma).$$

Now $\kappa = e^{j\theta}$ on C; also the zeros and poles of $F(\kappa)$ are real or are conjugate complex numbers. Therefore by symmetry,

$$[\text{ang } F(\kappa)]_C = 2\left[\text{ang } F(e^{j\theta})\right]_{\theta=0}^{\pi}.$$

If this angle is $2L$ right angles we have

$$L = 2(Z_C - P_C) - \sigma. \tag{26}$$

Thus from (25) and (26) we deduce

$$L = 2(P_C' - Z_C') + \sigma, \tag{27}$$

corresponding to **10.5** (4). But for stability, $Z_C' = 0$. If in addition we have $P_C' = 0$, the necessary and sufficient condition for stability becomes

$$L = \sigma. \tag{28}$$

In order to determine L we plot $A(e^{j\theta})$ and observe the number of right angles through which the line IP turns, I being the point -1 and P a point which moves along the locus from the point $\theta = 0$ to $\theta = \pi$. This locus is of course the analogue of the Nyquist diagram. Like the latter, as $\theta \to 0$ it tends to infinity in a direction depending on the order σ of the system. As $\theta \to \pi$ it tends to a point on the real axis; this is, however, not the origin in general.

15.5　Transform methods

Transformation methods, as applied to systems that operate continuously throughout, can be extended to cover systems that contain sampling elements. With these methods, functions of continuous time will be represented by their Laplace or Fourier transforms while sequences will be represented by z-transforms. Operations on the former will be effected by multiplying by functions of p while operations on the latter will correspond to multiplication by functions of z. In order to complete the set of necessary rules we must find the transform equivalents of the operations of sampling and pulsing.

Considering the latter first, let the sequence u_r have z-transform $u°(z)$. Then

$$u°(z) = \sum_r u_r z^{-r}.$$

Since

$$\mathbf{P}u_r = \sum_r u_r \delta(t - rT),$$

we have

$$\mathfrak{L}\mathbf{P}u_r = \sum_r u_r e^{-rpT} = u°(e^{pT}). \tag{1}$$

Again, if $u(t)$ has Laplace transform $u^*(p)$,

$$u(t) = u^*(\mathbf{D})\delta(t) = u^*(\mathbf{D})\mathbf{P}\delta_r,$$

so that

$$\mathbf{S}u(t) = \mathbf{S}u^*(\mathbf{D})\mathbf{P}\delta_r = u_p^*(\mathbf{E})\delta_r,$$

using the notation introduced in **13.5** and **15.2**. Thus, using **13.5** (10), we have

$$\mathfrak{Z}\mathbf{S}u(t) = u_p^*(z). \tag{2}$$

By combining (1) and (2) we have the result

$$\mathfrak{L}\mathbf{P}\mathbf{S}u(t) = u_p^*(e^{pT}). \tag{3}$$

An important special case of (3) is

$$\mathfrak{F}\mathbf{P}\mathbf{S}u(t) = u_p^*(e^{j\omega T}). \tag{4}$$

Observe that if $\Omega = 2\pi/T$, the sampling frequency, then

$$e^{j(\omega + \Omega)T} = e^{j\omega T + 2\pi j} = e^{j\omega T}.$$

The Fourier transform of a pulsed sequence is therefore a periodic function of ω with period Ω. In other words, a function consisting of a train of impulses in the time domain is periodic in the frequency domain. If we recall the reciprocal nature of a function and its Fourier transform, this property corresponds to the one which allows a periodic function in the time domain to be expanded in a Fourier series. This, as is shown in **6.3** (8) and (9), means that the Fourier transform is a sequence of impulses.

A direct relation between $u^*(p)$ and $u(e_n^{*j\omega T})$ can be found as follows. Consider the train of unit impulses

$$\delta_T(t) = \sum_{r = -\infty}^{\infty} \delta(t - rT). \tag{5}$$

This is a periodic function with period T. We shall find a Fourier series for it in the form

$$\delta_T(t) = \sum_{n=-\infty}^{\infty} c_n e^{jn\Omega t}.$$

Using **4.3** (2) and **6.3** (3) and the fact that $\delta_T(t) = \delta(t)$ when $\frac{1}{2}T < t < \frac{1}{2}T$, the coefficients c_n are given by

$$c_n = \frac{1}{T}\int_{-\frac{1}{2}T}^{\frac{1}{2}T} \delta_T(t)\, e^{-jn\Omega t}\, dt = \frac{1}{T}\int_{-\frac{1}{2}T}^{\frac{1}{2}T} \delta(t)\, e^{-jn\Omega t}\, dt = \frac{1}{T}.$$

Thus
$$\delta_T(t) = \frac{1}{T}\sum_{n=-\infty}^{\infty} e^{jn\Omega t}. \tag{6}$$

As in **6.3**, the difficulties associated with the non-convergence of this series can be overcome by the use of more advanced methods of summation. If this result is accepted we can proceed as follows.

$$\mathbf{P}Su(t) = \sum_r u_r\, \delta(t-rT) = u(t)\,\delta_T(t) = \frac{1}{T}\sum_n u(t)\, e^{jn\Omega t}.$$

Taking Laplace transforms,

$$u_p^*(e^{pT}) = \frac{1}{T}\sum_{n=-\infty}^{\infty} u^*(p-jn\Omega), \tag{7}$$

using property (I) of **5.4**. For Fourier transforms the equivalent result is

$$u_p^*(e^{j\omega T}) = \frac{1}{T}\sum_{n=-\infty}^{\infty} u^*\{j(\omega-n\Omega)\}. \tag{8}$$

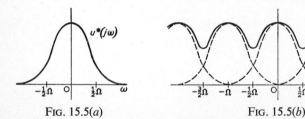

FIG. 15.5(*a*)   FIG. 15.5(*b*)

Figs. 15.5(*a*) and (*b*) show graphs of the Fourier transforms of $u(t)$ and $\mathbf{P}Su(t)$ and the way in which the latter is derived from the former. The dotted curves in fig. 15.5(*b*), which represent the individual terms of the summation in (8), are identical in shape with the curve in fig. 15.5(*a*). The transform of the pulse train is therefore formed by adding the functions represented by the dotted curves.

One consequence of (8) that is immediately apparent from the graphs is that if $u(t)$ contains no harmonic component with frequency exceeding $\frac{1}{2}\Omega$ then $u_p^*(e^{j\omega T}) = u^*(j\omega)$ when $-\frac{1}{2}\Omega < \omega < \frac{1}{2}\Omega$. It follows that if the pulse train is passed through an ideal low-pass filter whose band width is $\frac{1}{2}\Omega$ the original function $u(t)$ will be reproduced. In other words, if a given signal contains no sinusoidal component with frequency exceeding Ω_1, complete knowledge of the signal is preserved on samp-ling, provided the sampling period does not exceed π/Ω_1.

In the special case where $u(t)$ is sinusoidal with frequency ω_1 we have

$$\mathbf{PS}\, e^{j\omega_1 t} = e^{j\omega_1 t}\delta_T(t) = \frac{1}{T}\sum_n e^{j(\omega_1 + n\Omega)t}. \tag{9}$$

Alternatively, in terms of Fourier transforms, if $u(t) = e^{j\omega_1 t}$ then $u^*(j\omega) = 2\pi\,\delta(\omega - \omega_1)$, so that

$$u_p^*(e^{j\omega T}) = \Omega\sum_n \delta(\omega - \omega_1 - n\Omega). \tag{10}$$

Either of these results shows that the effect of sampling and pulsing a purely sinusoidal function is to introduce an infinite number of sinu-soidal sidebands with equal amplitudes but with frequencies in arith-metical progression, the common difference being Ω. As was shewn in **14.5**, the introduction of sinusoidal components with frequencies not present in the input function $u(t)$ is characteristic of time-variant opera-tions, of which the operation **PS** is of course an example.

The basic formulae (1) and (2) of this section can be used to obtain relations connecting the Laplace, Fourier or z-transforms of the input and output of any sampling system. Consider for example the servo shown in fig. 15.4(a). The basic equations are

$$x(t) = A(\mathbf{D})\mathbf{P}c_r, \tag{11}$$

where

$$c_r = \frac{1}{1 + A_p(\mathbf{E})}u_r. \tag{12}$$

Taking transforms and using (1)

$$x^*(p) = A(p)c^\circ(e^{pT}), \tag{13}$$

where

$$c^\circ(z) = \frac{u^\circ(z)}{1 + A_p(z)}. \tag{14}$$

Substituting, we have

$$x^*(p) = \frac{A(p)u^\circ(e^{pT})}{1 + A_p(e^{pT})}. \tag{15}$$

The inverse transform $x(t)$ of this function of p can be found by one of two methods. First, using (7) we can express $A_p(e^{pT})$ in terms of $A(p)$, and $u^\circ(e^{pT})$ in terms of an equivalent function. If a finite number of terms of the series in (7) is used the resulting approximation to $x^*(p)$ will be a rational function of p. The corresponding approximation ot

$x(t)$ can then be found by the methods of Chapter 3. This method is practicable only if the infinite series involved converge so rapidly that an adequate approximation is given in Ω in each case by a small number of terms.

The alternative method is to express $x^*(p)$ in partial fractions. Since $x^*(p)$ has an infinite number of poles the number of these fractions will be infinite; the process of determining them is involved but not impracticable. The resulting terms, when transformed into functions of t, can be grouped to form generalised Fourier series for the transient and steady state response.

A more restricted but much more manageable problem is to determine the harmonic content of the ripple in the output in conditions for which the error sequence c_r is constant. Consider for example the above system with $A(\mathbf{D}) = K/\{\mathbf{D}(\mathbf{D}+\lambda)\}$. It was shown in **15.4** (15) that the error sequence $c_r = u_r - x_r = (\lambda/K)\nabla u_r + \dots$. It follows that c_r is constant when the first differences of the input are constant. Substitution in (11) gives

$$x(t) = A(\mathbf{D})c_r\delta_T(t) = \frac{Kc_r}{T\mathbf{D}(\mathbf{D}+\lambda)} \sum_{n=-\infty}^{\infty} e^{jn\Omega t}.$$

The non-periodic part of the output is obtained from the constant term in the series and is

$$\frac{Kc_r}{T\mathbf{D}(\mathbf{D}+\lambda)}1 = \frac{Kc_r}{T}(\lambda+\mathbf{D})^{-1}t = \frac{Kc_r}{\lambda T}\left(t-\frac{1}{\lambda}\right) = \frac{\nabla u_r}{T}\left(t-\frac{1}{\lambda}\right),$$

expanding the operator as in example 8 of **2.3**. If the input sequence is obtained by sampling a constant velocity input at then $\nabla u_r = aT$, so that the above expression is $at-a/\lambda$. The mean steady state error is therefore a/λ.

The ripple is given by

$$\frac{\lambda a}{\mathbf{D}(\mathbf{D}+\lambda)} \sum_{n=1}^{\infty} (e^{jn\Omega t}+e^{-jn\Omega t}) = \sum_{n=1}^{\infty} \frac{2\lambda a}{\mathbf{D}(\mathbf{D}+\lambda)} \cos n\Omega t.$$

Using again the methods of **2.3**, we have after some manipulation,

$$x(t) = at-\frac{a}{\lambda}+\frac{2\lambda a}{\Omega} \sum_{n=1}^{\infty} \frac{\lambda \sin n\Omega t-n\Omega \cos n\Omega t}{n(n^2\Omega^2+\lambda^2)}. \tag{16}$$

The amplitude of the nth harmonic of the ripple is

$$\frac{2a\lambda}{n\Omega\sqrt{(n^2\Omega^2+\lambda^2)}}.$$

With given values of λ and Ω this expression shows clearly the extent to which harmonics introduced by the sampling process remain in the output.

CHAPTER 16

INTERPOLATION SYSTEMS

16.1 Interpolation formulae

The problem of interpolation in its most general form is as follows. If a function $u(t)$ is given for a sequence of values of the independent variable t, we have to estimate the value of the function for other values of t. We assume here that the values of t for which u is given are equally spaced and that the common difference is T. Then we are in fact given the sequence u_r where $u_r = u(rT)$ for a sequence of integral values of r, the sequence being finite or infinite. Our problem is to determine $u(rT+sT)$, where s can be any number, not necessarily an integer. This value of u will be denoted by u_{r+s}.

The most common method of interpolation is effected by assuming that $u(t)$ varies linearly in the interval $rT \leq t \leq (r+1)T$. This gives

$$u_{r+s} = u_r + s(u_{r+1} - u_r) = (1-s)u_r + su_{r+1}. \tag{1}$$

This is referred to as linear interpolation or interpolation by proportional parts and is adequate in many applications, provided T is sufficiently small. However, there are many other situations where more elaborate formulae must be used. The usual way of obtaining these is to fit a polynomial of higher degree to a convenient number of consecutive points of the sequence u_r. We now show how this can be done.

The general polynomial in s of degree n contains $n+1$ disposable constants. It can therefore be made to fit $n+1$ values of the sequence u_r. Then if these values are $u_r, u_{r+1}, \ldots u_{r+n}$ we require the polynomial which takes the value u_{r+k} when $s = k$, for $k = 0, 1, \ldots n$. Consider the polynomial of degree n,

$$s(s-1)(s-2)\ldots(s-k+1)(s-k-1)\ldots(s-n). \tag{2}$$

Using the factorial notation defined in **13.1** (4) this can be written $s^{(k)}(s-k-1)^{(n-k)}$ or $s^{(n+1)}/(s-k)$. It clearly vanishes when $s = 0, 1, \ldots$ $k-1, k+1, \ldots n$ and takes the value $(-)^{n-k}k!(n-k)!$ when $s = k$. It follows from this that the polynomial

$$u_{r+s} = \sum_{k=0}^{n} \frac{(-)^{n-k}s^{(n+1)}u_{r+k}}{k!(n-k)!(s-k)} \tag{3}$$

satisfies the required conditions. This is *Lagrange's interpolation formula*. Observe that, even though it uses $n+1$ values of the sequence u_r, it can in special cases have degree less than n. To take an extreme case, if the first differences of u_r are constant the interpolation formula will be linear, however many values of the sequence are used.

An alternative approach is to write

$$u_{r+s} = E^s u_r = (1+\Delta)^s u_r.$$

The operator is now expanded, using the binomial theorem. Then if s is not a positive integer an infinite series will be obtained. If, however, the series is terminated or truncated after $n+1$ terms and the resulting series is denoted by $(1+\Delta)^s_n u_r$, we have

$$u_{r+s} = (1+\Delta)^s_n u_r = u_r + s\Delta u_r + \binom{s}{2}\Delta^2 u_r + \ldots + \binom{s}{n}\Delta^n u_r. \quad (4)$$

Now this is a polynomial of degree n in s, n being the degree of the last term. Moreover, it follows from Gregory's theorem (see **13.2** (9)) that if $s = k$, an integer $\leq n$, this polynomial is equal to u_{r+k}. It therefore satisfies the required condition and can be used as an interpolation formula. It is called the *Gregory-Newton formula*.

It can be verified that (3) and (4) are equivalent. The essential difference between them is that, whereas (3) is expressed entirely in terms of values of the original sequence, (4) uses differences of orders up to n. These differences appear in a difference table such as table 13.1(A) or (B) on a falling diagonal. Such differences were called forward differences in **13.1**.

We shall find it convenient to obtain formulae equivalent to (3) and (4) where the interpolating polynomial is made to fit the values $u_{r-m}, \ldots u_r, u_{r+1}, \ldots u_{r-m+n}$ of the sequence, m being any positive integer $\leq n$. These follow immediately from (3) and (4) if we replace r by $r-m$ and s by $s+m$, giving

$$u_{r+s} = \sum_{k=-\infty}^{\infty} \frac{(-)^{n-k}(s+m)^{(n+1)}u_{r+k-m}}{k!(n-k)!(s+m-k)}, \quad (5)$$

$$u_{r+s} = (1+\Delta)^{s+m}_n u_{r-m} = (1+\Delta)^{s+m}_n E^{-m} u_r. \quad (6)$$

Notice that the limits for k in (5) have been changed from $(0, n)$ to $(-\infty, \infty)$. This has been done to facilitate later manipulation. It is justified in all respects if we define $k!$ to be infinite when k is a negative integer.

Formulae (5) and (6) are the basis of all interpolation processes using numerical methods. For computation of isolated values it is usual, having selected a value of n to give sufficient accuracy, to arrange that s

shall lie between zero and unity and to choose r and m accordingly. The actual formula selected will depend on a number of factors, such as the type of tables and computing machines that are available. For example, to interpolate in the first interval of the sub-sequence defining the interpolation polynomial we take $m = 0$. This gives the Gregory-Newton formula (4). It is usually preferable, where possible, to arrange for the interpolation interval to be in the middle of the sub-sequence so that $m = \frac{1}{2}n$ or $\frac{1}{2}(n-1)$, according as n is even or odd. In this case the interpolation formula is usually expressed in the central difference notation (see **13.1**). Alternative formulae of this type are those of Gauss, Stirling, Bessel and Everett. Derivations of these are to be found in text books on numerical analysis, such as Whittaker and Robinson.†

Formulae for extrapolation can be obtained from (5) and (6) by putting $m = n$. An alternative form to these can be derived by using the relation $\mathbf{E}^s = (\mathbf{E}^{-1})^{-s} = (1-\mathbf{V})^{-s}$. This is

$$u_{r+s} = (1-\mathbf{V})_n^{-s}u_r = \left\{1 + s\mathbf{V} + \binom{s+1}{2}\mathbf{V}^2 + \ldots + \binom{s+n-1}{n}\mathbf{V}^n\right\}u_r, \quad (7)$$

since
$$\binom{-s}{k} = \frac{-s(-s-1)\ldots(-s-k+1)}{k!} = (-)^k\binom{s+k-1}{k}. \quad (8)$$

If we put $s = 1$ this formula gives a "predicted" value for u_{r+1}, the next number in the original sequence. This is

$$(1-\mathbf{V})_n^{-1}u_r = (1 + \mathbf{V} + \ldots + \mathbf{V}^n)u_r = \frac{1-\mathbf{V}^{n+1}}{1-\mathbf{V}}u_r$$

$$= (1-\mathbf{V}^{n+1})\mathbf{E}u_r = u_{r+1} - \mathbf{V}^{n+1}u_{r+1}. \quad (9)$$

Thus the actual and the predicted values of u_{r+1} differ by $\mathbf{V}^{n+1}u_{r+1}$.

16.2 Interpolation Operators

Accounts of interpolation as a numerical process are to be found in textbooks on numerical methods. We shall be concerned in this chapter to regard the process as a linear operation, namely that of generating a function $u(t)$ from a sequence u_r of sampled values. The operation is in fact the inverse of sampling. This operation is clearly multiple in the sense defined in **7.2**, since a given sequence u_r has an infinite number of interpolating functions. In fact any function $u(t)$ for which $u(rT) = u_r$ will serve. Put in another way, a general interpolating function should contain a complementary function equivalent to the aggregate of all functions that vanish at every sampling instant. Although we have no

† Whittaker, Sir Edmund and Robinson, G., *The Calculus of Observations.* Blackie (Glasgow, 1944).

occasion to consider such aggregates, we shall have to compare the merits of different functions interpolating the same sequence.

It will be assumed that the Lagrangian formula **16.1** (5) is used for interpolation in the interval $rT < t < (r+1)T$, the same values of n and m being used with each value of r. In other words when interpolating in any interval we use a polynomial fitted to $n+1$ consecutive values of u, m of which always precede the value at the lower end of the interval. It follows that when t passes through each value rT there is in general a change in the interpolating polynomial. Putting $\tau = t/T$ so that $s = \tau - r$, and denoting the function generated by $u_{n,m}(t)$, we have

$$u_{n,m}(t) =$$
$$\sum_{r=-\infty}^{\infty} \sum_{k=-\infty}^{\infty} \frac{(-)^{n-k}(\tau-r+m)^{(n+1)}u_{r+k-m}}{k!(n-k)!(\tau-r+m-k)}\{H(\tau-r)-H(\tau-r-1)\}. \quad (1)$$

The factor involving the step functions ensures that the term containing it is non-zero only when $r < \tau < r+1$. We now split this expression into two separate sums, one containing $H(\tau-r)$ and the other $H(\tau-r-1)$. In the latter, we replace r by $r-1$ and k by $k+1$ and then recombine the sums to give

$$u_{n,m}(t) =$$
$$\sum_r \sum_k \frac{(-)^{n-k}u_{r+k-m}}{\tau-r+m-k}\left\{\frac{(\tau-r+m)^{(n+1)}}{k!(n-k)!} + \frac{(\tau-r+m+1)^{(n+1)}}{(k+1)!(n-k-1)!}\right\}H(\tau-r).$$

Simplifying the expression inside the brackets, we deduce

$$u_{n,m}(t) = \sum_r \sum_k \frac{(-)^{n-k}u_{r+k-m}(\tau-r+m)^{(n)}(n+1)}{(k+1)!(n-k)!}H(\tau-r)$$

$$= \sum_r \sum_k (-)^{n-k}\binom{\tau-r+m}{n}\binom{n+1}{k+1}u_{r+k-m}H(\tau-r)$$

$$= \sum_r \binom{\tau-r+m}{n}H(\tau-r)\sum_k \binom{n+1}{k}(-)^{n+1-k}\mathbf{E}^{k-m-1}u_r,$$

replacing k by $k-1$. Thus

$$u_{n,m}(t) = \sum_r \binom{\tau-r+m}{n}H(\tau-r)(\mathbf{E}-1)^{n+1}\mathbf{E}^{-m-1}u_r$$

$$= \sum_r \binom{\tau-r+m}{n}H(\tau-r)\mathbf{E}^{-m-1}\mathbf{\Delta}^{n+1}u_r. \quad (2)$$

Now the binomial coefficient is a polynomial in τ of degree n. Let its expansion in powers of $\tau - r$ be

$$\binom{\tau-r+m}{n} = a_0 + a_1(\tau-r) + \frac{a_2}{2!}(\tau-r)^2 + \ldots + \frac{a_n}{n!}(\tau-r)^n. \quad (3)$$

Then $\binom{\tau-r+m}{n} H(\tau-r) =$

$$\left\{ a_0 + \frac{a_1(t-rT)}{T} + \frac{a_2(t-rT)^2}{2!T^2} + \ldots + \frac{a_n(t-rT)^n}{n!T^n} \right\} H(t-rT)$$

$$= \left\{ \frac{a_0}{\mathbf{D}} + \frac{a_1}{T\mathbf{D}^2} + \frac{a_2}{T^2\mathbf{D}^3} + \ldots + \frac{a_n}{T^n\mathbf{D}^{n+1}} \right\} \delta(t-rT), \quad (4)$$

using **6.5** (3). Substitution of this in (2) gives

$$u_{n,m}(t) = M_{n,m}(\mathbf{D})\mathbf{P}\mathbf{E}^{-m-1}\Delta^{n+1}u_r \quad (5)$$

where

$$M_{n,m}(\mathbf{D}) = \frac{a_0}{\mathbf{D}} + \ldots + \frac{a_n}{T^n\mathbf{D}^{n+1}}. \quad (6)$$

Complementary function terms associated with the inverse operator $1/\mathbf{D}^{n+1}$ in $M_{n,m}(\mathbf{D})$ should not be included, since the derivation of (4) shows this expression to be a particular integral. In order to ensure this, (5) can be written

$$u_{n,m}(t) = \Delta^{n+1}M_{n,m}(\mathbf{D})\mathbf{E}^{-m-1}\mathbf{P}u_r. \quad (7)$$

If this is done the complementary function, being a polynomial of degree n, will be cancelled by the operation Δ^{n+1} (see **13.1**). On the other hand, (5) indicates clearly the dependence of the interpolation process on the $(n+1)$th differences of the sequence u_r.

We see that if the sequence u_r is pulsed, interpolation is represented by the operator $I_{n,m}(\mathbf{D}) = M_{n,m}(\mathbf{D})\mathbf{E}^{-m-1}\Delta^{n+1}$. Since $\Delta = \mathbf{E} - 1$ and $\mathbf{E} = e^{T\mathbf{D}}$, this operator can be expressed completely in terms of $\mathbf{D}$. It is therefore time-invariant (see **14.2**). This important property will be the basis of much of the work of subsequent sections. Firstly, knowledge of the form of the operator provides a valuable process for synthesising automatic interpolation systems. Secondly, it makes possible the use of harmonic response methods for the estimation of the efficiency of a given interpolation formula. Thirdly, it enables the concept of the weighting function to be applied to interpolation.

The polynomials $M_{n,m}$ are best obtained by putting $r = 0$ in (3) before expansion. For example, to find $M_{3,2}(\mathbf{D})$, we have

$$\binom{\tau+2}{3} = \tfrac{1}{6}(\tau+2)(\tau+1)\tau = \frac{\tau^3}{6} + \frac{\tau^2}{2} + \frac{\tau}{3},$$

so that

$$M_{3,2}(\mathbf{D}) = \frac{1}{T^3\mathbf{D}^4} + \frac{1}{T^2\mathbf{D}^3} + \frac{1}{3T\mathbf{D}^2}.$$

Table 16.2(A) shows some of the more elementary interpolation operators.

n	m	$I_{n,m}(\mathbf{D})$
0	0	$\dfrac{\mathbf{E}^{-1}\Delta}{\mathbf{D}} = \dfrac{\nabla}{\mathbf{D}}$
1	0	$\dfrac{\mathbf{E}^{-1}\Delta^2}{T\mathbf{D}^2}$
	1	$\left(\dfrac{1}{T\mathbf{D}^2}+\dfrac{1}{\mathbf{D}}\right)\nabla^2$
2	0	$\left(\dfrac{1}{T^2\mathbf{D}^3}-\dfrac{1}{2T\mathbf{D}^2}\right)\mathbf{E}^{-1}\Delta^3$
	1	$\left(\dfrac{1}{T^2\mathbf{D}^3}+\dfrac{1}{2T\mathbf{D}^2}\right)\mathbf{E}^{-2}\Delta^3$
	2	$\left(\dfrac{1}{T^2\mathbf{D}^3}+\dfrac{3}{2T\mathbf{D}^2}+\dfrac{1}{\mathbf{D}}\right)\nabla^3$
3	0	$\left(\dfrac{1}{T^3\mathbf{D}^4}-\dfrac{1}{T^2\mathbf{D}^3}+\dfrac{1}{3T\mathbf{D}^2}\right)\mathbf{E}^{-1}\Delta^4$
	1	$\left(\dfrac{1}{T^3\mathbf{D}^4}-\dfrac{1}{6T\mathbf{D}^2}\right)\mathbf{E}^{-2}\Delta^4$
	2	$\left(\dfrac{1}{T^3\mathbf{D}^4}+\dfrac{1}{T^2\mathbf{D}^3}+\dfrac{1}{3T\mathbf{D}^2}\right)\mathbf{E}^{-3}\Delta^4$
	3	$\left(\dfrac{1}{T^3\mathbf{D}^4}+\dfrac{2}{T^2\mathbf{D}^3}+\dfrac{11}{6T\mathbf{D}^2}+\dfrac{1}{\mathbf{D}}\right)\nabla^4$

TABLE 16.2(A)

Notice that the simplest case of all, $n = m = 0$, corresponds to clamping. Notice also that terms in $1/\mathbf{D}$ appear if, and only if, $m = n$, that is, with extrapolation. Since $I_{n,m}(\mathbf{D})$ will be applied only to impulses, the output functions will have steps if, and only if, the systems are extrapolating.

16.3 Practical applications

In this section we show how the operational method can be used to devise and analyse the performance of systems whose purpose is to generate automatically interpolation functions for given sequences. To be specific we will assume that the interpolation formula makes use of forward differences of order up to and including the third. Then from table 16.2(A) with $n = 3$ and $m = 0$, and with $T = 1$ for simplicity, the output we require is

$$x(t) = (\mathbf{D}^{-4} - \mathbf{D}^{-3} + \tfrac{1}{3}\mathbf{D}^{-2})\mathbf{E}^{-1}\Delta^4 P u_r$$
$$= (\mathbf{D}^{-3} - \mathbf{D}^{-2} + \tfrac{1}{3}\mathbf{D}^{-1})C\Delta^3 u_r. \tag{1}$$

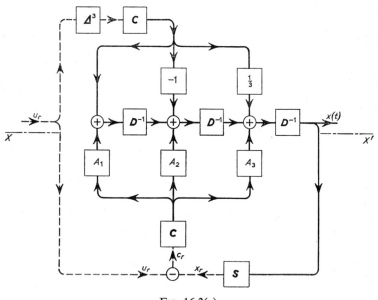

FIG. 16.3(a)

The polynomials which form $x(t)$ could in theory be generated by a series of three integrators in cascade. The way in which these would be linked to the input sequence u_r is shown in the portion of fig. 16.3(a) above the line XX'. Unfortunately, this open-loop system is not stable, since the output will contain the complementary function terms $\mathbf{D}^{-3}0$. There is in fact no provision for elimination of errors due to initial incorrect settings of the integrators or of instrumental errors arising subsequently. In order to stabilise the system it is necessary to introduce some form of monitoring feed-back. One possible arrangement is a system whose flow diagram is the whole of fig 16.3(a). The governing equation of this is

$$x(t) = (\mathbf{D}^{-4} - \mathbf{D}^{-3} + \tfrac{1}{3}\mathbf{D}^{-2})\mathbf{E}^{-1}\Delta^4 P u_r$$
$$+ (A_1\mathbf{D}^{-4} + A_2\mathbf{D}^{-3} + A_3\mathbf{D}^{-2})\nabla P(u_r - x_r), \tag{2}$$

where A_1, A_2 and A_3 are suitably chosen constants. Sampling (2) and using **15.2** (18) and the obvious relation $SI_{n,m}(\mathbf{D})P u_r = u_r$, we have

$$x_r = u_r + \mathbf{V}\{A_1 K_4(\mathbf{V}) + A_2 K_3(\mathbf{V}) + A_3 K_2(\mathbf{V})\}(u_r - x_r),$$

whence $[1 + \mathbf{V}\{A_1 K_4(\mathbf{V}) + A_2 K_3(\mathbf{V}) + A_3 K_2(\mathbf{V})\}]c_r = 0.$ (3)

The characteristic equation is obtained by replacing $\mathbf{V}$ by $1 - \kappa^{-1}$ in (3). When simplified this becomes

$$\kappa^3 + \kappa^2(\tfrac{1}{6}A_1 + \tfrac{1}{2}A_2 + A_3 - 3) + \kappa(\tfrac{2}{3}A_1 - 2A_3 + 3)$$
$$+ \tfrac{1}{6}A_1 - \tfrac{1}{2}A_2 + A_3 - 1 = 0. \quad (4)$$

By suitable choice of A_1, A_2 and A_3, the roots of (3) can be made to have any assigned values. Stability can therefore always be assured. Moreover, the transient response can be adjusted without affecting the steady state performance. For example, if $A_1 = 1$, $A_2 = 2$ and $A_3 = \tfrac{11}{6}$ all three roots of (4) are zero. In this case, whatever the initial settings on the integrators, the system will settle after three sampling intervals, with no subsequent error. It can be shown, however, that this arrangement makes the system rather sensitive to instrumental perturbations. This effect can be reduced by means of staleness weighting,† that is by making all three roots equal to α, a real number between zero and unity. This, however, delays the settling.

The same general principles hold when other interpolation operators are used. In fact, slightly more accurate interpolation is usually obtained if the operator is based on a central difference formula, for example with $n = 3$ and $m = 1$.

More generally, linear combinations of two or more operators can be used, the constant multipliers of different operators being chosen so that their sum is unity. For example, as was seen at the end of **16.2**, if an interpolation operator contains a term in $\mathbf{D}^{-1}$, the output has steps at the sampling instants. If, however, the operator contains a term in $\mathbf{D}^{-2}$ but not one in $\mathbf{D}^{-1}$, the output is continuous but its first derivative has steps. Its second derivative therefore has impulses. Such an arrangement would be unsuitable if the output load had appreciable inertia. This leads us to seek operators which contain neither $\mathbf{D}^{-1}$ nor $\mathbf{D}^{-2}$. Such an operator is $3I_{3,1} - I_{2,0} - I_{2,1}$. Substituting from table 16.2(A) and simplifying, it is found that this reduces to

$$\left\{\frac{3}{T^3 \mathbf{D}^4} + \left(1 - \frac{2}{\mathbf{V}}\right)\frac{1}{T^2 \mathbf{D}^3}\right\}\mathbf{E}^2 \mathbf{V}^4. \quad (5)$$

The system of fig. 16.3(a) can be regarded as an ordinary feed-back control loop with a feed-forward from the input. This type of control

† See Holt-Smith, Lawden and Bailey, *op. cit.* p. 189.

applied to continuously operating systems was mentioned briefly in **10.8**. Provided $m < n$ the sequence fed forward makes use at any instant of at least one future value of the input sequence u_r. It is because of this that it is possible to generate interpolating functions which, when the system has settled, have no errors or steps at the sampling instants whatever the form of the input. This type of system is therefore particularly useful for generation of functions of t available in advance in tabular form.

On the other hand, if the function must be generated as tabular values become available, some form of extrapolation or prediction must be used. In this case a different approach can be used. Unless steps in the output can be accepted it is impossible to ensure that there will be no steady state errors at the sampling instants without placing some restriction on the input sequence. We can, however, devise systems that give no steady state error provided that differences of u_r of some specified order all vanish.

Using **16.1** (9) it is seen that the $(n+1)$th differences of u_r, which are required for extrapolation, are provided directly by the errors at the sampling instants. No feed-forward from the input is therefore necessary, and such systems can operate entirely on error control. The most obvious type of extrapolation system is one based on the standard operator $I_{n,n}(\mathbf{D})$. This has, however, as was shown in **16.2**, the disadvantage of steps at the sampling instants. These can be eliminated by the introduction of suitable difference operators between the error and the integrators which generate the extrapolation polynomial.†

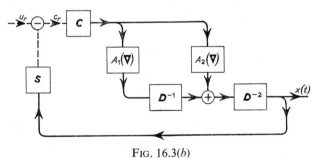

Fig. 16.3(b)

Consider for example the system of fig. 16.3(b), where

$$A_1(\mathbf{V}) = A_1' + A_1''/\mathbf{V},$$

and
$$A_2(\mathbf{V}) = A_2' + A_2''/\mathbf{V}.$$

† See Porter, A. and Stoneman, F., A New Approach to the Design of Pulse Monitored Servo Systems. *Proc. Inst. Elect. Engrs.* **97** Pt. II (1950), p. 597.

The governing equation is

$$x(t) = \left\{ \frac{A_1(\mathbf{V})}{\mathbf{D}^3} + \frac{A_2(\mathbf{V})}{\mathbf{D}^2} \right\} \frac{\mathbf{V}}{\mathbf{D}} \mathbf{P} c_r.$$

Sampling,

$$x_r = u_r - c_r = \mathbf{V}\{A_1(\mathbf{V})K_4(\mathbf{V}) + A_2(\mathbf{V})K_3(\mathbf{V})\}c_r.$$

Substituting for $K_3(\mathbf{V})$ and $K_4(\mathbf{V})$ from **15.2** (16) and (17), solving for c_r and expanding the resulting operator in powers of $\mathbf{V}$, the first term is found to be proportional to $\mathbf{V}^4 u_r$. The system is therefore of the fourth order, so that there will be no steady state errors if $\mathbf{V}^4 u_r = 0$. The stability and transient response of the system can be controlled by suitable choice of the constants $A_1{}'$, $A_1{}''$, $A_2{}'$ and $A_2{}''$.

The operations $1/\mathbf{V}$ appearing in $A_1(\mathbf{V})$ and $A_2(\mathbf{V})$ are both summations (see **13.3** (14)). These can of course be carried out before clamping. Notice that the order of this system, which is four, is equal to the number of integrations *and* summations in the control loop. This result is general.

16.4   Weighting functions

It was shown in **16.2** that the interpolation operator $I_{n,m}(\mathbf{D})$, which converts the pulsed sequence $\mathbf{P}u_r$ into $u_{n,m}(t)$, is time-invariant. There is therefore a fixed weighting function $W(t)$ corresponding to this operator with the property that

$$
\begin{aligned}
u_{n,m}(t) &= \int_{-\infty}^{\infty} W(t-t_1)\mathbf{P}u_r \, dt_1 \\
&= \int_{-\infty}^{\infty} W(t-t_1) \sum_{r=-\infty}^{\infty} u_r \delta(t_1 - rT) \, dt_1 \\
&= \sum_{r=-\infty}^{\infty} u_r W(t-rT).
\end{aligned}
\tag{1}
$$

This relation is a special case of **14.1** (6) in which $\phi(t, r) = W(t-rT)$. It follows that $W(t)$ is the function obtained by interpolating the sequence δ_r, defined in **13.5**. Alternatively, putting $t/T = \tau$ as before,

$$
\begin{aligned}
W(t) &= I_{n,m}(\mathbf{D})\delta(t) \tag{2} \\
&= \Delta^{n+1}\mathbf{E}^{-m-1}M_{n,m}(\mathbf{D})\delta(t) \\
&= \Delta^{n+1}\mathbf{E}^{-m-1}\binom{\tau+m}{n}H(\tau) \\
&= (\mathbf{E}-1)^{n+1}\binom{\tau-1}{n}H(\tau-m-1), \tag{3}
\end{aligned}
$$

using **16.2** (7) and (4).

Taking the simplest example, in which $n = 1$ and $m = 0$, this gives

$$W(t) = (\mathbf{E}^2 - 2\mathbf{E} + 1)(\tau - 1)H(\tau - 1)$$
$$= (\tau + 1)H(\tau + 1) - 2\tau H(\tau) + (\tau - 1)H(\tau - 1).$$

Thus
$$
\begin{aligned}
W(t) &= 0 && \text{if } \tau < -1, \\
&= \tau + 1 && \text{if } -1 < \tau < 0, \\
&= \tau + 1 - 2\tau = 1 - \tau && \text{if } 0 < \tau < 1, \\
&= \tau + 1 - 2\tau + \tau - 1 = 0 && \text{if } \tau > 1.
\end{aligned}
$$

The graph of $W(t)$ in this case is shown in fig. 16.4(a). The weighting function can be interpreted graphically in a way analogous to that used in fig. 8.4(e). Thus in order to calculate $u_{1,0}(t)$ for a given value of t we must first reverse the graph of the weighting function and displace it a distance to the right corresponding to t. We then multiply the sequence

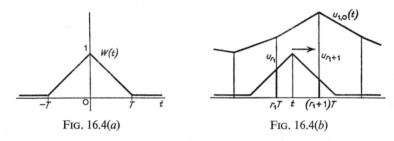

Fɪɢ. 16.4(a)   Fɪɢ. 16.4(b)

values by the intercepts of this graph on the corresponding ordinates and add the products. This is shown in fig. 16.4(b). It is clear that the function so generated is made up of the straight-line segments which join the ends of the ordinates representing the sequence values. This function is given by

$$u_{1,0}(t) = (1 - \tau + r_1)u_{r_1} + (\tau - r_1)u_{r_1 + 1}, \tag{4}$$

where r_1 is the greatest integer less than τ. Equation (4) is clearly in agreement with (1) and also with **16.1** (1).

The above process can be used to find the weighting function for the operator $I_{n,m}(\mathbf{D})$. A better method is as follows. Since

$$W(t) = I_{n,m}(\mathbf{D})\mathbf{P}\delta_r,$$

$W(t)$ can be obtained from **16.2** (1) by putting $u_0 = 1$ and all other values of u_r equal to zero. This is equivalent to taking from the double summation the terms for which $k = m - r$. This gives

$$W(t) = \sum_{r=-\infty}^{\infty} \frac{(-)^{n-m+r}(\tau - r + m)^{(n+1)}}{(m-r)!(n-m+r)!\tau}\{H(\tau - r) - H(\tau - r - 1)\}.$$

Expansion and rearrangement of the various factorials gives

$$W(t) = \sum_{r=m-n}^{m} (1-\tau)\left(1-\frac{\tau}{2}\right)\cdots\left(1-\frac{\tau}{n-m+r}\right)(1+\tau)\left(1+\frac{\tau}{2}\right)\cdots$$

$$\cdots\left(1+\frac{\tau}{m-r}\right)\{H(\tau-r)-H(\tau-r-1)\}. \quad (5)$$

Thus in the interval between each integral value of τ, $W(t)$ is a polynomial of degree n. The expressions for $W(t)$ obtained from (3) with $n = 1$ and $m = 0$ constitute a special case of the general formula (5).

Again, if $n = 2$ and $m = 0$,

$$\begin{aligned}
W(t) &= \tfrac{1}{2}(\tau+1)(\tau+2) && \text{if } -2 < \tau < -1,\\
&= 1-\tau^2 && \text{if } -1 < \tau < 0,\\
&= \tfrac{1}{2}(\tau-1)(\tau-2) && \text{if } 0 < \tau < 1,
\end{aligned}$$

and is zero otherwise. Fig. 16.4(c) shows a graph of this function.

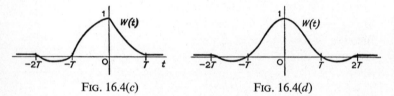

FIG. 16.4(c)   FIG. 16.4(d)

This method can be extended without difficulty to linear combinations of operators of the type $I_{n,m}(\mathbf{D})$. For example, it can be shown that the operator **16.3** (5) has weighting function

$$\begin{aligned}
W(t) &= \tfrac{1}{2}(\tau+2)^2(\tau+1) && \text{if } -2 < \tau < -1,\\
&= -\tfrac{3}{2}\tau^3 - \tfrac{5}{2}\tau^2 + 1 && \text{if } -1 < \tau < 0,\\
&= \tfrac{3}{2}\tau^3 - \tfrac{5}{2}\tau^2 + 1 && \text{if } 0 < \tau < 1,\\
&= -\tfrac{1}{2}(\tau-2)^2(\tau-1) && \text{if } 1 < \tau < 2,
\end{aligned}$$

and zero otherwise. This function, whose graph is shown in fig. 16.4(d), is continuous and has a continuous derivative. This operator is the simplest one for which the first derivative of the generated function is always continuous.

It usually happens in practice that the larger the value of n chosen, the more accurate is the value of the function obtained by interpolation for any value of t. It is natural, therefore, to investigate the behaviour of the interpolation operator as $n \to \infty$. If we assume in addition that both m and $n-m$ tend to infinity, the weighting function given by (5) tends to the infinite product

$$(1-\tau^2)\left(1-\frac{\tau^2}{2^2}\right)\left(1-\frac{\tau^2}{3^2}\right)\cdots$$

for all values of t. It is well known that this product converges to the limit $(\sin \pi\tau)/\pi\tau$. We have, therefore,

$$W(t) = \frac{\sin \pi\tau}{\pi\tau} = \frac{\sin \pi t/T}{\pi t/T}, \tag{6}$$

the graph of which is shown in fig. 16.4(e). If $I(p)$ is the Laplace trans-

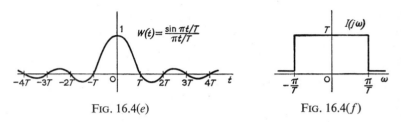

FIG. 16.4(e)   FIG. 16.4(f)

form of this function we can denote the corresponding operator formally by $I(\mathbf{D})$. This will be called the *ideal interpolation operator*. Using example 3 of **4.4**, the Fourier transform $I(j\omega)$ of $W(t)$ is the function which has the constant value T for $-\pi/T < \omega < \pi/T$ and is zero otherwise (see fig. 16.4(f)); that is

$$I(j\omega) = T\{H(\omega + \pi/T) - H(\omega - \pi/T)\}. \tag{7}$$

The practical significance of this result will appear in the next section.

It may be noted that the process of interpolation provides an example of a linear time-variant operation whose weighting function $W(t)$ does not vanish when $t < 0$.

16.5   Interpolation as a filtering process

One way of examining the effectiveness of a given interpolation process is to represent the various functions in the frequency domain. We will assume that the sequence u_r has been obtained by sampling a function $u(t)$ whose Fourier transform is $u^*(j\omega)$. Then it follows from **15.5** (8) that the Fourier transform of Pu_r is

$$u_p^*(e^{j\omega T}) = \frac{1}{T} \sum_{r=-\infty}^{\infty} u^*(j\omega + jr\Omega), \tag{1}$$

a function with period $\Omega = 2\pi/T$. Fig. 15.5(b) shows the graph of this function. If the operator $I_{n,m}(\mathbf{D})$ is used for interpolation, the function $u_{n,m}(t)$ generated has transform

$$u_{n,m}^*(j\omega) = I_{n,m}(j\omega)u_p^*(e^{j\omega T}). \tag{2}$$

Now **16.4** (7) shows that the ideal interpolation operator is equivalent to an ideal low-pass filter with band width $\pi/T = \frac{1}{2}\Omega$. If it happens that the original function $u(t)$ contains no harmonic components outside this band, $u_p^*(e^{j\omega T}) = (1/T)u^*(j\omega)$ when $-\frac{1}{2}\Omega < \omega < \frac{1}{2}\Omega$. It follows that the transform of the function generated is $u^*(j\omega)$. In these circumstances, therefore, interpolation will reproduce the original function $u(t)$.

The efficiency of an operator $I_{n,m}(\mathbf{D})$ with particular values for n and m can be judged by comparing $|I_{n,m}(j\omega)|$ with $I(j\omega)$. For example,

$$I_{3,1}(\mathbf{D}) = \left(\frac{1}{T^3\mathbf{D}^4} - \frac{1}{6T\mathbf{D}^2}\right)\mathbf{E}^{-2}\mathbf{\Delta}^4$$

$$= \left(\frac{1}{T^3\mathbf{D}^4} - \frac{1}{6T\mathbf{D}^2}\right)e^{-2T\mathbf{D}}(e^{T\mathbf{D}} - 1)^4,$$

since $\mathbf{E} = e^{T\mathbf{D}}$. Replacing $\mathbf{D}$ by $j\omega$,

$$I_{3,1}(j\omega) = \left(\frac{1}{T^3\omega^4} + \frac{1}{6T\omega^2}\right)(e^{\frac{1}{2}j\omega T} - e^{-\frac{1}{2}j\omega T})^4$$

$$= T(1 + \tfrac{1}{6}\omega^2 T^2)\left(\frac{\sin\frac{1}{2}\omega T}{\frac{1}{2}\omega T}\right)^4,$$

using equation (12) of Appendix 1. This function is compared with $I(j\omega)$ in fig. 16.5(a). This shows how, instead of the sharp cut-off of

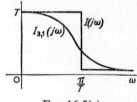

FIG. 16.5(a)

the ideal interpolator at $\omega = \frac{1}{2}\Omega$, interpolation with a finite value of n causes a gradual attenuation of the harmonic components as their frequency ω increases.

COMPLEX NUMBERS

The aggregate of positive and negative integers and fractions and terminating and non-terminating decimals constitute the *field of real numbers*. Given any two real numbers we can always carry out the elementary arithmetical operations of addition, subtraction, multiplication and division, with of course the single exception of division by zero. It is only when we come to apply more advanced operations that the limitations of this field become apparent.

The simplest example of this is given by the process of extraction of square roots, for since the square of any positive or negative real number must be positive, a negative number can have no square root. Again, a negative number has no logarithm; also there is no number (or angle measured in radians) whose sine exceeds unity.

All these limitations can be removed by extending the number field by the introduction of a number, denoted by j, which is defined to have the property $j^2 = -1$. This number can be multiplied by any real number to form an *imaginary number*. Finally, any real number and any imaginary number can be added to form a *complex number*. Thus we define a complex number as

$$z = x + jy$$

where x and y are real. We call x and y (or jy) the *real* and *imaginary* parts of z and denote them by $\mathscr{R}z$ and $\mathscr{I}z$.

We assume that complex numbers can be manipulated arithmetically like real numbers. Thus if two numbers $z_1 = x_1 + jy_1$ and $z_2 = x_2 + jy_2$ are equal, then $x_1 + jy_1 = x_2 + jy_2$, or $x_1 - x_2 = j(y_2 - y_1)$. Since non-zero real and imaginary numbers cannot be equal it follows that $x_1 = x_2$ and $y_1 = y_2$, so that two complex numbers are equal if, and only if, their real parts and their imaginary parts are equal respectively.

As has been stated, the introduction of complex numbers gives greater uniformity and completeness to the theory of elementary functions. For example, it can be shown that any complex number has two complex square roots and three complex cube roots. Also any complex number has a complex logarithm. Again, since a complex number consists of two separate parts, any equation in complex numbers is in effect a pair of equations in real numbers. It happens frequently that the equation in complex numbers is simpler in form and easier to manipulate than either of the two equations in real numbers. Put in another way, this means that it is often convenient to regard certain real quantities as the real or imaginary parts of appropriate complex quantities and to deduce their properties accordingly. As an example we show later that cosines and sines are the real and imaginary parts of complex exponential functions, which are much simpler to handle algebraically.

We consider now the arithmetic of complex numbers. It is easily seen that addition and subtraction are effected by adding or subtracting the real and imaginary parts separately. Multiplication is illustrated by the following example.

$$(3+2j)(1+3j) = 3+2j+9j+6j^2 = -3+11j.$$

Before discussing division we introduce the idea of the *conjugate* of a complex number z. This is formed by changing the sign of the imaginary part and is denoted by $\bar{z}$. Thus if $z = x+jy$ then $\bar{z} = x-jy$, so that

$$z\bar{z} = (x+jy)(x-jy) = x^2+y^2.$$

The product of any complex number and its conjugate is therefore a real number. This property enables us to find the real and imaginary parts of the quotient of two complex numbers. For example,

$$\frac{4+5j}{2+3j} = \frac{(4+5j)(2-3j)}{(2+3j)(2-3j)} = \frac{23-2j}{2^2+3^2} = \frac{23}{13} - \frac{2}{13}j.$$

Complex numbers have an important graphical representation. This is called the *Argand diagram* (see fig. A1(a)). In it, a complex number $z = x+jy$ is represented by a point P whose rectangular cartesian

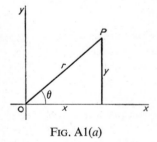

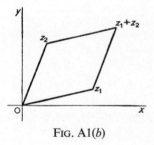

FIG. A1(a)   FIG. A1(b)

coordinates are (x, y). Alternatively, we can represent z by the vector OP. With this representation, addition of two complex numbers is represented by the parallelogram law of composition (see fig. A1(b)).

If the polar coordinates of the point P representing the complex number z are (r, θ), we call r the *modulus* or *magnitude* of z and denote it by $|z|$. Likewise θ is called the *argument* or *angle* of z and denoted by ang z. Then if $z = x + jy$,

$$r = |z| = \sqrt{(x^2 + y^2)}, \tag{1}$$

$$\theta = \text{ang } z = \tan^{-1}(y/x), \tag{2}$$

$$x = r \cos \theta, \qquad y = r \sin \theta. \tag{3}$$

The modulus r is taken to be positive and θ must be chosen so that equations (3) are both satisfied with positive r. A particularly useful relation is

$$z\bar{z} = x^2 + y^2 = |z|^2. \tag{4}$$

If z is a real number x, $|x|$ is the magnitude of x without regard to its sign, while ang x is 0 or π according as x is positive or negative. A useful inequality satisfied by the moduli of real or complex numbers is

$$|z_1 + z_2| \leq |z_1| + |z_2|. \tag{5}$$

This is obvious from fig. A1(*b*).

If we express a complex number in terms of its modulus and angle we have

$$z = x + jy = r(\cos \theta + j \sin \theta). \tag{6}$$

Using the series (3), (4) and (2) of Appendix 4 we deduce

$$\cos \theta + j \sin \theta = 1 - \frac{\theta^2}{2!} + \frac{\theta^4}{4!} - \dots + j\left(\theta - \frac{\theta^3}{3!} + \dots\right)$$

$$= 1 + j\theta + \frac{j^2\theta^2}{2!} + \frac{j^3\theta^3}{3!} + \dots,$$

or
$$\cos \theta + j \sin \theta = e^{j\theta}, \tag{7}$$

whence
$$z = re^{j\theta}. \tag{8}$$

Here we have assumed the exponential function of a complex number to be defined by the series

$$\exp z = e^z = 1 + z + \frac{z^2}{2!} + \frac{z^3}{3!} + \dots. \tag{9}$$

It can be proved from this definition that the index law is satisfied, that is,

$$e^{z_1 + z_2} = e^{z_1} \cdot e^{z_2}. \tag{10}$$

Replacing θ by $-\theta$ in (7) gives

$$\cos \theta - j \sin \theta = e^{-j\theta}. \tag{11}$$

By adding and subtracting (7) and (11) we deduce

$$\cos \theta = \frac{e^{j\theta} + e^{-j\theta}}{2}, \qquad \sin \theta = \frac{e^{j\theta} - e^{-j\theta}}{2j}. \tag{12}$$

Equation (7) states that $\cos \theta$ and $\sin \theta$ are the real and imaginary parts of $\exp j\theta$. As a special case of this, if x is a quantity that is varying harmonically with amplitude X, with (angular) frequency ω and with initial phase ε then

$$x = X \cos (\omega t + \varepsilon). \tag{13}$$

For many purposes it is convenient to regard x as the real part of $X \exp j(\omega t + \varepsilon)$. Not only does this allow us to use the index law (10), it also facilitates the differentiation of (13) one or more times.

An important property concerning the multiplication and division of complex numbers follows from (8). Let z_1 and z_2 have moduli r_1 and r_2 and angles θ_1 and θ_2. Then

$$z_1 z_2 = r_1 e^{j\theta_1} . r_2 e^{j\theta_2} = r_1 r_2 e^{j(\theta_1 + \theta_2)}, \tag{14}$$

so that

$$|z_1 z_2| = |z_1||z_2| \tag{15}$$

and

$$\text{ang} (z_1 z_2) = \text{ang} z_1 + \text{ang} z_2. \tag{16}$$

In other words, the modulus of a product is the *product* of the separate moduli and the angle of a product is the *sum* of the angles of the factors. Similarly

$$\left| \frac{z_1}{z_2} \right| = \frac{|z_1|}{|z_2|}, \qquad \text{ang} \frac{z_1}{z_2} = \text{ang} z_1 - \text{ang} z_2, \tag{17}$$

$$|z^n| = |z|^n, \qquad \text{ang} z^n = n \, \text{ang} z. \tag{18}$$

ALGEBRAIC EQUATIONS

Consider the quadratic equation

$$a_0 x^2 + a_1 x + a_2 = 0, \tag{1}$$

where the coefficients a_0, a_1 and a_2 are real.

This is well known to have two solutions, given by

$$x = \frac{-a_1 \pm \sqrt{(a_1{}^2 - 4a_0 a_2)}}{2a_0}. \tag{2}$$

Denoting the roots by α_1 and α_2, we can write (1), after division by a_0, in the form

$$(x - \alpha_1)(x - \alpha_2) = 0. \tag{3}$$

Then if $a_1{}^2 \geqq 4a_0 a_2$ the roots α_1 and α_2 will be real. Otherwise they will be conjugate complex numbers $\beta \pm j\gamma$. In this case (3) takes the form

$$(x - \beta - j\gamma)(x - \beta + j\gamma) = (x - \beta)^2 + \gamma^2 = x^2 - 2\beta x + \beta^2 + \gamma^2 = 0. \tag{4}$$

Notice that in general $(x - \alpha)(x - \bar{\alpha})$ is always a *real* quadratic form.

The problem of solving a quadratic equation is equivalent to that of factorising a quadratic form. It is often convenient to carry out the latter process by completing the square. The roots will then be real or complex according as the residual constant is negative or positive.

Example 1
$$x^2 + 4x + 1 = 0.$$
$$(x+2)^2 - (\sqrt{3})^2 = (x + 2 - \sqrt{3})(x + 2 + \sqrt{3}) = 0.$$
Hence
$$x = -2 \pm \sqrt{3}.$$

Example 2
$$x^2 + 5x + 9 = 0.$$
$$(x + \tfrac{5}{2})^2 + \left(\frac{\sqrt{11}}{2}\right)^2 = 0.$$
Hence
$$x = \frac{-5 \pm j\sqrt{11}}{2}.$$

Example 3 $x^2 + 1 \cdot 26x + 3 \cdot 47 = 0.$

                               $(x + 0 \cdot 63)^2 + 3 \cdot 07 = 0.$

Hence $x = -0 \cdot 63 \pm 1 \cdot 75j.$

We turn now to the general equation of order n,

$$a_0 x^n + a_1 x^{n-1} + \ldots + a_{n-1} x + a_n = 0, \tag{5}$$

in which the coefficients are again assumed to be real. It can be proved, but not unfortunately by elementary methods, that this equation has n roots. In general some of these will be real and some will be complex. The latter, however, will occur in conjugate pairs. If the roots are $\alpha_1, \alpha_2, \ldots \alpha_n$ the original equation can be expressed in the form

$$(x - \alpha_1)(x - \alpha_2) \ldots (x - \alpha_n) = 0. \tag{6}$$

Thus any polynomial of degree n can be expressed as the product of n linear factors, real or complex. Since complex roots occur in conjugate pairs the corresponding factors can be multiplied together as in (4) to give quadratic factors with real coefficients. We thus have the following important general theorem.

Theorem   Any polynomial with real coefficients can be expressed as the product of real linear and real quadratic factors.

Unfortunately, if $n > 2$ the solution of (5) involves in general a lengthy numerical process, since there is no simple formula corresponding to (2). Methods of solution are discussed in Appendix 9.

If (6) is multiplied out and the coefficients are compared with those of (5), we deduce the classical result that the sum of the products of all possible combinations of r of the n roots is $(-)^r (a_r/a_0)$. In particular,

$$\alpha_1 + \alpha_2 + \ldots + \alpha_n = -a_1/a_0, \tag{7}$$

$$\alpha_1 \alpha_2 \ldots \alpha_n = (-)^n a_n/a_0. \tag{8}$$

APPENDIX 3

SYNTHETIC DIVISION—REMAINDER THEOREM

When we require to divide one polynomial by another the usual method is to use long division. For example, to divide

$$x^4 + 4x^3 + 3x^2 + 3x + 12$$

by $x+2$, the working is as follows.

$$
\begin{array}{l}
x+2)x^4+4x^3+3x^2+3x+12(x^3+2x^2-x+5 \\
\quad\ \ x^4+2x^3 \\
\quad\ \overline{\quad\ \ 2x^3+3x^2} \\
\quad\ \ \quad\ \ 2x^3+4x^2 \\
\quad\ \ \overline{\quad\ \ \quad -x^2+3x} \\
\quad\ \ \quad\ \ \quad -x^2-2x \\
\quad\ \ \overline{\quad\ \ \quad\ \ \quad\ \ 5x+12} \\
\quad\ \ \quad\ \ \quad\ \ \quad 5x+10 \\
\quad\ \ \overline{\quad\ \ \quad\ \ \quad\ \ \quad\ \ 2}
\end{array}
$$

An examination of this method shows that the necessary arithmetic can be carried out much more compactly and expeditiously by a process using detached coefficients. Consider the general problem of dividing a polynomial $P(x)$ by $x+\alpha$, giving a quotient $Q(x)$ and a remainder R. Let

$$P(x) = p_0 x^n + p_1 x^{n-1} + \dots + p_{n-1}x + p_n$$

and

$$Q(x) = q_0 x^{n-1} + q_1 x^{n-2} + \dots + q_{n-1}.$$

Equating coefficients in the identity

$$P(x) \equiv (x+\alpha)Q(x) + R$$

gives

$$p_0 = q_0,$$
$$p_r = \alpha q_{r-1} + q_r, \qquad r = 1, 2, \dots n-1,$$
$$p_n = \alpha q_{n-1} + R.$$

Writing these in the forms

$$q_0 = p_0,$$
$$q_r = p_r - \alpha q_{r-1}, \qquad r = 1, \dots n-1,$$
$$R = p_n - \alpha q_{n-1},$$

shows that the coefficients $q_0, \ldots q_{n-1}$ and the remainder R can be calculated in turn, using at each stage the preceding coefficient. The working can be set out in tabular form as follows.

	p_0	p_1	p_2	p_3	$\cdots$	p_{n-2}	p_{n-1}	p_n
$\times(-\alpha)$		$-\alpha q_0$	$-\alpha q_1$	$-\alpha q_2$	$\cdots$	$-\alpha q_{n-3}$	$-\alpha q_{n-2}$	$-\alpha q_{n-1}$
	q_0	q_1	q_2	q_3	$\cdots$	q_{n-2}	q_{n-1}	R

After each number below the line is calculated as the sum of the two numbers immediately above, it is multiplied by $-\alpha$ and placed in the next vacant space above the line. This allows the next number below the line to be calculated, and so on. Thus with the above numerical example we have

$$\begin{array}{ccccc} 1 & 4 & 3 & 3 & 12 \\ \times(-2) & -2 & -4 & 2 & -10 \\ \hline 1 & 2 & -1 & 5 \mid & 2, \end{array}$$

showing that the quotient is $x^3 + 2x^2 - x + 5$ and the remainder 2.

This process, which is called *synthetic division*, is not restricted to linear divisors. Thus if we divide $P(x)$ by $x^2 + \alpha x + \beta$ the quotient $Q(x)$ will take the form $q_0 x^{n-2} + \ldots + q_{n-2}$ with a remainder $Rx + S$. The recurrence relations determining $q_0, \ldots q_{n-2}$, R and S are easily verified to be

$$\begin{aligned} q_0 &= p_0, \\ q_1 &= p_1 - \alpha q_0, \\ q_r &= p_r - \alpha q_{r-1} - \beta q_{r-2}, \qquad r = 2, \ldots n-2, \\ R &= p_{n-1} - \alpha q_{n-2} - \beta q_{n-3}, \\ S &= p_n - \beta q_{n-2}. \end{aligned}$$

In tabular form the working is as follows.

	p_0	p_1	p_2	p_3	$\cdots$	p_{n-2}	p_{n-1}	p_n
$\times(-\beta)$			$-\beta q_0$	$-\beta q_1$	$\cdots$	$-\beta q_{n-4}$	$-\beta q_{n-3}$	$-\beta q_{n-2}$
$\times(-\alpha)$		$-\alpha q_0$	$-\alpha q_1$	$-\alpha q_2$	$\cdots$	$-\alpha q_{n-3}$	$-\alpha q_{n-2}$	
	q_0	q_1	q_2	q_3	$\cdots$	q_{n-2}	R	S

As each number below the line is computed it is multiplied by $-\alpha$ and $-\beta$, the products being placed in the next vacant spaces in the third and second rows on the rising diagonal through the number. For example, to divide $2x^4 + 3x^3 - x^2 + 8x + 13$ by $x^2 + 3x + 2$, we have

$$\begin{array}{cccccc} & 2 & 3 & -1 & 8 & 13 \\ \times(-2) & & & -4 & 6 & -8 \\ \times(-3) & & -6 & 9 & -12 & \\ \hline & 2 & -3 & 4 \mid & 2 & 5. \end{array}$$

Thus the quotient is $2x^2 - 3x + 4$ and the remainder $2x + 5$.

This process can clearly be extended to the division of any polynomial by any other of smaller degree.

A useful application of the process of synthetic division is in the evaluation of polynomials for given numerical values of the variable x. We require in addition the *remainder theorem*, which states that if we divide a polynomial $P(x)$ by $x-\alpha$ the remainder is $P(\alpha)$. To prove this it is only necessary to substitute $x = \alpha$ in the identity

$$P(x) \equiv (x-\alpha)Q(x)+R. \tag{1}$$

For example, let us calculate $P(3)$ where $P(x) = x^4-4x^3+2x^2+x-2$. Dividing $P(x)$ by $x-3$, we have

$$
\begin{array}{rrrrr}
1 & -4 & 2 & 1 & -2 \\
\times 3 & 3 & -3 & -3 & -6 \\
\hline
1 & -1 & -1 & -2 \,| & -8,
\end{array}
$$

so that $P(3) = -8$.

This process is usually more rapid than direct substitution, particularly when the numbers involved are not simple integers. In such cases the computation can be carried out easily with the help of a slide rule or a desk machine, particularly one that has facilities for product transfer. For example, to evaluate $P(1{\cdot}57)$ when

$$P(x) = 1{\cdot}26x^3 + 1{\cdot}49x^2 + 0{\cdot}37x + 5.27,$$

the working is as follows.

$$
\begin{array}{cccc}
1{\cdot}26 & 1{\cdot}49 & 0{\cdot}37 & 5{\cdot}27 \\
\times 1{\cdot}57 & 1{\cdot}978 & 5{\cdot}445 & 9{\cdot}13 \\
\hline
1{\cdot}26 & 3{\cdot}468 & 5{\cdot}815 \,| & 14{\cdot}40,
\end{array}
$$

Thus $P(1{\cdot}57) = 14{\cdot}40$.

This method can be extended to the evaluation of $P(x)$ when x is a complex number $\beta+j\gamma$, a computation that can be tedious when carried out by direct substitution, even when only simple numbers are involved. In this case we divide $P(x)$ by $(x-\beta-j\gamma)(x-\beta+j\gamma) = x^2-2\beta x+\beta^2+\gamma^2$. The remainder is now a linear function $Rx+S$. If the quotient is $Q(x)$ we have the identity

$$P(x) \equiv (x^2-2\beta x+\beta^2+\gamma^2)Q(x)+Rx+S. \tag{2}$$

Putting $x = \beta+j\gamma$ in (2) we deduce

$$P(\beta+j\gamma) = R(\beta+j\gamma)+S = R\beta+S+jR\gamma.$$

In this way, except for the last step, the computation involves only real numbers. For example, to calculate $P(1+2j)$ when

$$P(x) = x^4 + 2x^3 - 4x^2 + 16x + 7,$$

dividing by $x^2 - 2x + 5$,

	1	2	−4	16	7
×(−5)			−5	−20	5
×2			2	8	−2
	1	4	−1	−6	12,

which gives $P(1+2j) = -6(1+2j)+12 = 6-12j.$

METHODS OF EXPANSION

The standard formula expressing an arbitrary function $f(x)$ in a series of ascending powers of x is *Maclaurin's expansion*,

$$f(x) = f(0) + xf'(0) + \frac{x^2}{2!}f''(0) + \frac{x^3}{3!}f'''(0) + \ldots \tag{1}$$

By direct application of this or by other methods the following familiar expansions can be deduced:

$$e^x = 1 + x + \frac{x^2}{2!} + \frac{x^3}{3!} + \ldots, \tag{2}$$

$$\cos x = 1 - \frac{x^2}{2!} + \frac{x^4}{4!} - \frac{x^6}{6!} + \ldots, \tag{3}$$

$$\sin x = x - \frac{x^3}{3!} + \frac{x^5}{5!} - \frac{x^7}{7!} + \ldots, \tag{4}$$

$$\tan x = x + \tfrac{1}{3}x^3 + \tfrac{2}{15}x^5 + \ldots, \tag{5}$$

$$\sec x = 1 + \tfrac{1}{2}x^2 + \tfrac{5}{24}x^4 + \ldots, \tag{6}$$

$$\sin^{-1} x = x + \tfrac{1}{6}x^3 + \tfrac{3}{40}x^5 + \ldots, \tag{7}$$

$$\tan^{-1} x = x - \tfrac{1}{3}x^3 + \tfrac{1}{5}x^5 + \ldots, \tag{8}$$

$$\log_e(1+x) = x - \tfrac{1}{2}x^2 + \tfrac{1}{3}x^3 - \tfrac{1}{4}x^4 + \ldots, \tag{9}$$

$$(1+x)^n = 1 + nx + \binom{n}{2}x^2 + \binom{n}{3}x^3 + \ldots \tag{10}$$

The first three of these series converge for all values of x, the next two only if $|x| < \tfrac{1}{2}\pi$, and the remaining four if $|x| < 1$.

The last series is of course the binomial theorem in its most general form. Here we have used the notation $\binom{n}{r}$ to denote the general binomial coefficient $n(n-1)(n-2) \ldots (n-r+1)/r!$. A very important special case occurs when $n = -1$, giving

$$\frac{1}{1+x} = 1-x+x^2-x^3+\ldots \tag{11}$$

or, replacing x by $-x$,

$$\frac{1}{1-x} = 1+x+x^2+x^3+\ldots. \tag{12}$$

An important requirement in this book is for efficient methods of expanding rational fractions, and for this Maclaurin's formula is not particularly suitable. If only two or three terms of the series are required it is better to use the binomial theorem, particularly (11) and (12), while if more terms are necessary, synthetic division is preferable. These methods are demonstrated in the following examples.

Example 1　　$\dfrac{1}{2+5x} = \dfrac{1}{2}\left(\dfrac{1}{1+\frac{5}{2}x}\right) = \frac{1}{2}(1-\frac{5}{2}x+\frac{25}{4}x^2-\ldots)$

$$= \tfrac{1}{2}-\tfrac{5}{4}x+\tfrac{25}{8}x^2-\ldots.$$

Example 2　　$\dfrac{1}{2-3x+4x^2} = \dfrac{1}{2}\left(\dfrac{1}{1-(\frac{3}{2}x-2x^2)}\right)$

$$= \tfrac{1}{2}\{1+(\tfrac{3}{2}x-2x^2)+(\tfrac{3}{2}x-2x^2)^2+\ldots\}$$

$$= \tfrac{1}{2}(1+\tfrac{3}{2}x-2x^2+\tfrac{9}{4}x^2+\ldots)$$

$$= \tfrac{1}{2}+\tfrac{3}{4}x+\tfrac{1}{8}x^2+\ldots.$$

Example 3　　$\dfrac{1-x}{1+2x} = (1-x)(1-2x+4x^2-8x^3+\ldots)$

$$= 1-3x+6x^2-12x^3+\ldots.$$

Example 4　$\dfrac{1}{2x+3x^2} = \dfrac{1}{2x}\left(\dfrac{1}{1+\frac{3}{2}x}\right) = \dfrac{1}{2x}(1-\tfrac{3}{2}x+\tfrac{9}{4}x^2-\tfrac{27}{8}x^3+\ldots)$

$$= \dfrac{1}{2x}-\tfrac{3}{4}+\tfrac{9}{8}x-\tfrac{27}{16}x^2+\ldots.$$

Example 5　　　　　　　　$\dfrac{1-x+x^2}{1+2x+3x^2}.$

Here we use synthetic division, arranged in *ascending* powers of x.

	1	-1	1	0	0	$\ldots$
$\times(-3)$			-3	9	-12	$\ldots$
$\times(-2)$		-2	6	-8	-2	$\ldots$
	1	-3	4	1	-14	$\ldots$

The required series is therefore $1-3x+4x^2+x^3-14x^4-\ldots.$

We conclude this appendix by mentioning Taylor's series, which is a generalisation of Maclaurin's formula. This is

$$f(a+h) = f(a) + hf'(a) + \frac{h^2}{2!}f''(a) + \ldots + \frac{h^n}{n!}f^{(n)}(a) + \ldots \tag{13}$$

EXERCISES   Obtain the first four terms of the expansions in ascending powers of x of the following fractions:

1. $\dfrac{1-2x}{1+3x}$,   2. $\dfrac{1}{2-x+x^2}$,   3. $\dfrac{1}{x^2+x^3}$,   4. $\dfrac{1+x+2x^2}{1+2x+4x^2}$.

APPENDIX 5

PARTIAL FRACTIONS

Consider the rational fraction $F(x) = (3x+8)/(x^2+5x+6)$. The denominator has factors $(x+2)(x+3)$. Let us investigate the possibility of expressing $F(x)$ as the sum of two fractions each of which has one of these factors as denominator. Assuming this to be possible, let

$$\frac{3x+8}{(x+2)(x+3)} \equiv \frac{A}{x+2} + \frac{B}{x+3}.$$

If the right-hand side is put over a common denominator and the coefficients of the numerators are equated we have $A+B = 3$, $3A+2B = 8$. The solution of these equations is $A = 2$, $B = 1$. We thus have the identity

$$\frac{3x+8}{(x+2)(x+3)} \equiv \frac{2}{x+2} + \frac{1}{x+3}.$$

We call the right-hand side of this identity the *partial fractions* of the left-hand side.

Let $F(x) = P(x)/Q(x)$ where $P(x)$ and $Q(x)$ are polynomials of degrees m and n. Then if $m < n$, $F(x)$ is a *proper rational fraction*. If $F(x)$ is not proper, it can be expressed as the sum of a polynomial and a proper rational fraction. The former is the quotient when $P(x)$ is divided by $Q(x)$ and the latter has the remainder as numerator.

Theorem 1   If $P/(Q_1Q_2)$ is a proper rational fraction and if P, Q_1 and Q_2 have no common factors, then this fraction can be expressed uniquely as the sum of two proper partial fractions with denominators Q_1 and Q_2. Thus

$$\frac{P}{Q_1Q_2} \equiv \frac{P_1}{Q_1} + \frac{P_2}{Q_2}.$$

This theorem will not be proved here.

By repeated application of Theorem 1 it is clear that if

$$Q(x) = (x-\alpha_1)(x-\alpha_2) \ldots (x-\alpha_n)$$

where $\alpha_1, \alpha_2, \ldots \alpha_n$ are all different, the partial fractions of $F(x)$ take the form

$$\frac{P(x)}{Q(x)} \equiv \frac{A_1}{x-\alpha_1} + \frac{A_2}{x-\alpha_2} + \ldots + \frac{A_n}{x-\alpha_n}. \qquad (1)$$

If the right-hand side is put over a common denominator the numerator will have degree $n-1$. By equating its coefficients to those of $P(x)$ we obtain n simultaneous equations that can be solved for the constants $A_1, A_2, \ldots A_n$.

This, however, is not the best way to calculate the constants. There is available an alternative method which allows them to be written down by inspection.

Theorem 2   Let $x-\alpha_1$ be a non-repeated factor of $Q(x)$ and let $Q(x) = (x-\alpha_1)Q_1(x)$. If

$$\frac{P(x)}{Q(x)} \equiv \frac{P(x)}{(x-\alpha_1)Q_1(x)} \equiv \frac{A_1}{x-\alpha_1} + \frac{P_1(x)}{Q_1(x)},$$

then

$$A_1 = \frac{P(\alpha_1)}{Q_1(\alpha_1)}.$$

Proof   If the above identity is multiplied by $x-\alpha_1$ we have

$$\frac{P(x)}{Q_1(x)} \equiv A_1 + \frac{(x-\alpha_1)P_1(x)}{Q_1(x)}. \qquad (2)$$

The result follows immediately if we put $x = \alpha_1$.

Example 1   Let $\dfrac{2x}{(x-1)(x-2)(x-3)} \equiv \dfrac{A_1}{x-1} + \dfrac{A_2}{x-2} + \dfrac{A_3}{x-3}$.

To find A_1 using Theorem 2, substitute 1 for x in the left-hand side after suppressing the factor $x-1$. This gives

$$A_1 = \frac{2.1}{(1-2)(1-3)} = 1.$$

Similarly $A_2 = \dfrac{2.2}{(2-1)(2-3)} = -4$ and $A_3 = 3$.

Hence $\dfrac{2x}{(x-1)(x-2)(x-3)} = \dfrac{1}{x-1} - \dfrac{4}{x-2} + \dfrac{3}{x-3}$.

If any two of the numbers $\alpha_1, \ldots \alpha_n$ are complex conjugates it is usual to combine the corresponding factors of the denominator to form a single quadratic factor with real coefficients (see Appendix 2, equation (4)). Then by Theorem 1, a factor $x^2+\beta x+\gamma$ in $Q(x)$ will lead to a partial fraction of the type $(Bx+C)/(x^2+\beta x+\gamma)$. The determination of the constants in simple cases of this type can be effected by a combination of the inspection method with the equating of coefficients.

Example 2 Let

$$\frac{1}{(x+1)(x^2+2x+3)} \equiv \frac{A}{x+1} + \frac{Bx+C}{x^2+2x+3}.$$

By inspection $A = \frac{1}{2}$. If we now equate the coefficients of x^2 and the constant terms in the numerators of this identity we have $A+B = 0$, $3A+C = 1$. Hence $B = -\frac{1}{2}$, $C = -\frac{1}{2}$, so that

$$\frac{1}{(x+1)(x^2+2x+3)} = \frac{1}{2(x+1)} - \frac{x+1}{2(x^2+2x+3)}.$$

When the denominator contains repeated factors, the corresponding partial fractions take a special form. Let $Q(x) = (x-\alpha_1)^k Q_1(x)$, where $Q_1(\alpha_1) \neq 0$. Then by Theorem 1

$$\frac{P(x)}{Q(x)} \equiv \frac{B_1(x)}{(x-\alpha_1)^k} + \frac{P_1(x)}{Q_1(x)}, \tag{3}$$

where $B_1(x)$ is a polynomial of degree $< k$. Let

$$B_1(x) \equiv A_1 + A_1'(x-\alpha_1) + A_1''(x-\alpha_1)^2 + \ldots + A_1^{[k-1]}(x-\alpha_1)^{k-1}. \tag{4}$$

Substituting in (3),

$$\frac{P(x)}{Q(x)} = \frac{A_1}{(x-\alpha_1)^k} + \frac{A_1'}{(x-\alpha_1)^{k-1}} + \ldots + \frac{A_1^{[k-1]}}{x-\alpha_1} + \frac{P_1(x)}{Q_1(x)}. \tag{5}$$

It is easily seen that the inspection method allows A_1 to be written down as $P(\alpha_1)/Q_1(\alpha_1)$. The other coefficients can be obtained by equating coefficients or by the following method. Multiply (5) by $(x-\alpha_1)^k$ and put $y = x-\alpha_1$.

$$\frac{P(\alpha_1+y)}{Q_1(\alpha_1+y)} = A_1 + A_1'y + \ldots + A_1^{[k-1]}y^{k-1} + y^k\frac{P_1(\alpha_1+y)}{Q_1(\alpha_1+y)}.$$

The constants $A_1, \ldots A_1^{[k-1]}$ are thus the first k coefficients in the expansion of the left-hand side in ascending powers of y. These can be obtained from Maclaurin's expansion or preferably by division or use of the binomial theorem.

Example 3 Let

$$\frac{1}{(x-1)^3(x+1)^2} \equiv \frac{A_1}{(x-1)^3} + \frac{A_1'}{(x-1)^2} + \frac{A_1''}{x-1} + \frac{A_2}{(x+1)^2} + \frac{A_2'}{x+1}.$$

Omitting the factor $(x-1)^3$ and putting $y = x-1$, we get the expansion

$$\frac{1}{(2+y)^2} = \tfrac{1}{4}(1+\tfrac{1}{2}y)^{-2} = \tfrac{1}{4}(1-y+\tfrac{3}{4}y^2\ldots),$$

so that $A_1 = \tfrac{1}{4}$, $A_1' = -\tfrac{1}{4}$ and $A_2' = \tfrac{3}{16}$. Similarly, omitting the other factor and putting $y = x+1$,

$$\frac{1}{(-2+y)^3} = -\tfrac{1}{8}(1-\tfrac{1}{2}y)^{-3} = -\tfrac{1}{8}-\tfrac{3}{16}y-\ldots,$$

so that $A_2 = -\tfrac{1}{8}$, $A_2' = -\tfrac{3}{16}$. We have therefore

$$\frac{1}{(x-1)^3(x+1)^2} = \frac{1}{4(x-1)^3} - \frac{1}{4(x-1)^2} + \frac{3}{16(x-1)} - \frac{1}{8(x+1)^2} - \frac{3}{16(x+1)}.$$

For more complicated fractions, such as those whose denominators contain two or more quadratic factors, an extension of the inspection method can be used. Let

$$\frac{P(x)}{(x^2+\beta x+\gamma)Q_1(x)} \equiv \frac{Bx+C}{x^2+\beta x+\gamma} + \frac{P_1(x)}{Q_1(x)}. \tag{6}$$

Multiply by $x^2+\beta x+\gamma$. Then

$$Bx+C = \frac{P(x)}{Q_1(x)} \tag{7}$$

if $\qquad\qquad x^2+\beta x+\gamma = 0.$

By repeated substitution of $-\beta x-\gamma$ for x^2, $P(x)$ and $Q_1(x)$ can be reduced to linear forms $ax+b$ and $cx+d$ (these forms, which are the remainders when $P(x)$ and $Q_1(x)$ are divided by $x^2+\beta x+\gamma$, can be derived alternatively by synthetic division). We continue the reduction as follows.

$$Bx+C = \frac{ax+b}{cx+d} = f + \frac{g}{x+h}, \tag{8}$$

where $f = a/c$, $h = d/c$ and $g = (bc-ad)/c^2$.

Finally, if $x^2+\beta x+\gamma \equiv (x+h)(x+k)+l = 0$ we have

$$Bx+C = f - \frac{g}{l}(x+k). \tag{9}$$

Now, whereas (6) is an identity, (7) and (8) are satisfied only for the two roots of the equation $x^2+\beta x+\gamma = 0$. But in (9) we have two linear forms which are equal for two values of x. They must therefore be identically equal.

T.L.S.—15

Example 4   Let

$$\frac{x}{(x-2)(x^2-x+1)(x-1)^2} \equiv \frac{A}{x-2}+\frac{B_1x+C_1}{x^2-x+1}+\frac{B_2x+C_2}{x^2-2x+1}.$$

By inspection, $A = \frac{2}{3}$. Using the above method by first putting $x^2-x+1 = 0$,

$$B_1x+C_1 = \frac{x}{(x-2)(x^2-2x+1)} = \frac{x}{-x(x-2)} = \frac{-1}{x-2}.$$

If we now write $x^2-x+1 = (x-2)(x+1)+3 = 0$ we have

$$\frac{1}{x-2} = -\tfrac{1}{3}(x+1),$$

so that $B_1x+C_1 = \tfrac{1}{3}(x+1).$

The same method can be used to give

$$B_2x+C_2 = \frac{x}{(x-2)(x^2-x+1)} = \frac{x}{x(x-2)} = \frac{1}{x-2} = -x,$$

since $x^2-2x+1=(x-2)x+1=0$. But

$$\frac{-x}{(x-1)^2} = -\frac{1}{(x-1)^2}-\frac{1}{x-1}.$$

The final partial fractions are therefore

$$\frac{2}{3(x-2)}+\frac{x+1}{3(x^2-x+1)}-\frac{1}{(x-1)^2}-\frac{1}{x-1}.$$

EXERCISES   Express in partial fractions:

1. $\dfrac{x^2+2}{x^3-7x+6}$,   2. $\dfrac{x^2}{x^3-5x^2+8x-4}$,   3. $\dfrac{x}{x^6-1}$.

APPENDIX 6

PROPERTIES OF OPERATORS

Definitions of the direct and inverse operators have been given in **1.3** and **2.2**. In this appendix we prove formally some of the properties stated in Chapter 2 and show to what extent these operators may or may not be manipulated algebraically. As in this chapter $P(\mathbf{D})$, $Q(\mathbf{D})$ and $S(\mathbf{D})$ denote polynomials in the operator $\mathbf{D}$, and u is a function of t.

Theorem 1 $\qquad P_1(\mathbf{D})\{P_2(\mathbf{D})u\} = \{P_1(\mathbf{D})P_2(\mathbf{D})\}u.$

This follows directly from **1.3** (2), (3) and (4) and is illustrated by a simple numerical example in **1.3**. It shows that direct operators are combined by algebraic multiplication and hence that they are commutative. We show now that a similar result holds for inverse operators.

Theorem 2 $\qquad \dfrac{1}{Q_1(\mathbf{D})}\left\{\dfrac{1}{Q_2(\mathbf{D})}u\right\} = \dfrac{1}{Q_1(\mathbf{D})Q_2(\mathbf{D})}u.$

For if x denotes the left-hand side, $Q_1(\mathbf{D})x = y$ where $Q_2(\mathbf{D})y = u$. Hence x is any function satisfying $Q_1(\mathbf{D})Q_2(\mathbf{D})x = u$.

We consider next the effect of commuting a direct and an inverse operator. It is assumed here as in Chapter 2 that the expression $\{1/Q(\mathbf{D})\}u$ is the general solution of the corresponding differential equation, being the sum of a particular integral and the complementary function $\{1/Q(\mathbf{D})\}0$. These are called the particular form and the complementary function of the expression.

Theorem 3 $\qquad Q(\mathbf{D})\left\{\dfrac{1}{Q(\mathbf{D})}u\right\} = u.$

This follows directly from the definition of the inverse operator.

Theorem 4 $\qquad \dfrac{1}{Q(\mathbf{D})}\{Q(\mathbf{D})u\} = u + \dfrac{1}{Q(\mathbf{D})}0.$

For if x denotes the left-hand side, $Q(\mathbf{D})x = Q(\mathbf{D})u$ or $Q(\mathbf{D})(x-u) = 0$ so that $x-u = \{1/Q(\mathbf{D})\}0$.

Theorem 5

If $\quad x_1 = \dfrac{1}{Q(\mathbf{D})}\{P(\mathbf{D})u\} \quad$ and $\quad x_2 = P(\mathbf{D})\left\{\dfrac{1}{Q(\mathbf{D})}u\right\} \quad$ then $\quad x_1 = x_2$

provided $P(\mathbf{D})$ and $Q(\mathbf{D})$ are mutually prime, that is, they have no common factor. If they have a common factor, x_1 has additional complementary function terms corresponding to this common factor.

Proof It is obvious that the aggregate x_1 is identical with the aggregate x where $Q(\mathbf{D})x = P(\mathbf{D})u$. Also x_2 belongs to this aggregate, for

$$Q(\mathbf{D})x_2 = Q(\mathbf{D})P(\mathbf{D})\frac{1}{Q(\mathbf{D})}u = P(\mathbf{D})Q(\mathbf{D})\frac{1}{Q(\mathbf{D})}u = P(\mathbf{D})u.$$

by Theorems 1 and 3. It follows that if x_1 and x_2 differ, they must do so in the complementary function terms $\{1/Q(\mathbf{D})\}0$. Now x_1 contains all these terms and so does $\{1/Q(\mathbf{D})\}u$; x_2 will do so also unless the operation $P(\mathbf{D})$ causes some or all of these to vanish. Let a typical term of $\{1/Q(\mathbf{D})\}0$ be $Ae^{\lambda t}$. Then $P(\mathbf{D})Ae^{\lambda t} = P(\lambda)Ae^{\lambda t}$. This will vanish if, and only if, $P(\lambda) = 0$, that is if $P(\mathbf{D})$ and $Q(\mathbf{D})$ have a common factor $\mathbf{D} - \lambda$. This proof can be extended to cover the case of repeated common factors.

As in **2.6**, the general rational fraction operator $F(\mathbf{D}) = P(\mathbf{D})/Q(\mathbf{D})$ is defined by saying that $x = F(\mathbf{D})u$ if $Q(\mathbf{D})x = P(\mathbf{D})u$. This means that the inverse operation is carried out *after* the direct operation. Thus

$$F(\mathbf{D}) = \frac{1}{Q(\mathbf{D})}P(\mathbf{D}). \tag{1}$$

Theorem 5 shows that reversal of the order of the operations has no effect provided $P(\mathbf{D})$ and $Q(\mathbf{D})$ are mutually prime. If, however, they have a common factor, complementary function terms are lost. Our definition of $F(\mathbf{D})$ in fact preserves maximum generality.

Theorem 6 $\qquad \dfrac{P_1(\mathbf{D}) + P_2(\mathbf{D})}{Q(\mathbf{D})}u = \dfrac{P_1(\mathbf{D})}{Q(\mathbf{D})}u + \dfrac{P_2(\mathbf{D})}{Q(\mathbf{D})}u.$

Denote the two terms of the right-hand side by x_1 and x_2. Then by definition $Q(\mathbf{D})x_1 = P_1(\mathbf{D})u$ and $Q(\mathbf{D})x_2 = P_2(\mathbf{D})u$. Adding,

$$Q(\mathbf{D})(x_1 + x_2) = \{P_1(\mathbf{D}) + P_2(\mathbf{D})\}u,$$

which proves the theorem.

Theorems 1 to 6 show that rational fraction operators can be broken down or combined by algebraic manipulation, with the reservations imposed by the fact that a direct operator and its inverse are not commutative. The most important of these reservations concern the processes of cancelling a common factor from the numerator and denominator and of multiplication of numerator and denominator by a common factor. The effects of these are respectively the elimination and the introduction of extra complementary function terms. For example,

$$\frac{1}{D+2} e^t = \tfrac{1}{3} e^t + A e^{-2t}, \tag{2}$$

but

$$\frac{(D+3)}{(D+2)(D+3)} e^t = \tfrac{1}{3} e^t + A e^{-2t} + B e^{-3t}, \tag{3}$$

being the general solution of $(D+2)(D+3)x = (D+3)e^t$, that is, of

$$(D+2)(D+3)x = 4 e^t.$$

Cancellation of common factors is not usually serious since the eliminated complementary function terms usually appear elsewhere, as happens for example in Theorem 7. The introduction of extra factors in the denominator should, however, be avoided since this can lead to false results arising from spurious complementary function terms.

Theorem 7   Rational fraction operators may be expressed in partial fractions.

Let $F(D) = \dfrac{P(D)}{Q_1(D)Q_2(D)}$ where $Q_1(D)$ and $Q_2(D)$ are mutually prime

and let $P(D) = P_1(D)Q_2(D) + P_2(D)Q_1(D).$

Then, using the abbreviated notation F for $F(D)$, and so on,

$$F = \frac{P_1Q_2 + P_2Q_1}{Q_1Q_2} = \frac{P_1Q_2}{Q_1Q_2} + \frac{P_2Q_1}{Q_1Q_2} = \frac{P_1}{Q_1} + \frac{P_2}{Q_2}.$$

Here we have first used Theorem 6 and then cancelled Q_2 and Q_1 from the two separate terms. This is permissible since the complementary function terms eliminated from the first term appear in the second term, and vice versa. By repeated application of this result any fraction may be broken down completely into partial fractions in the usual form.

Theorem 8   Rational fraction operators may be expanded in series of *ascending* powers of **D**.

Let $F(D) = P(D)/Q(D)$ be expanded by division in a series in ascending powers of **D** as far as the term in D^n. This series will usually start with a constant but it will start with a positive or with a negative power of **D** if **D** is a factor of the numerator or of the denominator. Let the series be $\ldots +a_{n-1}\mathbf{D}^{n-1}+a_n\mathbf{D}^n = A_n(\mathbf{D})$ and let the remainder, which will have $\mathbf{D}^{n+1}$ as a factor, be $\mathbf{D}^{n+1}S_n(\mathbf{D})$. Then

$$P(\mathbf{D}) = A_n(\mathbf{D})Q(\mathbf{D})+\mathbf{D}^{n+1}S_n(\mathbf{D})$$

or
$$F(\mathbf{D}) = A_n(\mathbf{D})+\frac{\mathbf{D}^{n+1}S_n(\mathbf{D})}{Q(\mathbf{D})}, \tag{4}$$

so that
$$F(\mathbf{D})u = A_n(\mathbf{D})u+r_n \tag{5}$$

where
$$r_n = \frac{S_n(\mathbf{D})\mathbf{D}^{n+1}}{Q(\mathbf{D})}u. \tag{6}$$

If $r_n \to 0$ as $n \to \infty$ we have $F(\mathbf{D})u = \lim_{n \to \infty} A_n(\mathbf{D})u$, which is a convergent infinite series. The convergence of series of this type is discussed in Appendix 7.

If, on the other hand, $F(\mathbf{D})$ is expanded formally in descending powers of $\mathbf{D}$, let the quotient be $\ldots +b_{n-1}\mathbf{D}^{-n+1}+b_n\mathbf{D}^{-n} = B_n(\mathbf{D})/\mathbf{D}^n$ and the remainder $T_n(\mathbf{D})/\mathbf{D}^{n+1}$. Then the corresponding operational identity is

$$\frac{P(\mathbf{D})}{Q(\mathbf{D})} = \frac{\mathbf{D}B_n(\mathbf{D})Q(\mathbf{D})+T_n(\mathbf{D})}{\mathbf{D}^{n+1}Q(\mathbf{D})},$$

which cannot be established without multiplying numerator and denominator by $\mathbf{D}^{n+1}$. Since this could introduce spurious complementary function terms, which as $n \to \infty$ could be of a very general nature, we do not use this process.

Theorem 9
$$F(\mathbf{D})(e^{\alpha t}u) = e^{\alpha t}F(\mathbf{D}+\alpha)u.$$

Denoting the left-hand side by x,

$$Q(\mathbf{D})x = P(\mathbf{D})(e^{\alpha t}u) = e^{\alpha t}P(\mathbf{D}+\alpha)u,$$

using **2.2**, property (IIa). But, by the same property,

$$Q(\mathbf{D})x = e^{\alpha t}Q(\mathbf{D}+\alpha)(e^{-\alpha t}x).$$

Hence
$$Q(\mathbf{D}+\alpha)(e^{-\alpha t}x) = P(\mathbf{D}+\alpha)u,$$

or
$$e^{-\alpha t}x = F(\mathbf{D}+\alpha)u$$

so that
$$x = e^{\alpha t}F(\mathbf{D}+\alpha)u.$$

As examples of the operational process we conclude by giving formal proofs of certain elementary rules used in Chapter 2. Consider first what happens when $F(\mathbf{D})$ operates on the constant unity. Taking the first term only of the expansion of $F(\mathbf{D})$, which by Taylor's theorem is $F(0)$, and using (5) with $u = 1$,

$$F(\mathbf{D})1 = \left\{F(0)+\frac{S_0(\mathbf{D})\mathbf{D}}{Q(\mathbf{D})}\right\}1 = F(0)+\frac{S_0(\mathbf{D})}{Q(\mathbf{D})}0.$$

Hence
$$F(\mathbf{D})1 = F(0) + \frac{1}{Q(\mathbf{D})}0, \tag{7}$$

provided $F(0) \neq \infty$. If $F(0) = \infty$, $F(\mathbf{D})$ will have the form

$$F_1(\mathbf{D})/\mathbf{D}^n = P(\mathbf{D})/\{\mathbf{D}^n Q_1(\mathbf{D})\}$$

where $Q_1(0) \neq 0$. We then have

$$F(\mathbf{D})1 = \left\{\frac{F_1(0)}{\mathbf{D}^n} + \frac{S_0(\mathbf{D})\mathbf{D}}{\mathbf{D}^n Q_1(\mathbf{D})}\right\}1 = \frac{F_1(0)t^n}{n!} + \frac{1}{Q(\mathbf{D})}0. \tag{8}$$

Complementary functions in the first term need not be written down since they are included in the second term.

Finally, using Theorem 9 we consider the effect of operating on $e^{\alpha t}$ with $F(\mathbf{D})$.

$$F(\mathbf{D})e^{\alpha t} = e^{\alpha t}F(\mathbf{D}+\alpha)1 = e^{\alpha t}\left\{F(\alpha) + \frac{1}{Q(\mathbf{D}+\alpha)}0\right\} = F(\alpha)e^{\alpha t} + \frac{1}{Q(\mathbf{D})}(e^{\alpha t}0).$$

Hence
$$F(\mathbf{D})e^{\alpha t} = F(\alpha)e^{\alpha t} + \frac{1}{Q(\mathbf{D})}0, \tag{9}$$

provided $F(\alpha) \neq \infty$. If $F(\alpha) = \infty$,

$$F(\mathbf{D})e^{\alpha t} = \frac{F_1(\mathbf{D})}{(\mathbf{D}-\alpha)^n}e^{\alpha t} = e^{\alpha t}\frac{F_1(\mathbf{D}+\alpha)}{\mathbf{D}^n}1 = e^{\alpha t}\left\{\frac{F_1(\alpha)t^n}{n!} + \frac{1}{\mathbf{D}^n Q_1(\mathbf{D})}0\right\}$$

or
$$F(\mathbf{D})e^{\alpha t} = \frac{F_1(\alpha)t^n e^{\alpha t}}{n!} + \frac{1}{Q(\mathbf{D})}0. \tag{10}$$

EXPANSION OF OPERATORS—
ASYMPTOTIC SERIES

In Appendix 6 a formal justification of the process of expanding the operator $F(\mathbf{D})$ in a series of ascending powers of $\mathbf{D}$ together with a remainder term is given. In this appendix we consider the general first order linear equation in detail, giving alternative derivations of the expansion and showing, by three examples, how convergent, divergent and asymptotic series can arise.

Writing this differential equation in the form

$$(T\mathbf{D}+1)x = f(t) \tag{1}$$

or

$$x = \frac{1}{1+T\mathbf{D}}f(t),$$

and expanding the operator by division, the remainder after n terms is found to be $(-T)^n\mathbf{D}^n$. Thus

$$x = \left\{1 - T\mathbf{D} + T^2\mathbf{D}^2 - \ldots + (-T)^{n-1}\mathbf{D}^{n-1} + \frac{(-T)^n\mathbf{D}^n}{1+T\mathbf{D}}\right\}f(t)$$

$$= f(t) - Tf'(T) + T^2f''(T) - \ldots + (-T)^{n-1}f^{(n-1)}(t) + r_n(t), \tag{2}$$

where the remainder $r_n(t)$ is given by

$$(1+T\mathbf{D})r_n(t) = (-T)^n\mathbf{D}^nf(t) = (-T)^nf^{(n)}(t).$$

Solving this differential equation, using the form **1.4** (6),

$$r_n(t) = -(-T)^{n-1}e^{-t/T}\int e^{t/T}f^{(n)}(t)\,dt. \tag{3}$$

A second method of obtaining the solution (2) is as follows. Applying **1.4** (6) to (1),

$$x = \frac{1}{T}e^{-t/T}\int e^{t/T}f(t)\,dt$$

$$= e^{-t/T}\left\{e^{t/T}f(t) - \int e^{t/T}f'(t)\,dt\right\},$$

integrating by parts. Thus

$$x = f(t) - e^{-t/T} \int e^{t/T} f'(t)\, dt.$$

Another integration by parts gives

$$x = f(t) - Tf'(t) + T\, e^{-t/T} \int e^{t/T} f''(t)\, dt.$$

Further repetition of this process gives the solution (2), with $r_n(t)$ as given in (3).

Yet another proof is obtained by writing (1) in the form

$$x = f(t) - T\mathbf{D}x,$$

and by repeatedly substituting this expression for x in the right-hand side. Thus

$$x = f(t) - T\mathbf{D}\{f(t) - T\mathbf{D}x\} = f(t) - Tf'(t) + T^2\mathbf{D}^2x = \ldots$$

$$= f(t) - Tf'(t) + T^2 f''(t) - \ldots + (-T)^{n-1} f^{(n-1)}(t) + (-T)^n \mathbf{D}^n x.$$

Since $\mathbf{D}^n x = \{\mathbf{D}^n/(1+T\mathbf{D})\}f(t)$, this form is equivalent to (2).

The form (2) with the remainder (3) which we have obtained from the differential equation (1) is always valid provided $f(t)$ can be differentiated n times within the range of values of t for which a solution is required. We consider now what can happen if n is made to tend to infinity. For this discussion to have a meaning $f(t)$ must of course have derivatives of all orders and these derivatives must have no discontinuity in the range considered. This condition imposes one limitation on the scope of the process. The most important limitation, however, arises from the requirement that the series obtained must be convergent or asymptotic. Moreover, if the series cannot be summed, it must give an adequate approximation after a few terms.

If we let n tend to infinity in (2), the right-hand side becomes an infinite series which converges to the required solution if, and only if, $r_n(t) \to 0$ as $n \to \infty$. Consider two examples.

Example 1 $\qquad\qquad (\mathbf{D}+3)x = e^{2t}.$

$$x = \frac{1}{3+\mathbf{D}} e^{2t} = \left(\frac{1}{3} - \frac{\mathbf{D}}{3^2} + \frac{\mathbf{D}^2}{3^3} - \frac{\mathbf{D}^3}{3^4} + \ldots \right) e^{2t}$$

$$= \left(\frac{1}{3} - \frac{2}{3^2} + \frac{2^2}{3^3} - \frac{2^3}{3^4} + \ldots \right) e^{2t}.$$

This series is convergent and has sum to infinity

$$\tfrac{1}{3}\frac{1}{1+\tfrac{2}{3}}e^{2t} = \tfrac{1}{5}e^{2t}.$$

The remainder is given by

$$r_n(t) = (-\tfrac{1}{3})^n e^{-3t}\int e^{3t}.2^n e^{2t}\,dt = \tfrac{1}{5}(-\tfrac{2}{3})^n e^{2t},$$

which tends to zero as $n \to \infty$.

Example 2 $(\mathbf{D}+2)x = e^{3t}.$

In this case it is easily seen that this method gives a divergent series and that $r_n(t) \to \infty$ as $n \to \infty$.

   Both of the above examples are of academic interest only, since the required particular integrals can be obtained much more simply by elementary methods. We consider now a third example, in which we obtain a useful solution that cannot be derived by other methods.

Example 3 $(\mathbf{D}+1)x = \dfrac{1}{12-t}.$ (4)

The general solution is

$$x = e^{-t}\int \frac{e^t\,dt}{12-t}.$$ (5)

This integral cannot be expressed in terms of a finite number of elementary functions. There can therefore be no solution of the differential equation in this form.

   Let us denote by $x(t)$ the particular integral that vanishes when $t = -\infty$ and consider what happens when we give t a particular value, say 2. The integral in (5) can now be expressed as a definite integral, thus

$$x(2) = e^{-2}\int_{-\infty}^{2} \frac{e^t\,dt}{12-t}.$$ (6)

By using available tables or by evaluating the integral numerically it is found that

$$x(2) = 0\cdot0915632\ldots.$$

On the other hand, if the operator is expanded we obtain the solution

$$x = (1-\mathbf{D}+\mathbf{D}^2-\mathbf{D}^3+\ldots)\frac{1}{12-t}+Ce^{-t}.$$

Since the series vanishes when $t = -\infty$ we can write formally

$$x(t) = \frac{1}{12-t} - \frac{1}{(12-t)^2} + \frac{2!}{(12-t)^3} - \frac{3!}{(12-t)^4} + \ldots,$$

whence

$$x(2) = \frac{1}{10} - \frac{1}{10^2} + \frac{2!}{10^3} - \frac{3!}{10^4} + \ldots.$$

Denote the nth term of this series by $u_n(2)$, the sum of the first n terms by $s_n(2)$ and the corresponding remainder by $r_n(2)$. Then

$$s_n(2) + r_n(2) = x(2).$$

Table A7 shows values of these three quantities for values of n from 1 to 12.

n	1	2	3	4
$u_n(2)$	0·1	−0·01	0·002	—0·0006
$s_n(2)$	0·1	0·009	0·092	0·0914
$r_n(2)$	−0·008	0·0016	−0·00044	0·00016

n	5	6	7	8
$u_n(2)$	0·00024	−0·00012	0·000072	−0·0000504
$s_n(2)$	0·09164	0·09152	0·091592	0·0915416
$r_n(2)$	−0·000077	0·000043	−0·000029	0·0000216

n	9	10	11	12
$u_n(2)$	0·0000403	−0·0000363	0·0000363	−0·0000399
$s_n(2)$	0·0915819	0·0915456	0·0915819	0·0915420
$r_n(2)$	−0·0000187	0·0000176	−0·0000187	0·0000212

TABLE A7

It appears from this that although the numbers $u_n(2)$ decrease in magnitude initially and have become very small when $n = 11$, subsequently they increase. The series therefore cannot converge. However, reference to the table shows that for values of n up to 10, $r_n(2)$ also decreases in magnitude and becomes very small. In fact $|r_n(2)| < |u_n(2)|$.

These phenomena, which we have verified numerically for a solution of a particular differential equation for a particular value of t, are found to occur widely in practice. For if we consider the general first order equation (1), already discussed, and assume that $T > 0$ and that the derivatives of $f(t)$ up to a certain order tend to zero as $t \to -\infty$, then from (2), $u_n(t) = (-T)^{n-1}f^{(n-1)}(t)$. Also, from (3), for the solution that vanishes when $t = -\infty$,

$$r_n(t) = -(-T)^{n-1} e^{-t/T} \int_{-\infty}^{t} e^{t_1/T} f^{(n)}(t_1) \, dt_1.$$

Notice that, since the variable t is now the upper limit, another symbol t_1 must be used as the variable of integration. Then for $-\infty < t_1 < t$, $e^{t_1/T} < e^{t/T}$, so that

$$\left| e^{t_1/T} f^{(n)}(t_1) \right| = e^{t_1/T} \left| f^{(n)}(t_1) \right| < e^{t/T} \left| f^{(n)}(t_1) \right|,$$

and

$$\left| r_n(t) \right| < T^{n-1} e^{-t/T} \int_{-\infty}^{t} e^{t/T} \left| f^{(n)}(t_1) \right| dt_1$$

$$= T^{n-1} e^{-t/T} e^{t/T} \left| \int_{-\infty}^{t} f^{(n)}(t_1) \, dt_1 \right|,$$

assuming further that $f^{(n)}(t_1)$ does not change sign for $-\infty < t_1 < t$. Performing the integration,

$$\left| r_n(t) \right| < T^{n-1} \left| f^{(n-1)}(t) \right| = \left| u_n(t) \right|.$$

The significance of this property in practice lies in the fact that if it is satisfied and if the terms of the series obtained by expanding the operator decrease initially, progressively better approximations to the particular integral can be obtained by taking the first term, the first two terms, the first three terms of the series, and so on up to a certain stage. Whether the series converges ultimately or not is immaterial. A series of this type is called *asymptotic* or *semi-convergent*. Returning to example 3, we can now say for values of t less than 12 that a particular integral which vanishes when $t = -\infty$ is given approximately by $1/(12-t)$, and the error arising does not exceed $1/(12-t)$. A better approximation is

$$x(t) = \frac{1}{12-t} - \frac{1}{(12-t)^2} + \frac{2}{(12-t)^3},$$

with an error not exceeding $2/(12-t)^3$.

With an equation of higher order, say $Q(\mathbf{D})x = f(t)$, the process of expansion of the operator is best carried out by division.

Let

$$\frac{1}{Q(\mathbf{D})} = q_0 + q_1 \mathbf{D} + q_2 \mathbf{D}^2 + \ldots + q_{n-1} \mathbf{D}^{n-1} + \frac{R_n(\mathbf{D})}{Q(\mathbf{D})},$$

where $q_0 + \ldots + q_{n-1} \mathbf{D}^{n-1}$ is the quotient and $R_n(\mathbf{D})$ the remainder after n steps in the division. Then $R_n(\mathbf{D})$ will contain $\mathbf{D}^n$ as a factor.

This gives

$$x = \frac{1}{Q(\mathbf{D})} f(t) = q_0 f(t) + q_1 f'(t) + \ldots + q_{n-1} f^{(n-1)}(t) + r_n(t)$$

where $r_n(t)$ is a solution of the equation

$$Q(\mathbf{D}) r_n(t) = R_n(\mathbf{D}) f(t).$$

The convergence or asymptotic nature of this expansion can be examined formally by the methods described above for first order equations if the operator $1/Q(\mathbf{D})$ is expressed in partial fractions.

If for a given function $f(t)$ the terms of this series decrease rapidly initially and become sufficiently small, the corresponding partial sums can usually be taken as approximations to the required solution without further examination.

Notice that, though the condition $|r_n(t)| < |u_n(t)|$ is sufficient to establish the asymptotic property of a series, it is not necessary. A more general definition is available. This is not, however, required in this book and will not be given here.

APPENDIX 8

STIELTJES INTEGRALS

Provided $f(x)$ satisfies certain general conditions the integral of $f(x)$ between the limits a and b can be defined as follows. Divide the interval (a, b) of values of x into n sub-intervals or increments and denote the rth increment by $\Delta_r x$. These increments need not be equal. Then if x_r is any value of x in the rth sub-interval, we have by definition

$$\int_a^b f(x)\,dx = \lim \sum_{r=1}^{n} f(x_r)\Delta_r x, \tag{1}$$

the limit being taken as $n \to \infty$ and as each $\Delta_r x \to 0$ in some prescribed manner. It can be proved that the value of the limit is independent of the manner chosen. Such an integral is usually referred to as a *Riemann integral*. Notice that the individual terms of this sum will tend to zero, but that the limit is in general finite and non-zero, since the number of terms tends to infinity.

We can generalise this idea by introducing another function $g(x)$ which is monotonic for $a \leq x \leq b$.† Assume in the first instance that $g(x)$ is continuous. Then if we replace increments of x in (1) by increments in $g(x)$ we can define the integral

$$\int_a^b f(x)\,dg(x) = \lim \sum_{r=1}^{n} f(x_r)\Delta_r g(x). \tag{2}$$

If $g(x)$ is differentiable in (a, b) then $\Delta_r g(x) = g'(x)\Delta_r x$ approximately. In this case (2) reduces to an integral of type (1), namely

$$\int_a^b f(x)\,dg(x) = \int_a^b f(x)g'(x)\,dx. \tag{3}$$

This gives, of course, the familiar process of change of variable in an integral. Notice that in this case also the individual terms of the sum in (2) tend to zero, since $g(x)$ is continuous.

† A function $g(x)$ is said to be *increasing* if $g(x_2) \geq g(x_1)$ for any pair of values of x_1 and x_2 in the interval (a, b) for which $x_2 > x_1$. Using a similar definition of a decreasing function, a function which is either an increasing function or a decreasing function is said to be *monotonic*.

Consider now what happens if $g(x)$ has a simple discontinuity or step at some point $x = X$ in the interval (a, b). Let the amount of this step be G. Then we can still define an integral by (2), but in this case the sum will always contain a term that does not tend to zero. The limit of this term is in fact $Gf(X)$. An expression of this type, in which $g(x)$ contains one or more simple discontinuities, is called a *Stieltjes integral*.

If we take the special case in which $g(x)$ has a finite number of steps $G_1, G_2, \ldots$ at the points $X_1, X_2, \ldots$ and is constant between these points, the only increments which make non-zero contributions to the sum in (2) are those which include the steps, so that

$$\int_a^b f(x)\, dg(x) = \sum_r G_r f(X_r). \tag{4}$$

The integral has now become a finite sum. Conversely, any sum of this type can be expressed as a Stieltjes integral.

This particular function $g(x)$ can be expressed in the form

$$g(x) = \sum_r G_r H(x - X_r),$$

where $H(x)$ is the unit step function. We can then write formally

$$g'(x) = \sum_r G_r \delta(x - X_r).$$

Substituting from (3) into (4) then gives

$$\sum_r G_r f(X_r) = \int_a^b f(x)\, dg(x) = \int_a^b f(x) \sum_r G_r \delta(x - X_r)\, dx. \tag{5}$$

Thus integrals involving impulses, of which those given in **6.3** (6) and (9) are examples, can be expressed as Stieltjes integrals and, if necessary, they can be discussed with complete rigour in this form.

APPENDIX 9

NUMERICAL SOLUTION OF EQUATIONS

The equation of degree n

$$f(x) = a_0 x^n + a_1 x^{n-1} + \ldots + a_n = 0 \tag{1}$$

can be solved easily when $n = 2$ using the familiar formula. Direct algebraic methods are also available for cubic or quartic equations. These, however, tend to be lengthy and are not much used in practice. In these cases use can be made of charts.[†] For equations of higher degree, numerical methods must be used. Even when n is 3 or 4 these are usually quicker and easier to apply than algebraic methods.

The classical numerical methods are those of Horner and Graeffe. These are described in standard textbooks on algebra.[‡] Both involve transformations of the equation which have the effect of separating the roots, thereby facilitating their determination. Both of these lead to difficulties, as indeed do all numerical processes, when the roots are close together or are complex. Graeffe's method can be modified to cover the latter case, but Horner's method is not applicable. In contrast with the method to be described, the main disadvantage of these methods is that neither provides any indication when an error is made in the computation.

Nowadays extensive use is made of *iterative methods*. Apart from the fact that they can be applied easily to equations of all types, these have the advantage that occasional numerical errors can be made without necessarily leading to incorrect values for the roots. Another point is that iterative methods are particularly suitable for automatic machines. This subject is too extensive for a full discussion here; we shall give instead a short account of the general principles, together with one or two simple examples.

Consider the quadratic equation

$$x^2 + 4x - 1 = 0. \tag{1}$$

[†] See for example Draper, C. S., McKay, W. and Lees, S., *Instrument Engineering*, Vol. 2. McGraw-Hill (New York, 1953).

[‡] See for example Uspensky, J. V., *Theory of Equations*, McGraw-Hill (New York, 1948).

A rough graph shows the roots are near $x = 0$ and $x = -4$. Observing that (1) can be written $x = 1/(x+4)$, we form a sequence of numbers from the recurrence relation

$$x_{n+1} = \frac{1}{x_n+4}. \tag{2}$$

Taking $x_1 = 0$ and using a table of reciprocals we deduce very easily the sequence $x_2 = 0.25$, $x_3 = 0.2353$, $x_4 = 0.2361$, $x_5 = 0.2361$, ...
It happens that this sequence converges to the root $-2+\sqrt{5}$. It is seen that the first four decimal places of this root have been obtained after only three steps. On the other hand, if we try to use this method for the other root, $-2-\sqrt{5} = -4.2361$, starting with say $x_1 = -4.25$ it is found that the sequence obtained diverges from this root. If, however, (1) is written $x = (x^2+1)/(2x+4)$ it is found that both roots are given correct to four decimal places after only two steps of the iteration

$$x_{n+1} = \frac{x_n^2+1}{2x_n+4}. \tag{3}$$

In order to examine the convergence in the general case, consider an equation $f(x) = 0$ which has a root $x = \alpha$. If the equation is transformed in some way (several will usually be available) to the form $x = g(x)$ we can set up an iteration

$$x_{n+1} = g(x_n), \tag{4}$$

starting from a value x_1 near α. Since $\alpha = g(\alpha)$ we have

$$x_{n+1}-\alpha = g(x_n)-g(\alpha) = (x_n-\alpha)g'(\alpha)+\tfrac{1}{2}(x_n-\alpha)^2 g''(\alpha)+ \ldots, \tag{5}$$

expanding by Taylor's theorem. Writing the error $x_n-\alpha$ as γ_n we have to a first approximation,

$$\gamma_{n+1} = \gamma_n g'(\alpha) = \gamma_{n-1}\{g'(\alpha)\}^2 = \ldots = \gamma_1\{g'(\alpha)\}^n. \tag{6}$$

The errors therefore form a geometrical progression which tends to zero if $|g'(\alpha)| < 1$. This is the condition for the iteration to converge. Clearly, the smaller $|g'(\alpha)|$, the more rapid the convergence. If, however, $|g'(\alpha)| > 1$ the sequence x_n will diverge or approach a root other than $x = \alpha$.

It is evident that the ideal value for $g'(\alpha)$ is zero. In this case $\gamma_{n+1} = \tfrac{1}{2}\gamma_n^2 g''(\alpha)$ and convergence is very rapid. An iteration for which $g'(\alpha) \neq 0$ is called a *first order process*, while if $g'(\alpha) = 0$ and $g''(\alpha) \neq 0$ it is a *second order process*. It can be verified that the formulae (2) and (3) used for solving (1) above correspond respectively to first and second order processes. In the former case with $\alpha = 0.2361$, $g'(\alpha) = -0.055$, which explains why the convergence is quite rapid.

T.L.S.—16

Iterative formulae for a given equation can usually be written in a number of forms, some of which will provide better convergence than others. These will in general give first order processes. We show now how to obtain a second order process for the equation $f(x) = 0$. If α is a root and $x_n = \alpha + \gamma_n$ an approximation, we have $f(x_n - \gamma_n) = 0$. Expanding by Taylor's theorem, $f(x_n) - \gamma_n f'(x_n) = 0$ approximately, so that $\gamma_n = f(x_n)/f'(x_n)$. Using this for the next approximation we have formed the iteration

$$x_{n+1} = g(x_n) = x_n - \frac{f(x_n)}{f'(x_n)}. \tag{7}$$

This is the well-known *Newton-Raphson formula*. It was used in fact to derive (3) above. It is easily verified that $g'(\alpha) = 0$, so that the process is a second order one.

As an example, consider the equation

$$x^3 + 3x^2 + 2x - 2 = 0, \tag{8}$$

for which $\qquad\qquad f'(x) = 3x^2 + 6x + 2.$

If a desk machine is used the working can be tabulated as follows.

	x_1	x_2	x_3	x_4	x_5
x	0	1	0·64	0·531	0·52146
$f'(x)$	2	11	7·069	6·03188	5·94452
$f(x)$	−2	4	0·771	0·057604	0·000477274
$f(x)/f'(x)$	−1	0·36	0·109	0·00954	0·00008028

The next step gives $x_6 = 0·5213797$. Since $f(x_6) = 7·72 . 10^{-8}$ we have found the root correct to seven decimal places.

A major part of the above computation lies in the evaluation of $f(x)$ and $f'(x)$. Since the latter is seen to change little in the later stages it need not be recalculated at every step. This has the effect of changing the process from a second to a first order one with a slight diminution of the rapidity of convergence, so that extra steps are required. It is a general principle with iterative processes that the more rapid the convergence the more complicated the formula used must be. The efficiency of a particular method must be judged by balancing numerical simplicity with speed of convergence.

Another point to be noticed is that it is not usually necessary to know an approximate value of a root before starting an iteration. An arbitrary value, for example zero, can often be taken for the first approximation x_1.

The other two roots of (8) can be found by dividing $f(x)$ by $x - x_6$ and solving the resulting quadratic equation by the ordinary method. This process can be used for any cubic equation and extended to equations of higher order that do not contain more than one pair of complex roots. The computation, however, becomes much more involved when there are two or more pairs of complex roots. Iterative formulae, such as (7), can still be used, but the labour of calculating $f(x)/f'(x)$ for complex values of x is much greater than for real values. It can, however, be reduced considerably if synthetic division is used (see Appendix 3).

It is more usual to obtain complex roots by obtaining first the corresponding real quadratic factor $x^2 + \beta x + \gamma$ of $f(x)$. This is done by means of a simultaneous iteration for the coefficients β and γ. Several alternative processes have been proposed, each having their own special merits. Synthetic division is a feature of all of these. Space does not allow a full account of these here and since clear descriptions are available elsewhere, we shall limit ourselves to a summary, with references.

Perhaps the simplest of these to carry out is that due to Shih-Nge Lin.† This is a first order process, so that its convergence is unpredictable. Modifications to this have been given by Friedman§ and by Aitken.† The former, though still a first order process, gives improved convergence. The latter is a second order process. Other second order processes are described by Milne‡ and by Hartree.§

The choice between these methods will vary from one equation to another. It will also depend on the skill and experience of the computer, who may well make use of transformations and other devices to expedite his work.

As has been mentioned already, iterative methods lend themselves naturally to the programming of digital machines. Alternatively, analogue machines can be constructed which enable roots to be found by means of a rapid sweep of the plane of the complex variable x.

EXERCISES   Obtain all the roots of the following equations:

1. $x^3 + 3x^2 + 2x - 5 = 0$,
2. $x^4 + 4x^3 + 6x^2 + 5x + 1 = 0$ (see exercise 1 of **9.4**).

† Aitken, A. C., Lin's Process of Iterated Penultimate Remainder, *Quart. J. Mech. and Applied Math.* **8** (1955) pp. 251–255.

‡ Milne, W. E., *Numerical Calculus*. Princeton University Press (1949).

§ Hartree, D. R., *Numerical Analysis*. Oxford University Press (1952).

Further references on this subject are given in the above papers and books.

APPENDIX 10

THE CRITERIA OF ROUTH AND HURWITZ

In this Appendix we give proofs of the criteria of Routh and Hurwitz, as stated in **9.4**.

Extending the argument of **9.3**, since for a stable system

$$\left[\text{ang } Q(j\omega)\right]_0^\infty = \tfrac{1}{2}n\pi,$$

the corresponding locus must cut the axes alternately in n points altogether and finish in the nth quadrant. To apply the general argument we make two modifications. First the locus is extended to include negative values of ω. To do this we reflect the portion for positive values in the real axis. This is shown by the dotted line in fig. A10(a) for the case $n = 5$. The second modification is to multiply $Q(j\omega)$ by $(-j)^n$. This is done to make the coefficient of ω^n real and positive and has the effect of rotating the locus clockwise through n right angles as

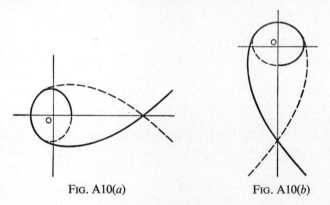

FIG. A10(a)   FIG. A10(b)

in fig. A10(b). The locus will then always finish in the fourth quadrant as $n \to \infty$. Further, it will cut the axes alternately in $2n-1$ points altogether. Now

$$(-j)^n Q(j\omega) = (-j)^n \{a_0(j\omega)^n + a_1(j\omega)^{n-1} + \ldots\}$$

$$= a_0\omega^n - a_1 j\omega^{n-1} - a_2\omega^{n-2} + a_3 j\omega^{n-3} + \ldots.$$

Separating this polynomial into real and imaginary parts we have

$$(-j)^n Q(j\omega) = f_0(\omega) - j f_1(\omega),$$

where

$$f_0(\omega) = a_0\omega^n - a_2\omega^{n-2} + a_4\omega^{n-4} - \ldots \tag{1}$$

$$f_1(\omega) = a_1\omega^{n-1} - a_3\omega^{n-3} + a_5\omega^{n-5} - \ldots \tag{2}$$

Since the locus cuts the axes alternately $2n-1$ times $f_0(\omega)$ and $f_1(\omega)$ must have n and $n-1$ real zeros respectively, and these must alternate. Also, since the locus is in the fourth quadrant when ω is large enough, both $f_0(\omega)$ and $f_1(\omega)$ tend to infinity as $\omega \to \infty$, so that a_0 and a_1 are both positive. The graphs of these polynomials are as in fig. A10(c).

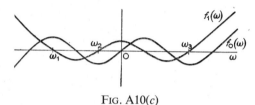

FIG. A10(c)

If we divide $f_0(\omega)$ by $f_1(\omega)$ the quotient is $a_0\omega/a_1$. Denote the remainder by $-f_2(\omega)$. Since

$$f_0(\omega) = \frac{a_0\omega}{a_1} f_1(\omega) - f_2(\omega), \tag{3}$$

at any zero ω_1 of f_1 we have

$$f_0(\omega_1) = -f_2(\omega_1). \tag{4}$$

Let ω_1 and ω_2 be consecutive zeros of f_1. Since f_0 has a zero between ω_1 and ω_2 (see fig. A10(c)), $f_0(\omega_1)$ and $f_0(\omega_2)$ have opposite signs. It follows from (4) that $f_2(\omega_1)$ and $f_2(\omega_2)$ also have opposite signs. Thus between each consecutive pair of the $n-1$ zeros of f_1 there is a zero of f_2. Since the degree of f_2 is $n-2$, it can have no other zeros. Let ω_3 be the greatest zero of f_1. Since $f_0(\omega_3) < 0$, (4) gives $f_2(\omega_3) > 0$. But f_2 has no zero greater than ω_3, so that $f_2(\omega)$ is positive as $\omega \to \infty$. Now

$$f_2(\omega) = \left(a_2 - \frac{a_0 a_3}{a_1}\right)\omega^{n-2} - \left(a_4 - \frac{a_0 a_5}{a_1}\right)\omega^{n-4} + \ldots \tag{5}$$

We deduce

$$a_2 - \frac{a_0 a_3}{a_1} > 0. \tag{6}$$

We have now shown that the zeros of f_1 and f_2 alternate in the same way as those of f_0 and f_1. The same argument shows that if a fourth polynomial $f_3(\omega)$ is formed by dividing f_3 into f_2 its leading coefficient must be positive, and so on.

Since Routh's first rule is simply a process for writing down the coefficients of the polynomials $f_0, f_1, f_2, \ldots$, the conditions for stability have now been established. We remark in passing that a sequence of polynomials related in this way are called *Sturm functions*; they have other interesting algebraic properties.

Writing down the first three rows thus,

$$a_0 \qquad\qquad a_2 \qquad\qquad a_4 \qquad\qquad a_6 \qquad\qquad \cdots$$

$$\qquad a_1 \qquad\qquad a_3 \qquad\qquad a_5 \qquad\qquad \cdots$$

$$a_2 - \frac{a_0 a_3}{a_1} \qquad a_4 - \frac{a_0 a_5}{a_1} \qquad \cdots$$

it is observed that the second and third rows are obtained from the first and second by replacing a_0 by a_1, a_1 by $a_2 - a_0 a_3/a_1$, and so on. Since the fourth row is obtained from the second and third in the same way as the third is obtained from the first and second, the fourth row can be obtained directly from the third by making the above substitutions. Likewise since the first, second and fourth rows and the second, third and fifth rows are similarly related, the fifth row can be written down from the fourth by the same substitutions. Since, however, we are only interested in the leading elements in each row it is only necessary to make the substitutions in these elements. Routh's second rule is now established.

In order to deduce the criteria of Hurwitz we observe that the third test function is $(a_2 a_1 - a_0 a_3)/a_1$, which is Δ_2/Δ_1. We now show that the substitutions of Routh's second rule converts this successively into Δ_3/Δ_2, Δ_4/Δ_3, $\ldots$. In fact, if these substitutions are made in Δ_r the result is Δ_{r+1}/a_1. Consider for example the case $r = 3$.

$$\Delta_3 = \begin{vmatrix} a_1 & a_3 & a_5 \\ a_0 & a_2 & a_4 \\ 0 & a_1 & a_3 \end{vmatrix}.$$

Making the substitutions, we obtain the determinant

$$\begin{vmatrix} a_2 - \dfrac{a_0}{a_1}a_3 & a_4 - \dfrac{a_0}{a_1}a_5 & a_6 - \dfrac{a_0}{a_1}a_7 \\[2ex] a_1 & a_3 & a_5 \\[2ex] 0 & a_2 - \dfrac{a_0}{a_1}a_3 & a_4 - \dfrac{a_0}{a_1}a_5 \end{vmatrix} = \begin{vmatrix} 1 & a_3 & a_5 & a_7 \\[2ex] 0 & a_2 - \dfrac{a_0}{a_1}a_3 & a_4 - \dfrac{a_0}{a_1}a_5 & a_6 - \dfrac{a_0}{a_1}a_7 \\[2ex] 0 & a_1 & a_3 & a_5 \\[2ex] 0 & 0 & a_2 - \dfrac{a_0}{a_1}a_3 & a_4 - \dfrac{a_0}{a_1}a_5 \end{vmatrix}.$$

If the first and third rows are multiplied by a_0/a_1 and added to the second and fourth rows respectively we have

$$\begin{vmatrix} 1 & a_3 & a_5 & a_7 \\ a_0/a_1 & a_2 & a_4 & a_6 \\ 0 & a_1 & a_3 & a_5 \\ 0 & a_0 & a_2 & a_4 \end{vmatrix} = \frac{1}{a_1} \begin{vmatrix} a_1 & a_3 & a_5 & a_7 \\ a_0 & a_2 & a_4 & a_6 \\ 0 & a_1 & a_3 & a_5 \\ 0 & a_0 & a_2 & a_4 \end{vmatrix} = \frac{\Delta_4}{a_1}.$$

This reasoning can be applied to the general determinant Δ_r. Finally it is only necessary to point out that if

$$\Delta_1, \quad \frac{\Delta_2}{\Delta_1}, \quad \frac{\Delta_3}{\Delta_2}, \quad \ldots \quad \frac{\Delta_n}{\Delta_{n-1}} > 0$$

then $\qquad\qquad \Delta_1, \quad \Delta_2, \quad .. \quad \Delta_n > 0.$

APPENDIX 11

STATISTICS AND PROBABILITY

Consider a set or distribution of N values of a variable u whose statistical properties we wish to discuss. In this context such a variable is usually called a *variate*. If a particular value u_r occurs f_r times in the set, f_r is called the *frequency* of this value. We call f_r/N the *relative frequency*. If we assume that one of these N values is chosen at random so that each has an equal chance of selection, the probability p_r that the selected value turns out to be u_r is f_r/N. In this sense therefore probability can be regarded as synonymous with relative frequency.

We now introduce a function $P(u)$, defined as the probability that the selected value is less than u. Then $P(u)$, whose graph is shown in fig. A11(a), increases with u in steps from zero to unity, being zero for

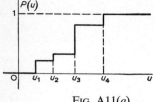

FIG. A11(a)

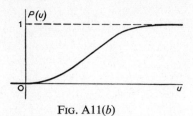

FIG. A11(b)

values of u less than the least of the set and unity for values greater than the greatest. For each value u_r of the set, $P(u)$ has a step of magnitude p_r or ΔP_r. Between successive values (in order of magnitude) it remains constant.

The main characteristics of a statistical distribution are measured by certain *parameters*, the most important of which is the *mean* or *average* μ. Then

$$\mu = (\textstyle\sum f_r u_r)/N = \sum u_r \Delta P_r. \tag{1}$$

Next in importance is the *standard deviation* σ, which is the root mean square deviation from the mean. This measures the dispersion of the distribution. For many purposes it is preferable to work with the square of σ, which is called the *variance*. We have

$$\sigma^2 = \{\textstyle\sum f_r(u_r-\mu)^2\}/N = \sum(u_r-\mu)^2 \Delta P_r. \tag{2}$$

We can call σ^2 the *second moment* of the distribution, where in general the kth moment is defined as

$$\mu_k = \sum (u_r - \mu)^k \Delta P_r. \tag{3}$$

The moments of higher order can be used to represent other more specialised characteristics of the distribution. Observe that μ_k is the average value of $(u_r - \mu)^k$; it is often called the *expected value* of $(u_r - \mu)^k$.

If N is large the graph of fig. A11(a) can be approximated by a smooth curve as in fig. A11(b). This means that the set is represented approximately by a continuously varying *distribution function* $P(u)$. This type of function can also represent a hypothetical distribution of infinite total frequency N. The probability increment or difference ΔP_r now becomes an infinitesimal *probability differential dP*, where

$$dP = P'(u)\, du. \tag{4}$$

The derivative $P'(u) = p(u)$ is the *probability density*. Then the probability that a value selected at random from the set has a value between two arbitrary values a and b ($a < b$) is

$$\int dP = \int_a^b p(u)\, du = P(b) - P(a). \tag{5}$$

As a special case, the probability that the selected value is less than b is

$$P(b) = \int_{-\infty}^b p(u)\, du \tag{6}$$

With this notation the mean, variance and kth moments are now given respectively by

$$\mu = \int u\, dP = \int_{-\infty}^{\infty} u p(u)\, du, \tag{7}$$

$$\sigma^2 = \int (u - \mu)^2 dP = \int_{-\infty}^{\infty} (u - \mu)^2 p(u)\, du, \tag{8}$$

$$\mu_k = \int (u - \mu)^k dP = \int_{-\infty}^{\infty} (u - \mu)^k p(u)\, du. \tag{9}$$

It is interesting and important to notice that these formulae can be made to cover the case when N is finite and not necessarily large if Stieltjes integrals, as defined in Appendix 8, are used. In this case the probability density $p(u)$ becomes a series of impulse functions of u and (7), (8) and (9) become equivalent to (1), (2) and (3).

We turn now to the case of a *bivariate distribution*. This is defined as a set of pairs of values of two variates u_1 and u_2, such as the heights and ages of a group of adult men.† The set can be represented, as in the univariate case, by a distribution function $P(u_1, u_2)$, which is the probability that, if a pair is selected at random from the set, the two values are respectively less than u_1 and u_2. Alternatively we can use a probability density $p(u_1, u_2)$. To show the relation between these observe that, generalising (6), the probability that the pair of values selected at random are respectively less than b_1 and b_2 is

$$P(b_1, b_2) = \int_{-\infty}^{b_2} \int_{-\infty}^{b_1} p(u_1, u_2) \, du_1 \, du_2. \tag{10}$$

Differentiating first with respect to b_2 and then with respect to b_1

$$p(b_1, b_2) = \frac{\partial^2 P(b_1, b_2)}{\partial b_1 \, \partial b_2},$$

or,

$$p(u_1, u_2) = \frac{\partial^2 P(u_1, u_2)}{\partial u_1 \, \partial u_2}. \tag{11}$$

The probability differential in this case, which is the probability that the variate values lie between u_1 and $u_1 + du_1$ and u_2 and $u_2 + du_2$ respectively, can be written

$$dP = p(u_1, u_2) \, du_1 \, du_2. \tag{12}$$

The distribution of u_1 independently of u_2 is given by the functions

$$P_1(u_1) = P(u_1, \infty)$$

or

$$p_1(u_1) = \int_{-\infty}^{\infty} p(u_1, u_2) \, du_2,$$

with similar definitions for $P_2(u_2)$ and $p_2(u_2)$. An important special case arises when $p(u_1, u_2) = p_1(u_1) p_2(u_2)$. It is easily shown that when this happens, $P(u_1, u_2) = P_1(u_1) P_2(u_2)$. Either of these formulae shows that the distribution of u_1 is the same proportionately for all values of u_2, and vice versa. In this case we say that the two variates are *statistically independent*. For example, if we recorded the heights and incomes of a large group of adult men we could expect these two variates to be independent statistically. This would not, however, be true normally of their heights and weights.

Parameters can be defined for bivariate distributions as in the

† Note that the symbols u_1 and u_2 now refer to different variates and not as previously in this Appendix to different values of the same variate.

univariate case. In particular the means and variances of u_1 and u_2 independently are given by the formulae

$$\mu_1 = \int u_1 \, dP, \qquad \mu_2 = \int u_2 \, dP, \tag{13}$$

$$\sigma_1^2 = \int (u_1 - \mu_1)^2 \, dP, \qquad \sigma_2^2 = \int (u_2 - \mu_2)^2 \, dP. \tag{14}$$

These expressions must be evaluated as double integrals, using (12).

A new parameter of special importance in the theory of linear systems is the mixed second moment or *covariance*

$$\mu_{12} = \int (u_1 - \mu_1)(u_2 - \mu_2) \, dP. \tag{15}$$

In order to investigate the significance of μ_{12} assume for simplicity that $\mu_1 = 0 = \mu_2$. Then if u_1 and u_2 are statistically independent,

$$\mu_{12} = \iint u_1 u_2 p_1(u_1) p_2(u_2) \, du_1 \, du_2 = \int u_1 p_1(u_1) \, du_1 \int u_2 p_2(u_2) \, du_2$$

$$= \mu_1 \mu_2 = 0.$$

On the other hand, if there is a linear relation $u_2 = ku_1$ between these variates (assuming for the present that k is positive),

$$\mu_{12} = \int ku_1^2 \, dP = k\sigma_1^2 = \sigma_1 \sigma_2.$$

In this case the non-dimensional quantity $\rho = \mu_{12}/\sigma_1 \sigma_2$ is unity. If k is negative it is easily seen that $\rho = -1$. It can be proved that this ratio can never exceed unity numerically, and that it can only equal unity when u_1 and u_2 are proportional. In general ρ is a number with modulus between zero and unity which is taken to measure the degree of linear dependence or correlation between u_1 and u_2. For this reason it is called the *correlation coefficient*.

These ideas can be extended to distributions of three or more variates. Although a complete definition of a stationary process involves parameters of these distributions, they do not appear explicitly in the optimisation theory of Chapters 11 and 12 and will not therefore be discussed here.

Consider now a random process, as defined in **11.1**, of which the signal $u(t)$ is a typical member. For a given value of t the values of $u(t)$ for different members of the ensemble form a set which defines a distribution function $P(u; t)$. From this we can calculate the mean, variance and higher moments at time t using the formulae

$$\mu(t) = \int u(t)\, dP(u; t), \qquad \mu_k(t) = \int \{u(t) - \mu(t)\}^k dP(u; t). \qquad (16)$$

If, however, the process is stationary $P(u; t)$ will, by definition, be independent of t and can be written $P(u)$. It follows that μ and μ_k are independent of t, being given by

$$\mu = \int u\, dP = \int_{-\infty}^{\infty} u p(u)\, du,$$

$$\mu_k = \int (u - \mu)^k dP = \int_{-\infty}^{\infty} (u - \mu)^k p(u)\, du.$$

These two parameters are in fact the *ensemble averages* of u and $(u - \mu)^k$ respectively. We can define the ensemble average of any function $f(u)$ of u as

$$E\{f(u)\} = \int f(u)\, dP, \qquad (17)$$

so that $\mu = E(u)$ and $\mu_k = E\{(u - \mu)^k\}$.

The corresponding time averages of $u(t)$ or of any function of $u(t)$ for a particular signal of the ensemble are obtained by taking averages in the usual way over the finite time interval $(-T_1, T_1)$ and then letting $T_1 \to \infty$. Thus

$$T(u) = \lim_{T_1 \to \infty} \frac{1}{2T_1} \int_{-T_1}^{T_1} u\, dt, \qquad (18)$$

$$T\{f(u)\} = \lim_{T_1 \to \infty} \frac{1}{2T_1} \int_{-T_1}^{T_1} f(u)\, dt. \qquad (19)$$

In addition to the series of univariate distributions $P(u, t)$ a general random process also defines a whole range of multivariate distributions. For example, if $u(t)$ is a particular signal of the ensemble and if $u_1 = u(t_1)$ and $u_2 = u(t_2)$, a bivariate distribution is formed by taking pairs of values of u_1 and u_2 over the whole ensemble for fixed values of t_1 and t_2. Let the distribution function in this case be $P(u_1, u_2; t_1, t_2)$. If the process is stationary this function will not be changed by a shift in time. It will, therefore, depend only on the difference $t_2 - t_1$ and not on t_1 and t_2 individually. Denoting this difference by τ the function can therefore be written $P(u_1, u_2; \tau)$.

With this distribution defined, an ensemble average of any function of u_1 and u_2 can be taken. The only one that will concern us, however, is the autocorrelation function $\phi_u(\tau)$, given by

$$\phi_u(\tau) = E(u_1 u_2) = E\{u(t)u(t+\tau)\} = \int u(t)u(t+\tau)\,dP. \qquad (20)$$

If the mean value of $u(t)$ is zero, $\phi_u(\tau)$ is the covariance of u_1 and u_2. In other words it measures the extent to which values of a particular signal $u(t)$ at times differing by τ are related statistically. If in fact these values are independent, $\phi_u(\tau)$ will be zero. In general we can expect that $|\phi_u(\tau)|$ will decrease as τ increases.

Instead of the ensemble average of $u_1 u_2$ we can form the time average

$$T\{u(t)u(t+\tau)\} = \lim_{T_1 \to \infty} \frac{1}{2T_1} \int_{-T_1}^{T_1} u(t)u(t+\tau)\,dt. \qquad (21)$$

As stated in **11.2** this is in fact usually taken as the definition of the autocorrelation function.

If we specify that a given stationary random process is ergodic we imply that for all its members, except a number of negligible probability measure, the time average of any function of u_1, u_2, $\ldots$ is equal to the corresponding ensemble average. For example

$$T\{u(t)\} = E\{u(t)\}$$
$$T\{u(t)u(t+\tau)\} = E\{u(t)u(t+\tau)\}.$$

The ergodic hypothesis implies that a typical signal of the ensemble has the same statistical characteristics as the ensemble as a whole. The practical significance of this lies in the fact that when correlation functions cannot be estimated as ensemble averages using theoretical considerations, the corresponding time averages taken from a typical observational record can be used.

APPENDIX 12

SPECIAL RANDOM PROCESSES

Let a random process be defined as the ensemble of sinusoidal functions

$$u(t) = a_1 \cos(\omega_1 t + \alpha_1), \tag{1}$$

where each function has the same amplitude a_1 and frequency ω_1, but with phase angles α_1 uniformly distributed between 0 and 2π. Then

$$u(t)u(t+\tau) = \tfrac{1}{2}a_1^2 \cos(2\omega_1 t + 2\alpha_1 + \omega_1 \tau) + \tfrac{1}{2}a_1^2 \cos\omega_1\tau. \tag{2}$$

Taking the ensemble average for different values of α_1, the autocorrelation function is seen to be $\tfrac{1}{2}a_1^2 \cos\omega_1\tau$. If we now take a more general ensemble of functions $u(t)$ with the same frequency ω_1 in which the phases α_1 are uniformly distributed and the amplitudes a_1 have a distribution with root mean square value A_1,

$$\phi_u(\tau) = \tfrac{1}{2}A_1^2 \cos\omega_1\tau. \tag{3}$$

This process provides an example of a case where the autocorrelation function does not decrease as τ increases. This is not surprising since the periodicity of the individual functions provides a relation between their values at times differing by a time τ, however large τ may be. Notice that if $u(t)$ is the voltage applied to a unit resistance, $\tfrac{1}{2}A_1^2$ is the mean power dissipated.

If we introduce now a second ensemble

$$v(t) = a_2 \cos(\omega_2 t + \alpha_2), \tag{4}$$

$$u(t)v(t+\tau) = \tfrac{1}{2}a_1 a_2 [\cos\{(\omega_1 + \omega_2)t + \alpha_1 + \alpha_2 + \omega_2\tau\} + \\ + \cos\{(\omega_1 - \omega_2)t + \alpha_1 - \alpha_2 - \omega_2\tau\}].$$

Provided $\omega_1 \neq \omega_2$, the ensemble average is zero, so that $\phi_{uv}(\tau) = 0$.

These results, together with **11.2 (9)**, enable us to state that for an ensemble for which

$$u(t) = \sum_r a_r \cos(\omega_r t + \alpha_r), \tag{5}$$

$$\phi_u(\tau) = \tfrac{1}{2}\sum A_r^2 \cos\omega_r\tau. \tag{6}$$

Here the frequencies ω_r can be any finite or infinite set of numbers which are all different. Using **6.3** (11) it follows that the spectral density is given by

$$\Phi_u(j\omega) = \tfrac{1}{2}\pi\sum A_r^2\{\delta(\omega-\omega_r)+\delta(\omega+\omega_r)\}, \qquad (7)$$

which is a series of impulses in the frequency domain, whose amplitudes are proportional to the mean power of the components of corresponding frequency.

Finally in this group we consider ensembles which can be broken down into components of type (1) for which the different frequencies are continuously distributed. If we assume that the distribution of these components is defined by a *power density* function $P(\omega)$, so that the components having frequencies between ω and $\omega+d\omega$ have mean power $P(\omega)\,d\omega$, (6) now becomes

$$\phi(\tau) = \int_0^\infty P(\omega)\cos\omega\tau\,d\omega.$$

Using **4.4** (5) and (6) and the fact that $\phi(\tau)$ is an even function, we have

$$P(\omega) = \frac{1}{\pi}\int_{-\infty}^\infty \phi(\tau)\cos\omega\tau\,d\tau = \frac{2}{\pi}\int_0^\infty \phi(\tau)\cos\omega\tau\,d\tau.$$

Comparison with **11.3** (4) shows that

$$\Phi_u(j\omega) = \pi P(\omega). \qquad (8)$$

We thus have a physical interpretation of $\Phi_u(j\omega)$ which, incidentally, justifies the name *power spectral density*.

White noise is defined in **11.2** as a process for which $\phi_u(\tau) = 0$ when $\tau \neq 0$. Since $\phi_u(0)$ is the mean square value of $\{u(t)\}^2$, it cannot be zero. In order that it shall have a significant effect in a system it must be infinite. This can be arranged by making $\phi_u(\tau)$ an impulse function. Therefore we consider the case $\phi_u(\tau) = k\delta(\tau)$. It follows immediately that $\Phi_u(j\omega) = k$, which is independent of ω. Thus white noise is a stationary random process with a flat frequency power spectrum. This indeed provides an alternative definition.

The third widely used form of a stationary random process can be defined in a number of ways. Let $\ldots t_1, t_2, t_3, \ldots$ be a sequence of successive points on the time scale located at random so that on average there are β such points per unit time. Such a sequence is said to have a *Poisson distribution*. We assume that in each interval between successive points $u(t)$ is constant, that the values in successive intervals are independent, and that the mean square value of $u(t)$ is unity. The graph of a typical function $u(t)$ is shown in fig. A12(a). More precisely, let

$u(t) = u_r$ for $t_r < t < t_{r+1}$. Then if t and $t+\tau$ lie in the same interval, $E\{u(t)u(t+\tau)\} = E\{u_r^2\} = 1$, while if they are in different intervals it is zero. In order to calculate $\phi_u(\tau)$ we must calculate the probability that there is no point of the sequence t_r in the interval $(t, t+\tau)$. Divide this interval into n equal small intervals τ/n. The probability that there is no point of the sequence in one particular small interval is $1 - \beta\tau/n$,

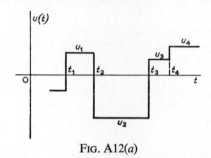

FIG. A12(a)

so that the probability that there is no point in any of the intervals is $(1 - \beta\tau/n)^n$. If we now let $n \to \infty$, using a well-known exponential limit, the required probability becomes $e^{-\beta\tau}$. Multiplying this by $E\{u_r^2\}$ gives $\phi_u(\tau) = e^{-\beta\tau}$, provided $\tau > 0$. But $\phi_u(\tau)$ is an even function. We thus have

$$\phi_u(\tau) = e^{-\beta|\tau|}. \tag{7}$$

It is shown in **11.3** that the corresponding spectral density is

$$\Phi_u(j\omega) = \frac{2\beta}{\omega^2 + \beta^2}. \tag{8}$$

It can be proved that similar expressions for $\phi_u(\tau)$ and $\Phi_u(j\omega)$ are obtained (with 2β replacing β) if $u(t)$ takes the constant values ± 1 alternately in intervals determined by a sequence of points on the time scale having a Poisson distribution. Yet a third way of obtaining this type of ensemble is to pass white noise of mean power density 2β through a filter whose operator is $1/(\mathbf{D} + \beta)$. This is immediately evident from **11.3** (9) and (13).

MATRICES

A matrix is a set of numbers or elements arranged in a rectangular array of rows and columns thus,

$$\begin{pmatrix} a_{11} & a_{12} & a_{13} & \ldots & a_{1n} \\ a_{21} & a_{22} & a_{23} & \ldots & a_{2n} \\ . & . & . & \ldots & . \\ a_{m1} & a_{m2} & a_{m3} & \ldots & a_{mn} \end{pmatrix}.$$

This matrix can be denoted by $\{a_{ij}\}$ or simply by A. A matrix like A having m rows and n columns is said to have *order* (m, n) or $m \times n$. In particular, if $m = 1$ or $n = 1$ we have a matrix consisting of a single row or a single column of elements. Such matrices are called *row matrices* or *column matrices* respectively. If $m = n$ the matrix is *square*.

Two matrices are equal if and only if their corresponding elements are equal. Thus $\{a_{ij}\} = \{b_{ij}\}$ if $a_{ij} = b_{ij}$ for all i and j. Then equal matrices must necessarily have the same order.

Matrices have their main applications in the manipulation of linear transformations and linear equations. To this end, rules are laid down for the addition and multiplication of matrices. First, the sum of two matrices of the same order is the matrix, each of whose elements is the sum of the corresponding elements of the given matrices. Thus if $C = A + B$, where $A = \{a_{ij}\}$ and $B = \{b_{ij}\}$, then

$$\{c_{ij}\} = \{a_{ij} + b_{ij}\}. \tag{1}$$

In order to multiply a matrix by a number λ, each element must be multiplied by λ, so that

$$\lambda\{a_{ij}\} = \{\lambda a_{ij}\}. \tag{2}$$

The product AB of two matrices A and B is defined only if the number of columns in A is equal to the number of rows in B. Let the orders of these matrices then be (m, n) and (n, p) respectively. The individual elements of the product matrix C are then defined by the relation

$$c_{ij} = \sum_{k=1}^{n} a_{ik} b_{kj}. \tag{3}$$

Thus the element in the ith row and jth column of the product matrix is formed by taking the elements of the ith row of A and of the jth column of B. Corresponding pairs are then multiplied together and the products are added. The elements used to form c_{ij} are shown in the following scheme.

$$
\overset{j}{\begin{pmatrix} & \cdot & \\ & \cdot & \\ i & \cdots & c_{ij} & \cdots \\ & \cdot & \\ & \cdot & \end{pmatrix}} = i\begin{pmatrix} \cdot & \cdot & \cdots & \cdot \\ & \cdot & \cdots & \\ a_{i1} & a_{i2} & \cdots & a_{in} \\ & \cdot & \cdots & \\ & \cdot & \cdots & \end{pmatrix} \overset{j}{\begin{pmatrix} \cdot & \cdot & b_{1j} & \cdot & \cdot \\ \cdot & \cdot & b_{2j} & \cdot & \cdot \\ \cdot & & & & \cdot \\ \cdot & & & & \cdot \\ \cdot & \cdot & b_{nj} & \cdot & \cdot \end{pmatrix}}
$$

$$\tag{4}$$

The product matrix C has order (m, p). As an example,

$$
\begin{pmatrix} a_{11} & a_{12} \\ a_{21} & a_{22} \\ a_{31} & a_{32} \end{pmatrix}\begin{pmatrix} b_{11} & b_{12} \\ b_{21} & b_{22} \end{pmatrix} = \begin{pmatrix} a_{11}b_{11}+a_{12}b_{21} & a_{11}b_{12}+a_{12}b_{22} \\ a_{21}b_{11}+a_{22}b_{21} & a_{21}b_{12}+a_{22}b_{22} \\ a_{31}b_{11}+a_{32}b_{21} & a_{31}b_{12}+a_{32}b_{22} \end{pmatrix}. \tag{5}
$$

Matrix multiplication is not in general commutative, that is, BA is not necessarily equal to AB. Indeed, in the above example BA does not exist, since $m \neq p$. However, matrix products when they exist are associative and distributive. Thus if A, B and C are any three matrices for which the appropriate sums and products can be formed, it can be proved that

$$(AB)C = A(BC), \tag{6}$$

$$C(A+B) = CA+CB. \tag{7}$$

EXERCISE If

$$A = \begin{pmatrix} 2 & 3 & -1 \\ 0 & 4 & 3 \end{pmatrix}, \quad B = \begin{pmatrix} 5 & 3 & -2 \\ 0 & -1 & 4 \\ 2 & 1 & 0 \end{pmatrix} \text{ and } C = \begin{pmatrix} 1 & 0 \\ 0 & 3 \\ -1 & 2 \end{pmatrix},$$

verify that $(AB)C = A(BC)$.

We show now how this definition allows linear relations between sets of numbers to be expressed in a compact form. Let y_1 and y_2 be homogeneous linear functions of x_1 and x_2, given by the relations

$$y_1 = b_{11}x_1+b_{12}x_2,$$

$$y_2 = b_{21}x_1+b_{22}x_2. \tag{8}$$

It is easily verified from (3) or (4) that these equations can be written

$$\begin{pmatrix} y_1 \\ y_2 \end{pmatrix} = \begin{pmatrix} b_{11} & b_{12} \\ b_{21} & b_{22} \end{pmatrix}\begin{pmatrix} x_1 \\ x_2 \end{pmatrix}, \tag{9}$$

or $Y = BX, \tag{10}$

where X and Y denote the column matrices representing the two pairs of variables. Again, if

$$z_1 = a_{11}y_1 + a_{12}y_2,$$
$$z_2 = a_{21}y_1 + a_{22}y_2, \qquad (11)$$
$$z_3 = a_{31}y_1 + a_{32}y_2,$$

we can write

$$Z = AY. \qquad (12)$$

Now if we express z_1, z_2 and z_3 directly in terms of x_1 and x_2 by eliminating y_1 and y_2 from (8) and (11) it is found on rearrangement that

$$z_1 = (a_{11}b_{11} + a_{12}b_{21})x_1 + (a_{11}b_{12} + a_{12}b_{22})x_2, \qquad (13$$

$$z_2 = (a_{21}b_{11} + a_{22}b_{21})x_1 + (a_{21}a_{12} + a_{22}b_{22})x_2,$$

$$z_3 = (a_{31}b_{11} + a_{32}b_{21})x_1 + (a_{31}b_{12} + a_{32}b_{22})x_2.$$

Comparison with (5) shows that these equations can be written

$$Z = (AB)X. \qquad (14)$$

This relation could have been written down directly by eliminating Y from (10) and (12), making use of (6).

The above application demonstrates the very considerable economy that can be achieved by the use of matrix notation.

This notation and algebra can clearly be extended to equations of the same type in any number of variables. The generalised forms of (8) and (11) can be written

$$y_i = \sum_j b_{ij}x_j, \qquad (15)$$

$$z_i = \sum_j a_{ij}y_j. \qquad (16)$$

These are equivalent to the matrix forms (10) and (12). Again, Z can be expressed directly in terms of X using (14). In particular, comparison of (15) with **14.1** (4) shows that the general linear operator converting one sequence into another is equivalent to a matrix of infinite order.

The similarity in form between the sum in **14.1** (4) and the integral in **14.1** (3), expressing the relation between the input and output functions associated with a general linear operator, suggests that the properties of matrices can sometimes be invoked to clarify the manipulation of such operators. For example, mention was made in **14.3** of the analogy between combination of operators and matrix multiplication.

A useful type of matrix is one in which the elements are operators.

Such operational matrices are particularly useful for the representation of systems with multiple inputs or outputs (see **14.6**).

The relation between linear operators and matrices is such that a knowledge of the properties of the latter can be very valuable, not only in the investigation of problems of a theoretical nature but also in the practical design of general linear systems. Comprehensive accounts of these properties are to be found in numerous textbooks.†

† For example, Frazer, R. A., Duncan, W. A. and Collar, A. R., *Elementary Matrices*. Cambridge University Press (1938).

ANSWERS TO EXERCISES

1.4 (6) $x = t - \frac{1}{2} + Ce^{-2t}$.

1.5 (8) $x = \frac{1}{2}e^{-3t} + Ae^{-t} + Be^{-2t}$.

1.6 (10) 1. $x = Ae^{-t} + Be^{-2t} + Ce^{-3t}$.

2. $x = Ae^{\frac{1}{2}(-5+\sqrt{53})t} + Be^{\frac{1}{2}(-5-\sqrt{53})t}$.

3. $x = e^{-5t/2}(A \cos \frac{1}{2}\sqrt{3}t + B \sin \frac{1}{2}\sqrt{3}t)$.

4. $x = Ae^{-t} + Be^{-3t} + Ce^{t}$.

5. $x = Ae^{-t} + Be^{t} + Ce^{-3t} + De^{3t}$.

6. $x = A \cos t + B \sin t + C \cos 3t + D \sin 3t$.

7. $x = Ae^{-2t} + e^{t}(B \cos \sqrt{3}t + C \sin \sqrt{3}t)$.

2.3 (19) 1. $x = \frac{1}{2}e^{-3t} + Ae^{-t} + Be^{-2t}$.

2. $x = e^{t} + e^{-2t}(A \cos 3t + B \sin 3t)$.

3. $x = (A - \frac{1}{4}t)e^{-2t} + Be^{2t}$.

4. $x = \frac{1}{5} \sin 2t + A \cos 3t + B \sin 3t$.

5. $x = \frac{1}{8} \sin 3t + e^{-4t}(A \cos 3t + B \sin 3t)$.

6. $x = t - \frac{1}{2} + Ae^{-2t}$.

7. $x = \frac{1}{2}t^{4} - t^{3} + \frac{3}{2}t^{2} - t + \frac{1}{2} + Ae^{-2t}$.

8. $x = t^{2} - 2t + e^{-\frac{1}{2}t}(A \cos \frac{1}{2}\sqrt{3}t + B \sin \frac{1}{2}\sqrt{3}t)$.

9. $x = (t - 2)e^{-t} + (A + Bt)e^{-2t}$.

10. $x = e^{-3t}\{(\frac{1}{64}t + A) \cos 4t + (\frac{1}{16}t^{2} + B) \sin 4t\}$.

11. $x = \frac{1}{2}(\sin t - \cos t) + e^{-\frac{1}{2}t}(A \cos \frac{1}{2}\sqrt{3}t + B \sin \frac{1}{2}\sqrt{3}t) + Ce^{-t}$.

3.3 (29) 1. $x = 28e^{-3t} - 23e^{-4t}$.

2. $x = e^{-5t}(\cos 4t + \frac{7}{4} \sin 4t)$.

3. $x = \frac{1}{3} + 3e^{-t} - \frac{1}{3}e^{-3t}$.

4. $x = e^{-3t} - 2e^{-2t} + e^{-t}$.

5. $x = \frac{1}{8}e^{t} - \frac{1}{8}e^{-t}(\cos 2t + \sin 2t)$.

6. $x = \frac{1}{25}(3 \cos t + 4 \sin t) - (\frac{3}{25} + \frac{2}{5}t)e^{-2t}$.

4.2 (37) 1. $f(t) = \dfrac{kT^2}{6} + \dfrac{kT^2}{\pi^2}\left(\cos \Omega t - \dfrac{1}{2^2}\cos 2\Omega t + \dfrac{1}{3^2}\cos 3\Omega t - \ldots\right)$.

2. $f(t) = \dfrac{kT}{8} - \dfrac{kT}{\pi^2}\left(\cos \Omega t + \dfrac{1}{3^2}\cos 3\Omega t + \ldots\right) +$

$$\dfrac{kT}{2\pi} + (\sin \Omega t - \tfrac{1}{2}\sin 2\Omega t + \ldots).$$

4.4 (42) $c(\omega) = \dfrac{1}{\pi\omega^2}(1 - \cos \omega T_1)$.

5.2 (47) $\dfrac{2T_1}{p}\sinh pT_1 - \dfrac{2}{p^2}(\cosh pT_1 - 1)$.

9.4 (98) 1. Stable.   2. Unstable.

13.3 (149) 1. $x_r = r - \tfrac{7}{2} + 2^{-r}A + 3^{-r}B$.
2. $x_r = \tfrac{1}{7}2^r + A + B\cos \tfrac{2}{3}r\pi + C\sin \tfrac{2}{3}r\pi$.

14.6 (175) 1. $x_1 = e^{-t} - e^{-2t}$, $x_2 = 2e^{-t} - 2e^{-2t}$.
2. $x_1 = 4(e^t + e^{-t} - e^{2t} - e^{-2t})$,
$x_2 = -4e^t + 4e^{-t} + 5e^{2t} - 5e^{-2t}$.

Appendix 4 (221) 1. $1 - 5x + 15x^2 - 45x^3 + \ldots$
2. $\tfrac{1}{2} + \tfrac{1}{4}x - \tfrac{1}{8}x^2 - \tfrac{3}{16}x^3 - \ldots$

3. $\dfrac{1}{x^2} - \dfrac{1}{x} + 1 - x + \ldots$

4. $1 - x + 4x^3 - 8x^4 + \ldots$

Appendix 5 (226) 1. $-\dfrac{3}{4(x-1)} + \dfrac{6}{5(x-2)} + \dfrac{11}{20(x+3)}$.

2. $\dfrac{1}{x-1} + \dfrac{4}{(x-2)^2}$.

3. $\dfrac{1}{6}\left(\dfrac{1}{x-1} + \dfrac{1}{x+1} - \dfrac{x-1}{x^2+x+1} - \dfrac{x+1}{x^2-x+1}\right)$.

Appendix 9 (243) 1. $x = 0{\cdot}9042, -1{\cdot}9521 \pm 1{\cdot}3112j$.
2. $x = -0{\cdot}2755, -2{\cdot}2207, -0{\cdot}7519 \pm 1{\cdot}0339j$.

INDEX

INDEX

INVENTORY 74

INVENTORY 1983